At Stormy Time

**The Story of Charles Coleman Parker
and Upper Iowa University**

Richard A. Barker

Cover Design: David Oliva   www.versalgroup.com
Managing Editors: Cliff Clark, David Mallick

Published in the United States by Versal Books.
Versal Books is a division of Versal Editorial Group, Inc.

Versal Editorial Group, Inc.
10 High Street
Andover, MA 01810 U.S.A.

ISBN 1-58018-162-7
First Edition

Printed in Canada
10 9 8 7 6 5 4 3 2 1

"Well, well try anything once, come hot, come cold!
If we're not foolish young, we're foolish old."

—Geoffrey Chaucer, *The Knight's Tale*

Contents

I

In the time since the passing of the affairs set forth in this account, I have grown to doubt somewhat the authenticity of my perception of events. The further removed from it I become, the more fantastic it seems. Still, I am confident that I know some things for certain. First, the character who dominated my life for that period was a real person at one time, although he had been dead for most of a century before our encounter. Second, my memory of those events remains as sharp to me today as it did five minutes after they occurred. Many of the things that he and I discussed I have been able to verify in historic documents, but many others I could not. Whether it is mostly fact or fiction I cannot tell, but it seems to be worth setting down in writing. I know there are others who may be seeking, as I was, something that has been lost. I shall leave it to you, dear reader, to sort out the reality from the imagination. I have always felt that truth is more a celebration of faith than a pedagogue of knowledge. Well, maybe I haven't always felt that way.

It all began, as much as anything has a beginning, on a bright morning in May of the year 2000—the final year both of the century and of the millennium. An hour and a half of driving brought my vehicle to the traditional front entrance. They had indicated that I should look for the building with the green goddess on top, and there it was.

I had carefully planned the seventy-five mile route from Dubuque, but Fayette slipped by me before I realized that I was through the town. There should have been a sign directing me to the university, but approaching on Highway 150 from the south there was not. I turned around on the straight, level stretch of highway north of town, and proceeded back. A reverse in course on the road to a new beginning should be taken as a bad omen, but the hopelessness of my situation provided only for humble acceptance of whatever may come. Good or bad, this is my path.

The slope of the valley drew me east of the highway where I discovered the preponderance of the town. A short drive through the small, mostly deserted downtown area yielded glimpses of expansive lawns to my left that, to my experienced eyes, could only be a college campus. The green goddess imposed herself through the trees, and beckoned me to the shallow hill from which she commanded the town.

After parking on the street in front of the campus, I sat for a moment to compose myself. Mozart's Requiem had been playing my emotions all the way up—not the whole of the piece, just that portion which obviously came by his hand. Whenever the soul yearns for inspiration, suffers to hear the voice of God, it is there in Mozart; whenever hope is awash in mundane tedium and self-recrimination, it is rekindled by the massively optimistic harmonies and by the intricate resolution; whenever faith stumbles over doubt, the Requiem Mass will steel the resolve. A tidal wave of cosmic might rends the spirit from its pathetic earthy manifestation to propel it toward the infinite, and to elevate it to an eternity of glory. Ok, I'm ready.

I slid from the driver's seat to the ground, my vehicle necessitating a descending exit, and reached into the back seat for my suit coat. Spring was giving way to a yawning summer, which had yet to oppress the landscape with its heat and humidity. Still, it was warm enough to promise a long, uncomfortable day inside of buildings that were unquestionably clear of debt to their builders before there was air conditioning.

A short hike brought me to an arch guarding the walkway up the hill to the goddess' building. A small plaque on the left side of the arch caught my attention. It said "*Superior Universitas Iowensis, Fayettae, Deo Duce MDCCCLVII*: Upper Iowa University." A good name; a strong name; a name that heralded academic tradition and integrity. But, having lived in the region for two years, and having heard much more often of its competitors, I wished rather than believed the name to reflect its true character.

I paused for a moment to survey the stretch of ground about me when a small, rounded granite boulder resting on the grass about thirty feet distant arrested my gaze. At first, I was unaware that my gaze had been arrested. Eventually, the subconscious part of my brain began to inform the conscious part that this gray, crystallized stone was not native to this area. I noticed a plaque fixed to the stone. Given that I had time to spare, I meandered over to read it; no doubt it was a memorial. Sure enough, on the plaque was lettered the following:

THIS TREE WAS PLANTED
--BY--
CHARLES COLEMAN PARKER, M.D.
BORN IN OHIO, SEPT. 12, 1823
HE CAME TO FAYETTE SEPT. 12, 1855
RIDING HORSEBACK FROM LOUISVILLE, KY
FIRST PROFESSOR OF NATURAL
SCIENCE IN UPPER IOWA UNIVERSITY
SURGEON 12TH IOWA INFANTRY
DIED JAN. 12, 1906
THE BELOVED PHYSICIAN

I looked up at the tree directly behind the stone, which was a maple, and determined that it could not have been planted more than twenty or thirty years ago. The plaque did not say when the tree was planted, but it would have to have been before 1906. The original tree must have died. It was nice that they replaced the tree rather than remove the stone. Old institutions always have such appealing traditions and histories.

For a moment, my imagination was filled with images of this fellow. The university must have hired him all the way from Kentucky. They probably did not fly him out for an interview, so it would have been accomplished through correspondence. Ah, the good old days. That would have been quite a ride in 1855. He did everything on the twelfth; he even joined the twelfth. Two of those things were in September; hmm, he arrived here on his birthday. Interesting. He must have been a stereotypical academic of his day—unmarried, pious, and poor as a church mouse, beginning his new life with all of his possessions in his saddlebags. There was no small resemblance to myself, I thought, except for the married and the pious parts. Wonder if he married someone from here; or, maybe he simply lived the monastic life everyone expects from academics. He served in the Civil War; that must have been difficult for a medic. He must have also served as the town doctor. I wonder why he planted this tree—it must have been for some special occasion. I suppose I'll never know. He must have been popular; that is an affliction I have never suffered.

I turned toward the sidewalk and began the ascent to the building. The hill challenged my considerable bulk. I had been spoiled in the past decade, teaching in small institutions where the distance from the parking area to the building could be measured in feet. Before that, working in a large factory as I did, the trek from my car to my office could be as much as half a mile. I seem to be heavier now; I'm not sure why.

At the crest of the hill stood the three-story stone edifice that must have been the first building on campus. An engraved facing stone just below the second floor window above the entrance in the center of the building read "Founded 1857 By Mr. & Mrs. Rob't Alexander & S. H. Robertson." This fortunate occurrence relieved my curiosity about the Latin numerals on the plaque at the bottom of the hill that I had not troubled myself to figure out. Wait a minute! Didn't that M.D., what's-his-name, come here in '55? I can't remember. It does not matter.

Above the central entrance to the building, a semicircular marble plate that seemed out of place must have been added during a renovation project to cover what could only have originally been a window over the door. It read "Alexander Dickman Hall, 1857-1963." That would indicate the year of the renovation, no doubt.

In front of the doorway stood two lighted pillars

of the same native stone used for the facing of the building with the year 1916 engraved in their bases. Were they a gift from the Class of '16? The pillar on the right had a plaque attached with the words "In Honor of President Richard Watson Cooper, 1909-1916."

Fixed to the building, adjacent the doorway, were bronze plaques. On my right, the plaque read "In Memory of F Company, Third Iowa Volunteer Infantry." Hmmm... a standard Civil War Memorial. The plaque on my left read "UIU Student Soldiers of the Twelfth Regiment, Iowa Volunteer Infantry."

I was suddenly struck with the idea that students here, young men, these men listed on the plaque, had willingly, even cheerfully, left the shelter of the university to fight and even die. I had abrupt images and sensations that I still cannot explain. I imagined myself witness to tearful good-byes and optimistic reassurances, many to end in tragedy. The best of these good-byes would effect extended inconvenience and hardship. I jolted myself back to reality by visualizing the scenes of my own generation's response to war. There was no plaque celebrating the students' enthusiasm for Vietnam. This was the sort of institution where young men of little interest in academics would take refuge from the draft. What a difference a century can make.

The first interview would not take place for another few minutes, so rather than intrude upon the last moments of solitude that my handlers would have to finish their real work, I determined to see what could be learned in the lobby. As I stepped through the outer door, I noticed a plaque fixed to the wall on my left. It read "Lieut. Colonel Jacob Abernethy, Third Iowa Volunteer

Infantry, killed in front of Atlanta, Georgia, July 21, 1864. The first of the students from U.I.U. and the first man to enlist from Fayette County."

Again, I felt those strange sensations. Jacob must have enlisted as a private and rose through the ranks—not hard to do in that war if you had a fair amount of gumption and lived long enough. He would be labeled "gung-ho" by my comrades-in-arms, most of whom did not enlist. An unexpected sadness overwhelmed me when I realized that he never finished his studies, and never carried out his life plans. He was probably never married. He certainly missed most of the important things one may savor on the quest for meaning in adult life. He was probably never fired either.

Shaking off this glut of emotion—it must be a Mozart hangover—I turned my attention to a glass display case inside the lobby. Within were photographs of what must be the school choir. It was a small group; there were no more than a dozen singers in any photo. In the upper right-hand corner was a program for a wind ensemble concert. That they have an ensemble is encouraging. The pieces listed in the program included *California Girls* and *Rolling on the River*. Ewww!

While the original versions of these pieces stand with some of the greatest music ever performed, ensembles have about as much chance at a passable interpretation of them as the Cubs have of winning the World Series. What evil sadist selected these things? I hoped I would never find out.

A voice broke my concentration. "Good morning," it said.

I looked up to see a young African-American

woman, obviously a student, bouncing down the stairs. First glance gathered that she was bright, energetic, and not the least bit reserved. That, along with her ethnicity, a rarity in this part of Iowa, was a positive indication that there was indeed substance to this institution. Institutions that attract high quality minority students do so for a reason.

"Well, it is morning," I replied. "I'll let you know later if it was any good."

"Well," said she, in a cheerful voice, "you do that. And whatever good you find, how about sending some of it in my direction?"

"I will do that," said I, as she exited the door opposite the one I entered.

My outlook was brightened considerably. It was just about time to climb the staircase to the third floor where Lynn told me I would find her office. A quick stop in the restroom on the second floor assured me that my hair was neat and that my clothing was straight, as though appearance really mattered on a fifty-three-year-old overweight slob, who owed the best of his demeanor to the attentiveness of his caring and ever-hopeful wife.

A flash of surrealistic time found me sitting across the desk from the Division Chair for the first of a daylong round of interviews. Lynn was a pleasant woman; younger than I, knowledgeable, perceptive, and no shrinking violet. She seemed to be of a character well-suited to the role of Chair. It was another sign of substance that the institution boasted a larger-than-usual number of women in key positions.

This session set the tone for the day by its particular want of the confrontational banter that normally characterizes academic interviews. I was eager to display my somewhat impressive academic record, but no one seemed to care about it. I was ready with my defensive remarks about why I was seeking employment, but there was no challenge to defend against. The interviews with other faculty members went similarly, and lunch at a local cafe passed by with little, if any, job-related discussion.

Back in action after lunch, I made my presentation to a group of professors and staff members who could be persuaded to fill the seats left vacant by students on summer vacation. I materialized my best strategic management jargon, but the blank stares informed me that only the business faculty was prepared to hear it. It did not matter. The others were there primarily to verify that fire did not shoot out of my nose, or that my head did not rotate completely around as I spoke.

The day went so smoothly, I was to the final interview before I knew it. As I was introduced to the Vice President, I remembered the warning I had received that he can fill the time to overflowing with conversation. He led me into his office and sat down with me at a small round table. The ensuing colloquy was more like a friendly visit than like an interview.

"What's going on at Clarke?" he said, finally.

I knew that sooner or later someone would bring up the subject of my previous employment. His was a most interesting tact—getting to the point without being provocative.

"Do you want the truth or the cover story?" said I, as though there was really an option.

"The truth," said he, plainly.

"They built two buildings without any capital funds," I said, trying to sound as objective as possible. "A hatchet man was brought in as an Interim AVP, and was told to trim the budget. He looked through the faculty list for those of us who were highly paid who did not have tenure. He cut six of us in one day. We were all white males, all highest paid in our departments, all over fifty, and only one was Catholic as far as I know. There was a series of suspicious resignations, and some others were simply denied tenure. Since then, something over 15 faculty have left or have announced their intentions to leave. Vice Presidents are gone; the place is a mess."

"Do you intend to do anything about it?" he asked.

"No," I replied, flatly. "What for? I never felt accepted there. Brother John hired all of us to bring in some academic integrity, particularly to the graduate program. Most of what it took him eight years to build was wiped out in one semester. I have never enjoyed being where I was not wanted. I offered to take less money, but they turned me down. I think they're trying to pretend that money isn't the issue. I don't know what else it could be. My student evaluations were good. It can't be service; I was on several committees, and I played in several ensembles. It surely can't be scholarship. I knew they were paying me too much when I came in. They're replacing me with adjuncts."

"Why do you think they want to hide money problems?"

"Because of what happened at the University of Dubuque last year."

"Ah," said the V.P., who must have been familiar with that situation.

I suddenly had the feeling that he was going to make me an offer. If so, it would be extremely unusual. Normally in academia there are a number of candidates interviewed in a process that can take months before an offer is made.

"I would not want to be paid more than the institution could afford," I said, in anticipation of a circumstance that a rational mind would take to be highly improbable.

The V.P. wrote something on a small piece of paper and slid it across the table to me. There it was! An actual dollar figure. He was making me an offer. It was fairly lower than what Clarke was paying me, but it was realistic.

"This is what I can offer," said the V.P.

It is customary in such situations to ask for time to consider the offer. The unusual nature of this situation granted that as an option, but not an advisable one. I had other alternatives, but something told me that there was more going on than casual appearance would have it. If ever there was a case of all roads leading to Rome, this was it. As with most other circumstances in my life, I had no real choice.

"Then I shall accept," I said, with no hesitation. I will be the last to reject someone who actually wants me. Being genuinely appreciated is something I have experienced but rarely in my life.

We spoke some more about employment expectations and conditions, and then he gave me over to Lynn, informing her that I had accepted an offer.

As we were leaving, he called to Lynn from his office door. "I've done my job," he said, and turned to disappear inside.

A few niceties and informalities later, I was back standing beside my vehicle trying to assess the ontological standing of what I had just experienced. It seemed like an illusion. *The last time I stood here I was unemployed*, I thought, struggling to assimilate the outcome of the day's events. I was so distracted that I took some wrong turns, and was obliged to retrace my steps several times on the drive home. This was going to be a long commute.

Over the next month, I made several trips to campus to move into my new office and to adjust to the long drive. It was not really any more time than one might spend commuting twenty miles in San Diego in the stop-and-go traffic on the freeway. At least this was continuous movement through beautiful, hill-saturated farm country. There were but five stop signs and no traffic lights between my driveway and the campus. It would prove to be unusual to have more than one vehicle ahead of me at any stop sign.

My office was in the southwest corner of the third floor of the Old Main Building; Alexander Dickman-Hall. I had a corner office because it was the back portion of a classroom now dedicated to my use. A wall had been constructed in the rear of the classroom to create the office, the partition rising to within a foot of the ceiling to let the air circulate. It was a large space with two windows, one to the west looking down on the entrance to the university and on the town of Fayette, and the other to the south, looking across the newly beautified landscape of the campus. Both vistas were superb—better than any I have had in an office.

I moved only a small portion of my book collection, now tired of moving and gun-shy regarding longevity. A short time was all that was required to set up my new quarters, so I set aside an interlude to sit quietly and construct a psychological map of the space to allow for more effective movement.

I have always been fascinated with old buildings, wondering who lived there and what they were like; what happiness, what sadness, what genius, what folly rang through these walls? It is a shame that so much of the world remains closed forever to the pitiful limitations of conscious realization. I hope that when I die, I can know more than I do now.

If only these walls could talk.

II

A lone rider reined in his horse at the crest of the ridge. He sat upright in his saddle, as though there was not a tired bone in his body. Before him, in the hollow, was a good deal of open field. Eight wooden buildings were scattered about the flatland of the valley, the largest of these was opposite from where he sat, maybe half a mile or more distant. Four or five hundred yards beyond that building was another ridge, about as high as the one upon which he had paused, which marked the northern end of the valley.

To his left, a tree-lined ridge ran west for about a quarter mile before it angled north, giving a box-like appearance to that side of the valley. The road he was traveling ran straight for the north ridge in front of him, and up a shallow hill rising slowly above the valley floor. Upon this small rise, just east of the road, construction was underway. The new building looked to be a massive undertaking compared to the other structures.

This must be the village they spoke about in Independence. "Follow the road north until you cross the Mission Trail," they said, "it'll be right in front of you; you can't miss it." He was not altogether sure about following their advice at first. They were ruffians hanging out in front of Plane's Hardware Store, teamsters mostly. Their demeanor could best be described as careless. They seemed like honest men, but you would never know if they were pulling your leg.

These men had just driven the nearly impassable road through the sloughs east of Independence. They came from Dubuque bringing loads of hardware, most of which Plane would eventually sell to the Army at Fort Dodge. Many broken-down wagons would have littered that path—abandoned by drivers who did not know the tricks, drivers who just gave up—had not every scrap of wood from abandoned wagons been used for the supports needed to move the cargo. These men knew the tricks, and they never gave up. They were men hardened by their work, and not above handing some greenhorn a bit of that hardship.

The rider paused, thoughtfully. "This is a most pleasant prospect indeed," he said, softly to himself. The hardworking teamsters had not exaggerated. This was the sort of place he had been seeking.

He lifted the hat from his head to wipe his brow with a cloth. His hair was thick and dark, setting off the lightness of his skin. So much was the contrast of light and dark about his head as to be remarkable. His neatly trimmed beard helped to elongate the oval shape of his face. Brown, wide-set eyes reflected his kind and gentle nature, and brightened what his wife of nearly two years thought was the most handsome face she had ever seen. He was slight in stature, but it was a smallness that escaped notice. His trim frame was agile and compact, and hinted both of inner and outer strength.

"Now we shall discover whether this place is as good as it is beautiful," he thought, as he urged his horse onward.

Picking his way slowly down the steep, rocky incline, he noticed the variety of trees that populated the groves on either side of the road. Botany was his avocation, a love affair inspired by his mother's affection for all organisms great and small. Respect all living things, she had told him, and God will respect you.

The air was cool with the onset of autumn, but the bright colors of fall had not yet begun to grace the branches. All about him was the deep green of the thicket, beset as it was with interplay of sunlight and shadow.

The short but steep descent brought him to the floor of the valley. There, branching from the road that ran into town, the Mission Trail made a sharp angle to the right to weave its southeasterly path through the rolling hills toward Dubuque. The village lay on the road ahead.

A score of workmen near a wagon at the construction site caught his attention. Alongside the wagon was a pile of quarried stone destined for the new building. He urged his horse in that direction. It was growing late in the afternoon, and he will need lodging for the night. Spying one of the workmen emerging from the site, he inquired about an inn—was there such a thing in this village?

"You can try the Davis place," said the workman, as he pointed to the largest of the buildings in the village, about two hundred yards away toward the river.

Thanking the workman, the rider directed his horse toward the indicated building, which sat a short distance from the river. It looked like a large, two-story house, and did not appear to have been designed as a hotel. Its box-like appearance did not boast of any ornamentation. It was about forty-five feet long and about twenty-five feet across. Before its front door, which was positioned near the south edge of its length facing east, was a semicircular gravel drive for carriages to turn about. When the rider was within a few rods of the house, a man appeared at the door carrying a bucket. The man with the bucket did not notice the rider at first, but when he did, the rider called out.

"Is this the Davis place?"

"Why yes," said the man, who seemed to be about fifty years of age. "I'm Moses Davis. People 'round here call me Mo. Who might you be?"

"I am Charles Parker. My friends call me C.C. Might I apply for a room tonight?"

"We got a room for you," said Mo. "You can leave your horse in the stable out back. There's plenty of hay. It gets charged with the room."

"That will do fine," replied Charles.

"There's somethin' else you should know," said Mo, "I got two kids down sick, and I ain't sure what's wrong with 'em."

"I will look at them," said Charles, "I'm a surgeon."

"You're a doctor?" cried Mo. "I'd be much obliged."

Charles lowered himself slowly from the saddle, every corner of his body screaming with agony from the long ride. Mo assisted him, mostly out of joy at the prospect of help for his children. While Charles attempted to revive his aching limbs, Mo led the horse to the lean-to that passed for a stable.

"Show me to them," said Charles, beginning to feel that he could walk under his own power again.

The entry area opened upon a large parlor and adjoining dining room. Collectively, these rooms were used as a tavern. There were eight bedrooms upstairs. As Charles was escorted into the parlor, he could see a woman in the kitchen preparing supper and a teenaged girl setting the large dining table. The older woman was holding a small child with her left arm as she tended to pots on the stove with her right. The child was a girl of three or four who was resting her head on her mother's shoulder while her legs dangled loosely. The woman looked up from her stove with a pained expression.

"This here's my wife, Martha," said Mo. "Martha, this here's Doc Parker. He's come to look at the children, an' he'll be stayin' the night."

Martha removed the pot she was stirring from the stove, and wiped her right hand anxiously on a towel.

"Oh, God bless you," she said, in a troubled voice now laced with relief. "We're worried sick about the children. It started with the boy, and then this one come down with it. They just keep gettin' worse. We don't know what to do."

"I'll do what I can, Mrs. Davis," said Charles, in a soothing voice.

"The boy's upstairs," said Mo, as he led Charles to a narrow, winding stair. Martha followed close behind, carrying her little girl.

In a room in the corner of the floor above were three beds. One contained a boy of about six, and into the adjacent bed Martha carefully laid her daughter. They were sick all right. Mo brought a chair over, and Charles sat himself to begin the examination.

"I'll need some hot water and towels," he said to

Mo, who, with Martha, left immediately to fetch them. It was a trick Charles had learned from his mentor to keep the hovering parents away and busy for at least a few minutes. Charles always thought that sending them for something gave them a sense of participation and comfort.

Some time later, Charles descended the stairs to the main floor. He tried to sound encouraging as he delivered the bad news.

"I'm afraid they have typhoid fever," he said. "They are in very bad condition. I will stay and care for them as long as I am needed. I have some medicine with me that may help."

"Are you sure it's typhoid?" Mo asked, anxiously.

"Yes, quite sure," said Charles. "I had it myself some years ago. Are there any hospitals nearby?"

"There's the one in Dubuque," said Mo, "but that's it as far as I know."

"It would be too difficult to move them that far," said Charles. "I will do what I can here, and we can move them to a hospital when they improve."

If they improved, they would recover and would not need a hospital, but Charles was not optimistic about the prognosis. He wished to convey the gravity of the situation without offering a morbid prediction. He would be as positive as he could until the illness had run its course.

They were joined for supper by six workmen from the construction site who devoted their energy to eating rather than to speaking. Mr. and Mrs. Davis both seemed in a much better humor. They were encouraged by the presence of a doctor. Charles was very concerned that the outcome would destroy that delicate trust, yet he did not have the heart to tell them of his deepest fears. He hoped he was mistaken.

The conversation at the dinner table was almost lighthearted. People on the frontier learn how to make the most of every moment, and to accept whatever happens with the conviction that life continues in spite of it.

"So, you come up from the south?" asked Mo, as he tore a piece of bread from a fresh loaf to sop up the gravy on his plate.

"Yes, I did," Charles answered, careful to swallow the peas he was chewing before speaking. "I came up from Independence this morning."

"Yeah, that town's really growin'," said Mo. "Lots of people movin' in to Buchanan County. You lookin' at land to buy?"

"Well yes," Charles answered, "in a manner of speaking. I had a letter from a colleague of mine by the name of Joseph Powell who moved to Independence from Ohio three years ago. He said it was a booming area, full of opportunity, but when I arrived, I found that he had died suddenly. I heard some people speaking about the building of a college here, so I came to see if this was a suitable place to move my family."

"It's as good a place as you'll find anywhere," said Mo. "I bought this here hotel because this is the next big boom town. Sam Robertson built this place. He an' his family was gonna move into it, but he decided that it'd work better as a inn an' boardin' house, so he built another house for himself over by his field, east of here. They brought in a slug o' workers to build the seminary, an' they gotta stay somewheres. It's small now, but I got three acres to expand on."

"Is that the college they are building on the hill?" asked Charles.

"Well, no," said Mo. "That's just the seminary. The college is gonna be built up on the south ridge, by the road you come in on."

"I did notice a large area staked out in lots south of the ridge," said Charles.

"Yeah, the Robertsons and the Alexanders got big plans for up there," said Mo. "The Colonel figures there's a lot of high class folks gonna move here because of the college, so they staked out a whole city up there. Since there ain't enough kids 'round here ready for college now, they decided to start with the seminary. They figure they can get the college built by the time the kids is ready."

"Is the Colonel an educator?" asked Charles, having not the smallest inkling who "the Colonel" was.

"Naw," said Mo. "He's a businessman. He started this town, well, really, he started the town of Westfield, up the river 'bout a half mile. He built the sawmill up there. Sam Robertson, one of his two son-in-laws, laid out Fayette here. Jim Robertson's his other son-in-law who got the land where the college is gonna sit. Sam donated the land for the seminary."

"It seems to be quite a project," said Charles. "Judging from the footing, it should be a very impressive building."

"Yup," said Mo, taking a swig from his cup of coffee. "Elizabeth wouldn't hear of no wood building. She insisted that it be made outta stone. They was gonna build it from rubble stones, but Charlie West, who come here from Brooklyn, New York, told 'em that it'd be much more hoity-toity if it was faced with limestone. Since the Colonel thinks hoity-toity is good for business, it is as you see it. I think its gonna cost 'em a lot more than they think. That's what I think."

"This supper is excellent," said Charles, finishing the last morsel on his plate. "Perfect for celebrating an anniversary."

"What anniversary?" spouted Mo, afraid that he had forgotten something important.

"Why," said Charles, "it is the anniversary of my birth, thirty-two years ago today."

"Oh, it's your birthday," said Mo, greatly relieved. "If we had known, we'd have thrown a party. That may still happen, 'cause folks know you're in town, and they're gonna want to come by and find out who you are."

With the gravity of prophesy written, Mo's words came to pass almost immediately as a knock on the door heralded the arrival of at least half the town.

It was the most important social event of the week, this being only Wednesday. After a hearty round of greetings, everyone gathered around the now crowded dining area to meet the new arrival. The highest in the social register were introduced first.

"This is Colonel Alexander," said Mo, "and this is his wife, Elizabeth."

"Pleased to make your acquaintance," said Elizabeth, with great reverence, as she shook Charles's hand.

The Colonel just grunted as he squeezed the

surgeon's slender fingers. The Colonel looked exactly as a frontier Colonel should... tall, slim, alert. His face was weathered and sunburned, highlighted by his sandy red hair which was beginning to show streaks of gray. He was rough around the edges, but straightforward and honorable. He looked to be about sixty years of age, and eagerly embracing his role as the town's patriarch, both figuratively and literally.

Charles would learn later that the "Colonel's" title was the result of one week of service as a Private in Davidson's Mounted Dragoons, mobilized for service in Indiana for the Black Hawk War. The title must have stuck because it suited him so well.

"The Colonel tells me he once owned a tavern just like mine," said Mo, giving the big man the rib. "And, that's Elizabeth's seminary you can almost see the first floor of."

"Oh, it's not my seminary," she said, sternly. "I only said to Reverend Brunson that we have as much right to a good school as any other town. I don't think its right that I have to send Kate and Emily, those are my twin girls, off to Mount Pleasant or Mount Vernon just to get an education. Why can't we have a college right here in Fayette? So Robert, uh... the Colonel, and Sam, that is Sam Robertson, my son-in-law, you see him standing there, arranged for the building as you see it. We pressed John Griffen into service to oversee the construction. He was going to build a store, but we talked him into building the seminary first. The first floor should be done before year's end. We're hoping to get the Iowa Conference of the Methodist Episcopal Church to sponsor us."

"That is very interesting," said Charles, trying to mask his extreme fatigue.

"What about you, Doctor Parker?" asked Elizabeth, irrepressibly, "have you had experience with starting a school? Where did you do your medical study?"

"As it happens," said Charles, "my father founded the Clermont Academy in Clermont County, Ohio, where I was educated along with my brothers and sisters. My oldest brother, James, is still the principal there. I taught in the Academy for a short time before beginning my medical studies under the tutelage of Dr. William Johnson in Clermont County. I went to Starling Medical College in Columbus to complete my medical degree in 1850, and returned to Clermont to practice."

"Oh," exclaimed Elizabeth, "that's wonderful. We could sure use your help. Are you going to settle here?"

The room, hushed before her question was spoken, was now absolutely quiet. The profound silence was unsettling.

"I am considering it," said Charles, unwilling to commit himself further, but loath to disappoint these good people.

"What can we offer to get you to settle here?" said the Colonel, getting to the point in a gruff voice.

"This is such a beautiful valley," said Charles. "If you are building a college, this should be a thriving community before long. Am I to understand that you have no doctor in town?"

"That is correct, sir," replied the Colonel. "We need one if we are to thrive, as you say."

"Are you married?" asked Elizabeth.

"Yes," answered Charles. "My wife, Sarah, and our baby boy await my return in Ohio."

"Do you belong to a church there?" asked Elizabeth, hopefully.

"Sarah has been a member of the Methodist Episcopal Church all of her life," answered Charles. "I joined before we were married."

"Oh, that is wonderful," exclaimed Elizabeth, encouraged by this connection with the newcomer. The local Methodist Episcopal congregation had been formed in Fayette just that summer.

"It's Doc Parker's birthday today," Mo announced, thinking that a good party would be more convincing than questions about church. "I'm gonna serve a round of drinks for everybody."

"When were you born?" asked the Colonel, in his normal woodsy manner, as Mo positioned himself behind the small bar.

"September twelfth, 1823," Charles replied, with a sense of pride. His age made him something of an elder and the respect he was being accorded here was a vast improvement over the minimal salience he experienced at home.

"Hmm," mused the Colonel, "it's '55 now, so that'd make you, uh, thirty-two."

"Yes, indeed it would," replied Charles, with a smile.

As the Colonel turned his prominent nose toward the bar, Elizabeth slid into the chair next to Charles. She looked younger than the weathered Colonel, but still must be at least in her mid-fifties. She was plain in the manner of nearly all frontierswomen. She wore the traditional bonnet of white linen, and a black dress that covered her from her chin to her toes. Her dark, deep-set eyes were narrow and unadorned, and they pierced you to the soul. Beneath her small, chiseled nose, her mouth was thin and pulled back into a determined line that dropped slightly below center plane at its corners.

Elizabeth reminded Charles a great deal of his own mother in many ways. Her countenance declared her religious devotion, that no-nonsense approach to solving life's problems that Charles likened to his mother's trademark piety. Beneath the stern exterior, there was a vivacious energy and insatiable curiosity, which gave her an aura of youth. Elizabeth was a determined woman with specific objectives who exercised control over everyone about her with little tolerance for diversion or frivolity. She bore the consciousness of her mortality with the zeal of a missionary who had a certain agenda to complete before God's final call. Charles was, at present, the target of her zealousness, and no sign of fatigue or indifference on his part would dissuade her.

"Well," said she, obviously brimming with questions, "how did you and your wife, her name is Sarah, right? How did you meet?"

"I first met Sarah when she came to Clermont Academy to study," Charles began, realizing that he would not be released to retire until Elizabeth had been satisfied. "She was just a young girl then, and I had no inclinations toward any woman. I went off to Columbus to study, and I saw her again when I returned to Clermont to practice. We were very good and close friends, but we were still not ready to make anything permanent of it. I joined her church to be close to her. In 1852, I was chosen Demonstrator of Anatomy at Starling, so I returned to Columbus thinking to make my life there and hoping to convince her to eventually join me, but alas, I was forced to resign after a bout of typhoid fever. The small quarters I was assigned were just too confined for my health. The stench of chemicals and formaldehyde that constantly assaulted my sinuses was just more than I could bear, so I moved back to Clermont. I am not sure whether it was her idea or mine, but in either case we were married in October two years ago. It is nearly our anniversary, on the fourth, and I hope to arrive back in Ohio in time to celebrate with Sarah and our dear little boy."

"Oh," cooed Elizabeth, "what's your little boy's name?"

"William," answered Charles, with no small measure of pride, "William Lakin Parker. He was named for Sarah's father, William Lakin, and for my grandfather, William. I also have an older brother named William, and Sarah has a younger brother named William. Choosing his name was an easy way to honor both families. Our son is only seven months old; he was born last February."

"Your family is from Ohio?" asked Elizabeth, knowing full well that few families had been there for more than one generation. She desired to know everything about him, but was mindful to avoid being overly assertive, lest he shrink from exposure.

"Well," said Charles, slowly, "there is no short answer to that question."

Charles was hoping that Elizabeth would have had her fill of conversation so that he could retire, but there was no sign of any such circumstance. Cultured and well-bred strangers did not happen into town with any regularity. When they did, the custom was to wrest all possible society from them before the opportunity vanished.

In addition to gathering information for its entertainment value, Elizabeth had an ulterior motive—to connect the stranger to the town and its people to encourage him to settle here. They needed him desperately, not only for health care, but he would also be a tremendous asset for the new college.

Seeing that she was awaiting his response with great anticipation, Charles continued with the short version of the long story. "About 1640, five Parker brothers sailed over from Wiltshire, England—I think their names were Abraham, Jacob, James, Joseph, and John—to settle in Woburn, Massachusetts. Jacob represented my line of the family, which eventually settled in Malden, Massachusetts. My great-great grandfather was named Thomas, and he built a mansion in Malden that is still known today as the old Parker homestead. My grandfather, William, was a cabinetmaker who prospered by selling many of the products of his labor in the West Indies. He bought the family land in Ohio, some twelve hundred acres, sight unseen; I think it was called the Ohio Company's Purchase at the time."

"My father, Daniel, was born in 1781 in Newburyport, Massachusetts, but he did not stay there long. Sometime in 1788, my grandfather packed up the family belongings in a covered wagon, left behind everything he had built in Massachusetts, and moved west to settle on his land in Ohio. They managed to travel only as far as Western Pennsylvania, south of Pittsburgh near the point where the Youghiogheny and the Monongahela Rivers come together, before they had to stop because of the Indian wars. My father told me that because there were no houses available, the family was obliged to live in a sheep pen that a kind farmer was willing to provide them for a month."

"Since there was no apparent letup in the wars, my grandfather took a job as a cabinetmaker and hired out my father and his brothers to work on farms in the local area. After a time, my grandfather rented some land and founded a sawmill, the wood from which he used to build flatboats. Eventually, he bought a farm in what was called the *'forks of Yough'*."

"In 1802, my grandfather again packed the family belongings, this time in two flatboats he had fashioned for that purpose, and again left everything behind to move to Meigs County on Leading Creek. He built a cabin there in Rutland, Ohio, and died in 1825 when I was two. I never knew him, but I wish I had had the opportunity."

"That is very interesting," said Elizabeth, sincerely. "So your father became a farmer?"

"Ah, yes," said Charles, wistfully, rolling his head to the side, "my father."

After a brief pause, Charles said "that is a long and twisting tale. Are you sure that you care to hear it?"

"Of course I do," said Elizabeth, with that tone of voice that is frequently used to answer a silly question.

Charles sighed to himself. He wished that she would be anxious to join the revelry that had already taken on a life of its own apart from his presence, but her fixation on his story had not waned in the least. Besides, she did not appear to be the sort of person who would be interested in spontaneous celebration for its own sake.

"My father," said Charles, with a tone of resignation, "learned his father's cabinet trade. And when he came of age, he set up a cabinet making business in Kyger Bottom in Gallia County, Ohio. He also studied scripture at home, and 'round about 1805 he gave up his business to preach the Gospel full time. He originally joined the Halcyon Church, but that dissolved after a brief period of duration."

"Father decided that the Bible does not teach endless punishment, but instead it teaches the final restoration to holiness and happiness. And so, he preached without an affiliation. Having no affiliation meant that he still had to work to support himself, so he and his brother, my Uncle John, designed and patented a hemp-breaking machine and a washing machine. Father went into business with a partner by the name of Alvin Bingham. Around 1809 and 1810 they traveled all over Ohio, Kentucky, and Tennessee, and sometimes as far south as New Orleans, making and selling their machines; my father preaching the Gospel."

"In October of 1816, he married my mother, whose name at the time was Priscilla Ring. They met when my father was invited by Mr. James Kennedy to preach in Point Pleasant. It was in June previous to their marriage. My mother was first married to a merchant seaman, named Benjamin Ring, who died when his schooner capsized off the coast of Massachusetts. The year after, she immigrated from Hallowell, Maine to New

Richmond, Ohio in the same manner as Grandfather had come, by flatboat on the Ohio River. When she arrived, she grew very sick with malignant fever, and the only child of her first marriage died. She was taken in by Mr. Kennedy and his family to their house in Kentucky, and she boarded with them while she taught school there. The schoolhouse in which she taught was directly across the Ohio River from Point Pleasant and one mile upstream."

"Well," continued Charles, with a slight smile playing about his lips, "my father tells me that Mr. Kennedy invited him to spend the night, as was customary with traveling ministers. And thither also was invited my mother, at the time unknown to my father except for their brief introduction before his sermon. He spent the evening deeply engaged in conversation with the mysterious widow in black, whom he had first seen as she made her way across the river to the meeting with the Kennedy party. He tells me also that he was smitten, and proposed marriage a few weeks later after only a few meetings with her. His proposal was met with the diffidence he claims he fully expected from a young woman—she was only twenty-three—of such great virtue, and who had faced such hardship."

"Father was persistent, as he is in all things, and when his character became better known to Mother, she accepted him. Their engagement happened to coincide with the wedding plans that Mr. Kennedy had made for his daughter, Florilla. So, they were married together in the Kennedy home, the place where their acquaintance had begun and where it had flourished. That is why my oldest brother's name is James Kennedy Parker; he's the one I mentioned who is the Principle Teacher in

Clermont Academy. Mother's parents were Hugh and Priscilla Mulloy of New England. She was born in Litchfield, Maine in May of 1793."

"So," inquired Elizabeth, "did your father settle then in Ohio?"

"Yes," replied Charles, "Father bought ninety-two acres and built a house in Mt. Hygiene, which is near New Richmond. That is where he built Clermont Academy in 1839. His object, and that of Mother, was to provide an education for their children that was superior to what was available in that country at the time."

After a brief pause, Charles inquired, "Did you and the Colonel come from back east?"

He was hoping that she would be reluctant to reveal much about their personal life, and thus provide him with the moral upper hand if he should refuse to continue the discussion.

"That is, as you say, a long and twisting tale," said she, with an uncharacteristic sparkle in her eye. "But since you have agreed to tell your tale, so I shall tell mine."

This was not the answer for which Charles was hoping, but it was too late to stop it now. She continued, and he politely accepted her confidence.

"When I was fourteen," she began, lifting her gaze to Heaven, "I first heard my call to the church. I accepted God's plan for my life, and became a Methodist. I was so enraptured by God's message that I would not rest until everyone else had heard it also. There was, at the time, a handsome young farmer who lived with his brother near my folks' place in Brooksville, Indiana that I especially thought should hear the Word."

"Well," she said, lowering her eyes from their former position to Charles by way of an earthly aside, "he was not a good listener. I tried in vain for two years to break through to him, so in the end I had to marry him to make sure that he followed the straight and narrow path."

Charles was suddenly taken by this revelation of a subtle and pleasing sense of humor not ordinarily expected from a person of Elizabeth's character. More than a lapse of seriousness, it represented a deep emotional bearing that was entirely humanitarian, and it indicated that, for her, love was more important than almost anything else.

"That was the year of 1816," she continued, "the same year apparently that your parents were married."

"Yes," Charles mused, "that is an interesting coincidence."

"After we were married," said Elizabeth, "we moved to Connersville, Indiana, where Robert worked as a hatter. But that sort of work made a noticeable mark on his health. It must have been the chemicals, as you said affected you in your work. Robert took up farming, but in 1825 he decided that we needed a better climate. To tell the truth, his health was still not its best. So we packed up our belongings in an ox cart, and moved to Lafayette, Indiana. On the way, Robert bought some apple trees to plant an orchard. When we got to Lafayette, we did not have much money, so Robert cut down a tree and made a small shelter out of the rails. I used some quilts to make it a cozy little house that we lived in until Robert made a proper cabin. We lived very well there, except for the period of the Black Hawk War. In 1832, Robert was obliged to join the militia to protect us. That was of short duration, however, and he was soon back to work on the farm."

"After ten years of building it, Robert sold that farm for a good profit, and we moved to Parish Grove, Illinois. That was about 1836. That's where Robert built the inn that Moses loves to rib him about. We did very well there too except that I thought that Chicago was becoming too wild a place for raising children. He finally sold that place for a good profit, and we moved here in 1849."

Elizabeth fell silent. Charles at first believed that she had been satiated, but soon realized from her demeanor that she now wanted him to continue with his part of the story. She did not want to appear overbearing, but she was attempting to assess his general character. She was negotiating for this intimacy in a tit-for-tat exchange of family histories.

Charles sat quietly for a moment, until a sudden urge to confess overwhelmed him. Perhaps it was extreme fatigue, but he felt a strong desire to declare certain things to the open air. In this near wilderness, were the perfect conditions for shedding the mantles of social station. Here you are accepted for who you are and not for what your history has anticipated of you. Here you may voice what is in your heart and expect that it will be taken for just what it is. He did not foresee any objection from Elizabeth to his pursuit of this discourse.

"Father can be a difficult man to live with," he began. "He is highly principled but, sometimes, well... he is a highly complex man. He has not always been as accessible to his children in the manner in which one expects a father to be. I love him dearly, but I fear I shall never have the opportunity to know him well. His theology is not of the common way, and is understood only by him. Yet, he is content with his belief and is as unshakeable in his faith as any I have known. When he was appointed Pastor of the First Restorationist Church of Cincinnati, he was not well accepted. His views on certain issues were—rather, still are—somewhat radical. He was misunderstood and maligned, but gradually he won acceptance from the congregation because his heart is pure and well intentioned. Father has restrained himself from discussing his views on theology with the students in Clermont Academy even though James imbues the subject matter with prayers and scripture. Father thinks this the prudent course, lest the parents of his patrons accuse him of taking advantage of his position. Still, he and Mother are very adamant regarding the importance of moral and religious obligations."

"One project upon which he vigorously exercises his support is the fight against slavery. He and Mother are staunch abolitionists, something of which I wholly approve, I might add. Some years ago, Father supported the plan to colonize slaves as a means of abolishing slavery that was originally proposed by Bushrod, Washington, Madison, and Clay, but he soon realized that those men had no intentions of freeing their own slaves. In light of that insincerity, Father determined that the only answer was to free the slaves altogether and to let them choose their own destiny. Mother shares his conviction and his enthusiasm."

"We are not supporters of slavery around here,"

said Elizabeth, forcefully. "We believe everyone should have an equal chance at a good life, and that you should be able to reap the rewards of your hard work. The new seminary will be open to all students just for that reason."

"I am pleased to hear that," said Charles. "Father and Mother had the same intentions for Clermont Academy. It is open to people of all colors, all faiths, and all levels of social consequence. Among Clermont's students number several former slaves and the children of former slaves. Girls and boys are taught in the same apartment. James rejects corporal punishment as a tool of discipline. He governs through appeals to understanding and to conscience rather than to any principle of fear. Studies are aimed at the promotion of growth and well-being. A lyceum currently thrives to nurture composition and rhetoric."

"That is my wish for Fayette Seminary," said Elizabeth, ardently. "It shall be an opportunity for all to get an education."

"Father is rather idealistic," said Charles, still pursuing his disclosure, "and does not always embrace the realities of the world. Mother, however, is more grounded in the pragmatic courses of living. She is a very strong, forceful, and pious activist. She spares no quarter in her guidance of the deportment of others. Mother demands excellence in word and deed, and she does not settle for less than perfection."

"You know," he added, leaning forward slightly, as though he were revealing a deep, dark secret, "everyone calls her Mother Parker. She does not condone drinking or frivolous behavior of any sort."

He sat back in his chair and a slight scowl

clouded his face as he spoke. "She is everyone's mother."

Charles now regretted the course of his conversation, which for him amounted to an outburst. The boundaries of social grace had been clearly compromised, and he was about to apologize for his indiscretion when, to his surprise, Elizabeth took up his torch.

"Oh," she said softly, her voice quivering with emotion, "my dear Martha. My dear little girl passed from us two years ago next month. She would have been sixteen this year. She was so beautiful and so full of life."

Elizabeth dropped her head slightly and folded her hands into her lap. Presently, she looked up at Charles.

"Do you know what she did, my sweet Martha?" she said, looking into his face with tears welling up in her eyes. "She stood up on that hill one day and she said 'what a lovely view, wouldn't it be lovely to be buried here.' Well, she died a few months after that. There was nothing we could do but bury her in the spot that she picked out. You might have seen it from the Mission Road coming in. I miss her so much."

Elizabeth paused momentarily. She held her eyes in a steady downward gaze; she seemed to be having an internal discussion. Finally, she looked up into Charles's eyes and said directly "Robert is a good man, but sometimes I wish he would be more sensitive. Do you know that he will not allow services to be held in our house? When the minister comes to town, we must go to my daughter Elizabeth's. She and James are very devote, and they welcome regular services. Robert will allow the minister to come for dinner, but he will not tolerate any discussion of religion in his presence."

They held each other's hands and shared their emotions quietly together. It was a rare moment for both of them; they were no longer strangers, but now connected in common experience.

The crowd in the room was dissipated somewhat, folks mindful that tomorrow was another full day of work. If anyone was aware of what was transpiring between Charles and Elizabeth, there was no sign of it. They all knew full well of Elizabeth's ability to work magic when something important was at stake. So, they left her to do her work.

Charles rose early the following morning to look in on the children. He had slept soundly, but was not well rested. The children seemed a little better. Still, he was not optimistic about their condition. It would be at least another few days before he could begin to think of leaving. He had given his word.

After breakfast, he decided to walk down to the river. It was the sort of river that would run a mill, but would not accommodate a flatboat for any distance. Its bed was gravel and its water clear, which would indicate healthy conditions. The air was warmer than it had been the previous day, and Charles was grateful for a respite from his long ride. He sat for a time on the bank, looking down into the shallow water. A leaf was running with the current, floating effortlessly by, moving in and around the contours of the flow. He stared into the static patterns created by the flowing water, and a sense of peacefulness embraced him as a mother embraces her child.

"This is a lovely place," he thought. He wondered how Sarah would like it. She would tell him that it was his choice, but he was always careful to consider her feelings. She, like himself, was gentle and giving, and would not object to his decision if it was well intentioned.

Sarah's image filled his mind as he thought of her. His favorite memory of her was of the time they had their first picnic after they were married. She had fixed such good things to eat, and the sunny outdoors was so refreshing. He could picture her petite form as she sat on the blanket with her legs folded under her skirt. Her soft blue eyes were intensified by the reddish tint to her naturally wavy hair. It was the perfect beginning to the perfect marriage. Charles would not be content if she was not happy. She liked much the same things that he liked. He could imagine her pleased with what she would find in this place. He was sure that she would trust his judgement.

He pondered the responsibilities of providing for his family, and wondered what sort of life the future would hold in this pocket of semi-civilized wilderness. While many areas of Iowa were bustling and thriving, this region in the northeast portion of the state was sparsely settled. There was no railroad here as yet. Besides, witnesses still living could describe Indian massacres that occurred near this spot in gory detail. That may have been what kept many settlers away.

Still there was an irresistible charm and the new seminary and college would almost certainly establish Fayette as a population center. Elizabeth had said that Fayette would be the county seat when that sort of thing was finally decided. Yes, there were many good reasons for moving here.

He rose and walked further upstream along the bank. After a little distance, he could see the sawmill. It was bustling with activity. Coming toward him, on the road that ran between the towns of Westfield and Fayette, was the Colonel. His profile announced him long before his face was discernable. As with most other things about him, his gait was deliberate and direct. His faculties were focused on the task before him to the exclusion of incidentals.

"Good morning, Colonel," said Charles, in a cheery voice.

The Colonel gave a small start, as though he had been deep in thought.

"Hello, Dr. Parker," he said, in measured tone.

"My friends call me C.C.," Charles said. That was mostly correct. The number of duplicated names in his family necessitated an efficient way of identifying the person of reference, so initials and pet names were used almost universally for the children. Sarah called him Charles because it was dignified, and because she felt it was more becoming of him. Privately, he was partial to Sarah's form of endearment, but he was concerned that it indicated a formality that was not consistent with his nature. Besides, he was not given to correcting those who had already built the habit, and it had become his habit as well.

"Very well, C.C.," replied the Colonel. "I was hoping to run into you today. I spoke with my foreman about building you a house. We can accommodate pretty much any price range. Would you like to live nearer or further from the river?"

Charles was taken aback somewhat by the

Colonel's presumption. He might have been offended, but for his realization that this was the Colonel's way of doing business. The Colonel routinely made decisions and took actions for others. He figured that if they objected, they would let him know. He was not a man to waste time waiting for the less decisive to make up their minds. Charles was more amused than offended. He appreciated the Colonel's directness, and he was very flattered by the obvious desire for him to reside and work in town.

"Let me think about it," Charles replied. "My first inclination is to locate nearer the river, but there are reasons to be further from it."

This was a good stalling tactic. He provided a sensible reason for holding the Colonel off without revealing that he was not firmly decided to make the move.

"Well, good!" said the Colonel, feeling that his initial objective was accomplished. "You will let me know. When will you be leaving to retrieve your family?"

"I have promised to take care of the Davis children until the danger has passed," said Charles. "I should know in a few days."

"Yes," said the Colonel, "and how are they doing?"

"They seem to be a little better," replied Charles, optimistically, "but only time will tell."

"Good!" said the Colonel, as he turned to continue his course for the construction site. "You will let me know."

As the Colonel strode away, Charles looked after

him wishing that Sarah were there with him to help him decide. He believed deep down that she was more sensible in these matters than he, even though she deferred all such decisions to him. Neither of them was wont to force opinions upon the other, nor upon anyone else for that matter. Often, reluctance to exercise their voices masked their volition, and was taken by some as indifference. At least they were alike in that respect.

Charles continued down the road to the mill. Careful not to become an obstacle, he watched its workings with fascination. He was not an expert in such things, but the operation seemed to him to be particularly efficient. No doubt, it reflected the Colonel's influence.

Into the following day, Charles had a number of conversations with local residents. A short ride through the countryside confirmed the descriptions of rolling hills and beautiful scenery of which the townspeople boasted. The soil was fertile, and the climate appeared to be generally healthy. This was certainly a place that would attract multitudes of settlers.

By Saturday, the fifteenth, Charles was nearly decided to make this beautiful valley home for his family. As if God were urging him in that direction by providing supportive omens, the condition of the Davis children improved dramatically. Responding to treatment, their recovery had accelerated over the past twenty-four hours, and it seemed that they would soon be free of the disease. He was grateful that he had not voiced his original opinion, and accepted these developments as an indication of his obligation to providence.

That evening, during the ritualized Saturday night

celebration at Mo's tavern, Charles announced his intentions. His disclosure brought a round of hoorahs and an outpouring of appreciation that was at least as embarrassing as it was gratifying. Mo called for a toast, which by protocol was the responsibility of the Colonel. The large, steady man rose to his feet with great ceremony, and raised his mug with great reverence.

"This evening," said the Colonel, his voice deep with the solemn dignity of the occasion, "we have been blessed with the final ingredient for our continued progress. We may leave here knowing that not only will the suffering of many be relieved, as has been demonstrated by the children of this house this day, but that the mark of civilization will be upon us and will be known to all, and that this township will boast one of the great cities of the West. To our industry, to our seminary, and to our greatest asset of all, our new town doctor."

As one, the crowd took a long drink. Another hearty round of hoorahs brought a flush to Charles's face. He was now beginning to worry whether or not he could live up to their expectations. Still, he had a high regard for providence, and had long ago resolved to go wherever it was indicated he should go. Be the outcome what it may, this was his destiny and he would make the most of it. His only regret now was that Sarah was not already here to join the celebration. He accepted this display of appreciation and deep gratitude with his characteristic humility because, as his mother had always told him, nothing, whether it's good or bad, is ever permanent, except Heaven.

That night, Charles awoke with a start. He sat bolt upright in his bed, his body permeated with an ominous sensation of foreboding. A quick check told him that all of his body signs were abnormal—pounding heart, shallow breathing, cold sweat, shaking limbs. Yet, these were symptoms of panic, not illness. Something was horribly wrong, yet he could not imagine what it could be. At first, he thought that it must be remorse about having committed to such a risky decision to move here. He laid his head back upon the pillow and tried to calm himself and drop back to sleep. It was a vain attempt. He moved about trying to find a comfortable position, but the deep sense of dread that now invaded him like a parasite would not let him rest.

Was it something he was dreaming? He could not remember. It was nothing he could explain. It must be something to create such a reaction. As he lay there mentally sorting out the possibilities for this circumstance as any good scientist would do, the desire to return home began to grow. While sleep did not come again to him, this desire began to take on the dimensions of urgency. Before the predawn light began to break up the night sky, Charles was up and packing for his return trip.

The morning was cold, and the horse's breath made clouds of steam as Charles cinched up the saddle. He carefully secured his saddlebags and arranged his gear for the long ride ahead. By the time Charles reentered the house, Mo was up and dressed and preparing for breakfast.

"Mornin'!" exclaimed Mo, in a cheery mood. "You headin' out?"

"Yes," replied Charles, "I think I must."

"The Colonel thought you might," said Mo. "He

said he was sendin' over one of his mechanics to take your order for a house this mornin'. Should be here any time."

"Ah," said Charles, considering that a few more moments of delay would not hurt, "that is good. I suppose a long journey should begin with a good breakfast."

Just as they all sat down to eat, the mechanic arrived. He joined them for breakfast, and they conducted their business. The Colonel had picked out a lot on Washington Street just half a block from the Davis place, the second lot south of the corner. The two-room house would be of modest price, but large enough to accommodate their needs with room to expand; they would begin work immediately, considering that winter was closing in. That being settled, Charles made arrangements with Mo for a room in which to stay on his return. The work would not likely be finished in time for their anticipated arrival. Thus completing his business, Charles lost no further time in making his way back to Ohio.

The return trip must be short and direct. Charles took the Mission Trail directly to Dubuque, and from there made a direct route through northern Illinois to Chicago, and then southeast through central Indiana to Cincinnati. Beyond Cincinnati was Point Pleasant where Sarah and their son were staying in the small house they had rented there. They had decided to reside in Point Pleasant after they were married to be near Sarah's mother, for whom she had been named. Sarah's father had died twelve years previous, and her mother's ability to care for herself had diminished in that time.

The trip took nearly two weeks, punctuated by storms and hardships. On many occasions, Charles was forced to take shelter for extended periods of bad weather. On other occasions there was no inn, so he was required to sleep on the ground. Swollen streams and ferries that had been broken up or swamped required hours of detour to bypass. Each day, each obstacle was met with stronger determination than the previous.

It was late in the evening when Charles rounded the turn that brought him to within sight of his home. As he dismounted, his heart pounded with anticipation. He could not wait to tell Sarah of his adventures. He would see to the horse later; now he must greet his wife and satisfy his longing for her warmth and embrace. Their son would be sleeping, but he should be happy to see his father.

The dimly lit parlor lay before him as he opened the front door. At first glance, everything appeared to be normal. No one was in the room. As he turned to close the door, he again had that strange sensation that he could not explain. It was the sense of foreboding that had been gnawing at him for the entire trip. He had thought it was the mental anguish that usually accompanies perilous and difficult travel, but the greatest dangers had passed. He should be releasing it now.

Turning again toward the center of the room, he felt a great apprehension. Taking care not to make noise lest he should disturb something—what it was he might disturb, he did not know—Charles stood still and scanned the room more closely. At first, he could not find Sarah. Finally, he spotted her sitting in a rocking chair in the darkest corner of the room. She had not said a word on his arrival. As he approached, he noticed that her gaze was fixed on some distant object in front of her. She was quietly rocking back and forth at a steady pace, and she did not seem to be aware of his presence.

"Sarah," he said, softly.

She stopped rocking and turned her head toward him, but her eyes were focused beyond, as though he was not standing there. He noticed the lines and dark circles under her eyes that indicated sleeplessness and extreme fatigue. Something was dreadfully wrong.

"Sarah," he repeated, "it's me, Charles. Sarah, are you all right?"

It was a long moment before she responded. Then, it was only a slight shaking of her head.

"Sarah," he pleaded, "what's wrong? Where's Will? Is he in our room?"

She slowly shook her head, but still she did not speak.

Charles moved slowly to her chair, and dropped to one knee.

"Sarah," he said, breathlessly, "Sarah, where is Will? Where is our little boy?"

She did not speak directly. She turned her head slightly to meet his eyes with her own. It was then that he could see the intense pain reflected in her eyes. He was now quite certain that his feelings of dread were not baseless. He was searching for something to say when she finally spoke.

"He died," she said, her voice coming from a thousand miles away.

"Oh, Sarah, no!" Charles cried softly, his voice quivering with shock and anguish. He lowered his head and began to sob as the events of the past few months flashed through his memory—how he had traveled and searched and planned, how he had envisioned his son by his side exploring their new life together. All of that would come to nothing.

It was a few minutes before he regained enough control and presence of mind to raise his head and to gather Sarah to him for a long overdue embrace. She did not resist, but she also did not reciprocate. She sat limp in his embrace for some time without moving.

Charles began to feel intense guilt for not being there, for not providing for his family when they needed him the most. He would never forgive himself for being absent when his presence might have made all the difference. He held his unresponsive wife closer to him in a plea for forgiveness.

"Oh Sarah," he said, when he could finally bring himself to speak, "I am so sorry."

He could speak no more.

Suddenly, letting loose the suffering and torment that had been compounding itself for what seemed like an eternity, Sarah began to wail. Her body was convulsing uncontrollably with grief. Charles was obliged to lay aside his own sorrow temporarily to continue holding on to her tightly, lest she fall to the floor and injure herself. Just at the point where he began to feel that his dwindling strength would fail him, she brought her arms up about his neck and held on to him tightly. Her convulsions subsided.

They slid gently to the floor together, weeping and sobbing, in an embrace of shared anguish that would bond them together for life in a way that no ordinary expression of love and commitment could do.

After what seemed like hours, the weeping subsided. It was replaced by a speechless exchange of emotion, which was eventually overcome by sheer exhaustion. They fell together into an unconscious slumber that lasted until well after the sun came up. When they finally rose from their position on the floor, they found it impossible to separate. Charles could not let her move beyond his reach, and Sarah was not interested in moving beyond it. They remained physically close for most of the day, expending effort only to satisfy the most basic needs. They lay in their bed together, having not enough energy to remove their clothing, drifting in and out of sleep. Neither could find a voice to speak.

By dusk, Charles could finally bring himself to leave her immediate presence to care for his horse. The poor beast had been tethered to the post in front of the house since the previous evening with no food or water, save for a bit of grass that grew around the post. Having been properly cared for the whole of the journey, he was none the worse for wear, and seemed to understand the gravity of the situation and its call for his patience.

When he returned to the house, Charles found Sarah preparing food for the both of them. She looked thin and pale; her face bore the lines of exhaustion. As she worked, he began the conversation slowly.

"Where is your mother?" Charles asked, not wanting to address the horrible event directly. He knew that Sarah would tell him all that happened as she found the strength to do so.

"She has taken ill," said Sarah, slowly, and with great effort. "She wanted to help, but you know she is not strong. William and Jimmy have tried to help as much as they can, but mother has needed them more than I. Elizabeth came the first week, but she has her own family to care for."

Not able to wait any longer, Charles had to know.

"Sarah," he said, softly, "what happened?"

She stopped what she was doing and looked into his eyes, her own filling with tears.

"Oh, Charles," she said, speaking his name for the first time since his arrival, "I... he..."

Sarah broke off as her head drooped and her body began to tremble; she was struggling to hold herself upright, with both arms braced against the counter, and weeping profusely. Charles moved to her and slid his arms around her to give support. She turned to him and draped her arms around his waist, still sobbing. He brought one hand up to gently massage the back of her neck; it was something he knew gave her great comfort.

"Forgive me," she finally said.

"It is I who should beg your forgiveness," said Charles, earnestly. "I would never have left you alone if I had known something so terrible would happen."

"There was nothing you could have done," she said, still clinging to him, showing no sign of letting him go. "I put him to bed just as always. Everything was fine. Just before retiring, I went to check on him. He was dead."

Sarah's voice began to break as she began to cry. After a moment, she pushed herself back slightly, sniffed, and wiped her tears with a hanky.

"There was nothing anyone could have done," she said, bravely. Then, raising her eyes to meet his, she said,

"I am sorry to have such terrible news for you on your return. If I had been sure of where you were, I would have tried to write."

"When did this happen?" Charles asked, suddenly wondering about certain feelings he had.

"Two weeks ago today," she said, drying her eyes again.

Charles felt weak. He moved to a kitchen chair with great difficulty. Instinctively, Sarah supported him until he sat down.

"Two weeks ago today," Charles began, incredulous, looking up into her face, "I woke up in the middle of the night with the most dreadful feeling. I knew something was wrong. I left immediately for home. Your letter would never have reached me."

They had both been prepared for losing children by every person who spoke to them on that subject. The rule on the frontier was to have many children, and some of them would survive. Charles was unusually fortunate in that all of his brothers and sisters were still living, but Sarah was only eight when her younger sister Martha and her younger brother Joseph died a few days apart of the same disease. Still, nothing can prepare you for the loss of your own child, particularly when it is your first.

Sarah stroked the back of his head as he sat. She knew that his suffering was at least as great as her own. That realization gave her strength somehow.

Charles did not begin to tell Sarah of his plans and adventures until the following day. He disclosed the details slowly, to allow her ample space for healing, beginning with the most important of them first. When the entire story had been told, they agreed that they should remove quickly ahead of the advancing winter season. The great tragedy that had befallen them did eliminate the complication of travel on the frontier with an infant. Whereas they might have postponed the move until the following spring, they were able to leave almost at once.

Aside from the opportunity to leave immediately, the urgency to do so was intensified by the sense that a new beginning would lessen the painful memories associated with their present home. Charles displayed an infectious enthusiasm for this new opportunity, and Sarah became absorbed with it as a means of diversion. Working toward their new goal was the best therapy anyone could have prescribed.

In less than a month, they settled their accounts, packed up their belongings, and arranged to have their furniture shipped by steamboat to Dubuque. From there, it would be shipped by ox cart over the Mission Trail to Fayette. There was nothing left to do but say goodbye to the family.

From the Journal of Priscilla Malloy Parker

Mount Hygiene, Oct. 28th 1855

We live here in two pleasant rooms of J.K. Parker's house.

On the 20th of last March we suffered the loss of our house and goods by fire being awakened from a sound sleep at 5 o'clock in the morning, found the kitchen full of raging flame then progressed too far to be extinguished, some who were sleeping in the house barely escaped with life. Thanks to merciful providence we were all saved from the devouring element, thus thrown into circumstances strange and embarrassing by the loss of our effects, yet this severe loss has revealed to us a wealth which is boundless and inappreciable in the sympathy and good affections of our friends.

Oct. 29th This day Charles and Sarah, our son and daughter in law have been here, they have us a short visit and the last before going to the far west.

On the first of Nov. Charles and Sarah left for their new home in Fayette Ville in Fayette County Iowa, at stormy time.

III

They were even less enthusiastic than usual. It had been a painful transition for me, from teaching primarily at the graduate level to teaching traditional undergraduates. It was obvious that none of them had read the assignment. There might have been one or two who read it, but they tend to be the sort of students who do not speak up in class. I try to make the class sessions into discussions, but it's hard to carry on a discussion all by yourself. As usual, it regressed into a lecture.

I did not need to see the clock to know what time it was; the shuffling of papers and books informed me that the large hand was approaching a specific mark. Their energy level increased by an order of magnitude as the allotted time for the class ran out. "Read chapter four," I called after the flurry of jackets and backpacks that disappeared through the door. I let out a great sigh and gathered up my papers and books. At least I did not have far to go. My office door was at the back end of the classroom.

As I walked through the doorway and turned toward my desk, I was surprised to see a figure silhouetted against the western window. At first, I thought it was one of the students, but a closer look confirmed that it was a smallish, elderly man dressed in an unusual-looking gray suit, staring out the window with his hands clasped behind his back.

Momentarily, I was consumed with speculation

over how in the world he managed to get in here. There is only one doorway to the office, and I had been facing it for the past hour. The only way in was through the front doorway of the classroom past me to the office. He was certainly not here when the class began. We are on the third floor, and the windows can only be opened from the inside and with great difficulty.

I was just about to say, "Can I help you?" in that tone of thinly disguised contempt and annoyance that civil servants, department store clerks, and French waiters so often use when he spoke first.

"It's gone," he said.

Taken off guard, I sheepishly blurted out, "What's gone?"

"My tree. My tree is gone."

What is he talking about? There was something eerie about this. I tried to say, "What the hell are you doing in my office?" but it came out "Which tree is that?"

"The one I planted out front," he said, turning slightly toward me. "The elm I dug up and carried down from Robertson's Woods. In fact, it looks as though the pine trees I planted are gone too."

Then he turned back to gaze out the window and added "but the elm was special."

He was a man of between sixty and seventy years of age, not much taller than five feet, with a tuft of gray hair on the top of his head and a full, neatly trimmed gray beard that gave him a very distinguished look. His voice was calm, slightly higher than normal pitch, with no edge to it at all.

As he stood there gazing out the window, something in the recesses of my head told me that I should know what this is all about. Gradually, like the sun rising over a mountain, the realization came to me of who this was. It's what's-his-name. The guy with the tree. Yeah, I'm sure that's it. Naw, it can't be. There's only one way to find out.

"Sure it's there," I said, as I sank into my chair. I did not want to be standing if I was right.

"Well," he said, "there is a tree there, but it's not mine. It's not an elm for sure, and it's much smaller than when I last looked upon it."

"It's a maple," I said.

"Then you know what happened to my elm?" he asked, forcefully, turning toward me.

It *is* what's-his-name. I hate it when I'm right. Fortunately, the complete absence of any menace in his continence helped me to suppress my natural panic impulses.

"Well, I don't know for sure," I said, as casually as I could. "I have heard that there was a big windstorm that took out most of the trees on campus in the 1970s."

"Oh," he said, and turned to gaze out the window again. "That must be what happened to my pine grove as well."

"There are a few very large pines still left on the north side," I said, with an artificial bubbly quality to my voice that was intended to approximate cheerfulness. "Maybe they are yours. You can see them from Duane's office."

I pointed diagonally across the building, hoping he would want to go see.

"By the chapel?" he asked, hopefully.

"What chapel?" I asked in return. "You mean the

Methodist Church on Clark Street?"

"No, no," he said, "the chapel next to North Hall. The one everyone attends twice daily."

"What North Hall?" I said. "You mean Colgrove-Walker Hall? We don't have a chapel."

"The North Hall where the Science Department resides," he said.

"The Science Division is located in Baker-Hebron," I said, "over there." With that, I pointed out my south-facing window.

He walked over to look.

After a moment, he said, "where is South Hall? Everything has changed so much. There has been a large addition to Henderson Library as well."

Then, looking around the room, he said, "I do not recognize this room, though I know this is Old Sem."

He let out a sigh, and then returned his attention to the view from the south window. I decided to wait for him to do whatever he was going to do. This was far out of my control.

After what seemed like a long time, he turned toward me again and said, "I am sorry. I should have introduced myself. I am Charles Coleman Parker. My friends call me C.C."

He reached out to shake my hand, and smiled warmly. I would have hesitated, but I was much too shocked to do anything but respond. His grasp felt normal enough, firm, not limp, not bone-crushing.

His brown eyes sparkled with intelligent perception. His manner was so gentle that I could not help but to be receptive. This was all very puzzling.

"Do you know who I am?" I asked.

"Of course," he responded, turning to look out the window again. "I am here to help you."

"Help me with what?" I asked.

"I don't know," he said, turning to look at me again, with a slight grin. "What's wrong with you?"

"What's wrong with me?" I huffed, with indignation. "There's nothing wrong with me."

He did not say anything, he just turned toward the window again.

"Well," I conceded, "maybe there are a few things wrong with me."

"That is a beginning," he said, and said no more.

After a very long pause, I felt the onus was mine to initiate some conversation. I'm not sure why I should have felt that way. Unless I was hallucinating, I was speaking with a ghost.

"May I ask a question?" I offered, hesitantly.

"Of course," he responded.

"What was so special about that tree?"

"The elm?" he asked, rhetorically. "It was the first tree planted on the grounds of the new seminary. I took it upon myself to bring some life to this barren ground. Everyone was so consumed with the problems of the fledgling school that no one thought to plant an ornamental garden to beautify the campus."

He paused for a moment. I was about to ask another question, when he added, "it was the last thing I saw before I died."

That took care of that question.

"Two days before I died," he continued, "I had just enough strength for one short walk. I came from my son's house on King Street, down to College, and up to

Washington. It was less than five blocks, but it was all I could manage. Fortunately, the weather was good, else I'd have stayed home. As Abraham Lincoln once said, in this place I passed from a young to an old man. The growth of that tree marked the progress of my life here; it bore witness to the happiness and the grief that passed through my family. That tree was there when four of our children were born, and it was there to condole with us over the untimely deaths of our only two daughters. It was there when I lost Sarah. That was a time when I was certain that I could not possibly continue living. Some of the most painful moments of my life happened in its presence, and after each tragic event the sight of that elm always encouraged me. It gave me great comfort to know that it would continue after me. And now it is gone."

"But you are here," I ventured.

He turned toward me, his melancholy reflection replaced by a smile, and said "indeed I am."

After a time, he said, "I wonder why they planted a maple and not another elm."

"There was a plague of Dutch Elm Disease running through this part of the country in the seventies," I said. "I suppose they thought a maple would be a better bet."

"Indeed," he said.

This *can't* be a hallucination, I thought, *I'm* not creative enough to think of all this.

"Do you believe in providence?" he asked, beginning to pace across my office floor as though he were inaugurating a lesson.

"I suppose I do," I ventured.

"Ah," he said, "that is good. It is providence that

brings you and I together."

"So that you might fix whatever's wrong with me?" I tried not to sound as sarcastic as I meant it.

"Just so," he said sincerely, "and that is where we can begin."

"What?" I blurted. "Where?"

He did not respond. He just looked at me with an expression on his face that I would come to see again many times after that.

"What?" I said. "My sarcasm?"

"I heard you speak to your students," he said. "You do not take them very seriously."

"First," I began, "they do not take their studies very seriously. And second, sarcasm is one of my most important defense mechanisms."

"Maybe so," he suggested, "but it creates a barrier between you and other people."

"That's what defense mechanisms usually do," I suggested back.

"Do you really need these defenses?"

"Well, yeah," I responded, defensively. "I am easily hurt, and these defenses help me to communicate with people and still protect myself from them."

"I see you've given this some thought," he said. "Have you considered that others see you as arrogant?"

"Well, yes," I responded. "Of course I'm arrogant. How else could I stand at the head of a classroom, in front of reasonably intelligent people, and pretend that I know something they do not?"

"I understand your argument," he conceded, "but I do not accept it. You are strong enough to not need your so-called defenses."

"I'm glad you think so," I retorted. "You have more faith in me than I do."

With that, he straightened up slightly and turned to the side. "That may be the real problem," he said, more to himself than to me.

He broke off the conversation and began to inspect the room. "These are interesting photographs you have here," he said, casually, as he paced toward my desk. "They have wonderful color to them. Did you paint them yourself?"

"They do not need to be painted," I said, still a little agitated. "The color is part of the photographic process."

"Interesting," he mused, "and of what is this a photograph?"

"That is a close-up of a Western Diamondback rattlesnake," said I, glad he asked about that particular picture. "It is there to remind me that you can indeed trust everyone. You can trust a snake to bite you if you give it the chance."

"I always found that if you allow them their leave, they will not bother you," he said.

Either he did not get my message, or he was sending one of his own. I was not sure. I have never considered myself to be the sort of person who needed anyone's help. Yet it was hard to deny the implications of this whole affair. Someone has gone to a great deal of trouble here, and so far it has not been me. His honest and endearing nature left no room for reproach. His manner was quite beyond any criticism that I could concoct. Had he been a headstrong, opinionated, cynical sort of fellow, such as I am, I could have fought him and probably won. But, it is hard to fight someone who does not deserve to be beaten. Maybe, for once in my life, I should be open to constructive criticism. Naw, I'm too old to change.

He continued looking at my pictures. "What is this one here?" he said.

"That's a shot of Black's Beach from the Torrey Pines glider port in San Diego."

"I am sorry," he said, "I cannot quite make it out."

"Ok," I said, trying not to sound impatient, "I am standing on the bluff looking down on the beach. The black area in the lower left-hand corner of the picture is the bluff. I'm about three hundred feet above the ocean. The white streaks are waves washing in. You can see three people walking along the sand right at the waterline."

"Ah," he said, "now I see it. I did not realize those tiny figures were people."

He turned toward me and said, in a wistful tone, "I have never seen the ocean."

"Never?" I asked, wondering why he can't just fly there now. "The picture below that one is taken from the same spot looking south toward La Jolla Cove. Scripp's Pier can be seen on the left, and that is a fishing boat heading out to sea on the right. The open Pacific lies in front of it; there is nothing but ocean between that boat and Japan."

"That is a very nice view," he said. "These are like works of art."

"There are many artists who work with photography," I said.

"You are an artist, then?!" said he, more as a

statement than as a question.

"Not really," said I. "These are just snap shots that turned out well."

"Ah!" he responded. "There were some photographic artists in my day, but it was a very difficult endeavor. And, their photographs were not as colorful as these."

"Modern technology has greatly simplified the process," I said. "It is possible for a novice like me to take good photographs with little real knowledge."

"Hmm," he said, "this one does not appear to be near the ocean; that rock must have been in a river to have been worn so smooth. Judging by the trees, which I assume to be of normal size, that is a very large rock, indeed. I do not think I have ever seen a rock so large. Yet, the river does not appear large enough to have been able to do its work."

"That is Lambert Dome in Yosemite Park," I said, "and it rises over a thousand feet above the valley floor. It is not the largest rock there. I took that picture because I spent so much time in and around that place, and climbing up and down that dome. You can't see it, but the Tioga Road runs right in front of it. I was standing at the edge of the Tuolumne Meadows campground, and that is the Tuolumne River you see. The dome was polished by a glacier. That whole area was shaped by glaciers."

"Where did you say that was?" he inquired.

"The eastern side of Yosemite Park," I said. The puzzled look on his face indicated that I should continue. "It's in Central California, in the high Sierras."

"Ah," he said. But, I had the feeling he still was

not sure where it is. He moved to the next one, which undoubtedly required some explanation.

"That," I said, "is some type of exotic white mountain goat. I took his picture at the San Diego Zoo. He's up there because his expression reminds me of some of my students." It was the same sort of clueless, goofy expression for which Stanley Laurel was famous.

He gave me that look again, and moved on. The next picture was fixed to the wall in the center of my desk at my eye level when I am seated. I had to slide my wheeled chair over to make way for him.

"That is a sketch of a Torrey Pine, drawn by a Japanese artist. I use it sometimes as something to occupy my eyes while I think."

"I have never heard of a Torrey pine," he said, bending over to peer closely at it.

"It is a particular variety that only grows in two places on earth," I said, "on a small island off the coast of California, and on a small stretch of coastal bluffs that make up Torrey Pines State Park in San Diego. It looks all gnarly the way it does because of the dryness. On the coast, it only rains about four to six inches a year. That is the only pine that can survive there without irrigation."

He lingered for a few minutes, studying the drawing, then moved on to the small cork bulletin board near the door upon which I had tacked a few odds and ends. His attention fixed on the poster advertising a business plan competition that featured a photo of the original entrance to San Diego State University.

"My alma mater," I said.

"What are these unusual plants here in the foreground?" he asked.

"The trees are date palms, and those shrubs are called bird of paradise," I answered, pointing them out. "The tree in back of the building is a eucalyptus."

He nodded and then read the three quotes I had printed on cards and pinned to the board. The first read "Well, well, try anything once, come hot, come cold! If we're not foolish young, we're foolish old... Chaucer."

"It's a translator's paraphrase of a line in the Knight's Tale," I said, when I thought he had finished it.

He did not respond, but continued reading the next one, upon which was lettered "Life is tough! It's tougher when yer stupid... John Wayne." I decided to suspend all comments until he asked a question.

He continued without comment, reading the third, which said "To do is to be... Nietzsche; To be is to do... Sartre; Do Be Do Be Do... Sinatra." He turned in my direction with a puzzled look on his face.

"Sinatra was a singer," I said. "It's a joke."

When his look did not change, I said, "It would be a great deal of explanation for a tiny amount of amusement. It's a poke at philosophy."

He seemed to accept that assessment, and moved across the doorway to the only picture in that corner of the room.

"That is an alpine meadow in the Sierras near Mount Conness," I said. "My wife took it."

"It is the most unusual collection of plants I have ever seen," he said, with awe.

"We were at about eleven thousand feet looking southeast toward Tioga Pass," I said. "It is above the tree line. Those dwarf shrubs you see are the tallest trees in the area. The weather is very harsh there, and that meadow would be under about thirty or forty feet of snow all winter."

He stood there studying that picture for at least fifteen minutes. I was becoming a bit impatient because I had a great deal of work to do. Still, this is not an experience one has every day, or at least I hope not. What did I have to do that mattered anyway?

Finally, he continued his circuit of the room, stopping at the old calendar I had put on the wall because I liked the pictures.

"Is this the year?" he asked, "nineteen hundred and ninety five?"

"You don't know what year it is?" I blurted out.

"No," he said, simply. "I do not know anything past nineteen aught five. For me, yesterday was January of nineteen aught six, and I remember little of that."

"What's it like?" I was compelled to ask.

"What is what like?" he responded.

"Dying," I said.

"I cannot say," he responded.

"You don't know?" I asked, incredulous.

"I cannot say," he said.

"You can't say, or you won't say?" I demanded.

"I cannot say," he said, with a slight smile.

"What is Boscobel?" he asked, reading the caption on the calendar.

He was obviously diverting attention from a subject he did not wish to discuss. I debated whether to answer him, or to press the other question.

"It's an old house in the Hudson Valley in New York that has been restored for tourists," I finally said. "People in the old days used to name their houses. We lived near there for seven years, and I must say I really miss the place. That is an old calendar that I put up just for reminiscence. The date today is December fifth, two thousand."

"Two thousand," he said, almost breathless.

I waited for him to say more, but he did not. Instead, he moved to the pictures on the south wall opposite my desk. Before reaching the pictures, he paused a long time to study the houseplant, sitting in a pot on the floor, that my wife had prepared for my office. He seemed to have a special interest in plants. I was glad that this one was in good shape, not that it was because of my careful attention.

"I do not know the name of that plant," I said, to head off the question I knew he was about to ask.

"It is a calathea," he said.

"Oh," was my reply.

Finally, he looked up at the first picture on the wall.

"That's me fishing in the Tuolumne River," I said. "My wife took it. I didn't catch a thing."

He moved to the next one.

"That is my wife in a meadow near Young Lakes in Yosemite," I said. "I had to take it to show her friends that she actually went camping." I would have mentioned that we were seven miles from the nearest road, but that would not impress a pioneer.

"Is this your wife also?" he asked, referring to a picture on top of the small bookcase.

"Yes," I said, "her name is Barbara."

"She is very beautiful," he said.

"I know," was my reply.

"She looks too young for you."

"I hope so. That picture is fifteen years old. She is less than four years younger than I am. She will turn fifty in a few months."

"You do not look that old," he said, turning to study my face.

"It's the fat," I said. "It fills in the wrinkles."

There was no response.

"These are your children?" he asked, turning back to the photos on the bookshelf.

"Jaime, my daughter," said I, mindful that Jaime is commonly a boy's name, "is twenty-three, and Cory is twenty-one."

From there, he moved to the last of the photos.

"That is a plant growing out of the rocks on top of Lambert Dome," I said, gesturing toward the picture of the dome on the north wall. "I do not know the name of the plant, I just thought it was interesting that it was growing without any apparent soil."

This photo he studied for some time. I took the opportunity to get on with the important business at hand.

"I'm going to eat lunch," I said. "I hope you brought your own." It was supposed to be a joke, but I did not know if he ate anything or not.

He looked as though he was about to say something when the bell began to ring as it did every hour on the hour. The bell loft was directly above my classroom door, and it interrupted every class I conducted with a minute and a half of ringing. Since the classes did not begin or end on the hour, it was most inconvenient and disruptive. Students, marginally motivated to begin with, were often lost for good after the bell. Pavlov could have made a great study of it.

The sound of the bell grabbed his attention. "Is there a fire?" he asked, anxiously.

"I hope not," I shouted. "It rings every hour."

"Oh," he said, when it finally subsided. "It was originally rung to wake the students living on this floor, and to put them to bed at night. Other than that, it was a fire alarm for the town."

"This was a dorm?" I asked, though I should not have been surprised. When there is only one building on campus, everything happens in that building.

"Yes," he mused. "In fact, this portion of it belonged to the ladies. The northern half belonged to the gentlemen. There was a wall in between, but there was no door. The first year, I remember the ladies were obliged to use a ladder to enter their sleeping chambers because the stairway for this half of the dormitory was not yet completed. Access to the bell was gained by a rope that descended down to the first floor, and was rung by the students who were assigned to the job."

"Work-study," I said, offhandedly.

"Pardon me?" he asked.

"Tell me about the bell," I inquired. "I have the impression that it is a great tradition here."

"Indeed it is," said he. "The bell was purchased by the first steward of Fayette Seminary before classes began. It was the year of eighteen hundred and fifty-six when David Poor ordered that bell from a company in Troy, New York. It weighed over twelve hundred pounds and it cost nearly five hundred dollars. That was equal to the principal's annual salary. It was brought by barge from New York and then brought by ox cart from Dubuque. It was installed, and first rung at a fund raising event on October thirtieth of eighteen hundred and fifty-six. I remember that date because it was the day following my son Daniel's birth. People came from all over the township to hear it. It was very grand. Some said it could be heard in surrounding townships. We took Danny to hear it for his first outing. It certainly had an effect, for he remained attached to the school all of his life."

He continued speaking with a sentimentality that occasionally crept into his expression. "Besides waking students at five in the morning, and signaling their bed time at ten in the evening, and signaling the beginning of services and meals, and being used as a fire alarm, it tolled the passing of important persons such as Elizabeth and Robert Alexander and Abraham Lincoln. It sent Company C of the Twelfth Iowa Regiment off to meet their glory, and it celebrated Lee's surrender at Appomattox."

"Five in the morning?" I said, with an incredulous tone.

"Yes," he said, "and they were expected to perform their chores and begin their studies before breakfast."

"That would never work with this generation of students," I said. "There are some who will not take a class at eight because they cannot get themselves out of bed and across campus by that hour."

He looked at me with a little smile. "Not all the students were enthusiastic about rising early," he said. "The Steward was obliged to keep two clappers in supply because students would remove them in order to sleep awhile longer undisturbed. One fellow, I recall, did not return the one he took until his twentieth reunion. When students were not endeavoring to silence the bell, they took great joy in ringing it out of turn. They would often sound false alarms, and the volunteer firemen in the town would be hopping mad when they found they had left their warm beds for nothing."

He paused for a long moment in silent reflection. Finally, he turned toward the west wall and said, "who is Joshua Lawrence Chamberlain?" He was reading the caption on the bottom of the poster featuring a photograph of the young general in uniform.

"He was the hero of Gettysburg," I replied. "You must have heard of him. He was a professor in Bowdoin College; he was Governor of Maine after the war."

There was no response.

"Weren't you in the Civil War?" I asked.

He shot me a glance that left no doubt on my part that discussion on that question was not forthcoming. By this time, I had determined to let him govern the conversation. I reserved the right to ask questions, but I saw no need to press him for answers. He did not seem to be in possession of any extraordinary knowledge, nor did he seem to have any particular supernatural powers. I found his apparent limitations quite surprising in view of my profound knowledge of ghosts, derived as it was from Hollywood movies. In light of his limitations, his purpose there was all the more puzzling.

"This is a very nice office," he conceded, "your students must enjoy coming in here."

"I cannot say they enjoy it," I admitted, "they

rarely come in. When they do, it is generally to have something signed or to explain why they have not done their work."

"They do not stop to admire these wonderful pictures?" he asked, with surprise.

"They do not seem to be that curious," I said. "It is possible that they feel uncomfortable staying in here for any length of time."

"Why do you suppose that is the case?" he said, obviously trying to make a point.

"Because it's haunted?" I ventured.

With that, he let out a burst of laughter.

"That was very good," he said, when his laughter finally subsided. "I cannot remember the last time I had a good laugh. It is good for the constitution, you know."

The whole mood had changed. I suggested that he seat himself, but he informed me that he did not experience fatigue, hunger, or thirst. That was good because, while I had enough lunch to make a complete meal for two, I was not in the habit of sharing. I was more in the habit of receiving my wife's leftovers.

Since I did most of the cooking at our house, I prepared large quantities of food on weekends specifically to be used by both of us for lunches during the week. It saved a great deal of time when three hours of my day was spent in transit. Today, I had a partitioned microwave dish with ham, scalloped potatoes, and broccoli. After heating the food in the microwave I brought into my office just for that purpose, I sat at my desk and began to eat. My tendency to get certain foods out of the way before savoring the more delectable ones lead me to attack the broccoli first.

"You should not eat too much of one food," he said, leaning over my shoulder. "You should eat one bite of each in turn. Do you intend to eat that entire plate full?"

"Are you my food coach now?" I said, somewhat irritated at this critical interruption of my feeding. Also, he was beginning to sound like my wife.

"I am merely offering sound medical advice," he retorted, a bit indignant that I should question his judgment. "I have made a study of the digestive system, and have concluded that it is best to present the stomach with a well balanced array of foods in their proper sequence. Following the meal, it is imperative that one should rest calmly to promote digestion."

"Did you conduct this research yourself?" I asked, with a more softened tone.

"I treated many digestive disorders in my time," he said, "and I have tried various procedures myself to observe their results. So, some of what I know is based on empirical observation. However, there was a lengthy study of the digestive processes conducted on a patient who had a window installed in his stomach that I followed in detail. That study also validated the importance of relaxation after eating."

I decided that arguing with him was not worth the effort, nor was I interested in offending him. He was such a pleasant fellow that he inspired my wish to earn his good opinion. He was growing on me.

Turning his attention from my eating, he took a great, sweeping survey of my office. And then, fixing his gaze on my computer, said "I must know what is the nature of this contraption."

"Are you in for a surprise," I said, turning it on.

For the next several hours, we surfed the Net. There are no words that would adequately characterize his amazement and delight. For me, it was sheer joy to witness such a true appreciation of discovery. We found his name in several places, along with pictures of people he had known, such as Elizabeth Alexander and James Robertson. But most of all, he enjoyed the botany sites. He learned very quickly how to explore the Web himself, and I left him engrossed in this activity which, I found out the following day, he pursued all night.

"Good morning," I said, upon discovering that he was still in my office, seated at the computer. I was not in the least dismayed to find him there, and would have been disappointed otherwise.

"Good morning," he said, without looking up from the screen.

I undertook my usual routine of organizing coat, lunch, and briefcase. When I was finished, I stood behind him to see what he had found. He was perusing a medical site.

"They have made the most amazing discoveries," he said, with an edge of excitement in his voice.

After a moment, he surprised me by asking if I always lock my door.

"Of course," I said, "there are many things here that I do not care to lose, not to mention that there are often exams and other confidential materials laying about."

"Ah," he said.

"Do you have an objection to locking doors?" I asked.

"I would not call it an objection," he said. "I suppose it is more of a phobia. One bleak winter day, I fell from my horse and broke my leg. There was no one about, but I managed to drag myself to a nearby cabin. Fortunately, the door was unlocked, and so I was able to open it and drag myself inside. The residents eventually returned and found me, but I am convinced that I should have died if that door had been locked. Since that time, I never locked a door."

"Well," I said, "that might have been okay in those days, but today an unlocked door is an invitation to be ripped off. Weren't you afraid someone would steal all your stuff?"

"They were welcome to anything they needed," he said. "Perhaps it is a sad comment that I never possessed much of value sufficient to tempt a thief."

"It could be that the people you knew were more honest than the ones I know," I said. "And that is a sad comment."

He did not respond to that, but returned his attention to the computer.

"Dr. Parker," I said, inquiringly, not able to bring myself to address him as C.C., "did you acquire any special knowledge or enlightenment when you died?"

"I do not know," he said, with a tone that indicated sincerity rather than evasion. "I cannot say for sure what happened. I appear before you as I was. I would not say that this is what I have become."

"Oh," I said. "That's helpful."

He gave me that look, and then said, "you will know soon enough. Try not to be impatient."

As I began to organize the items I would need for

the day's classes, he said, "if you had arrived earlier, we might have had more time for our discussions."

"You kept me late last night," I said. "I did not get home until after nine. By the time I ate and watched the news and packed a lunch, it was time for bed. I left home at eight this morning."

"But it is half past nine," he said, "and you are only just arrived."

"Well," I said, "it's a seventy-five mile drive from Dubuque."

"You live in Dubuque?" he said, astounded, "and you travel that distance every day?

"Every day," I said, "thanks to modern automobiles."

"Yes," he said, "I saw them on the computer. But I did not think that one could travel seventy-five miles in one hour and a half. That would be at a speed of fifty miles in an hour."

"My car is not particularly fast," I said, "but I can cruise at seventy-five to eighty miles an hour for extended periods. I can drive from here to Denver in eighteen hours, and to San Diego from there in another eighteen hours."

"That is amazing," he said. "It took us three weeks to reach Pike's Peak."

"You went to Pike's Peak?" I asked.

"Yes," he said, with a smile and an expression that indicated the presence of fond memories. "In eighteen hundred and fifty-nine, Ed Howe, Horace Derby, Will Lakin, Bill Fish, Noah Alexander, and I all traveled to Pike's Peak in a buckboard to hunt for gold. Let me tell you that Sarah was none too happy about it, especially when we returned empty-handed. It was quite an adventure though."

"Wives never seem to appreciate a good adventure," I said, "especially when they have to stay home and mind the children."

"You are very right," he said, with a tone of regret. "I should never have left her alone with Danny. I knew at the time that she was pregnant with Charles, who was born that August. It is fortunate that we did not stay long in Colorado, but I'm afraid that I would not learn my lesson until long after that time."

I was tempted to ask him to tell me that story, but I was running short of time and he seemed to be on to some memory that was causing him great pain. His sense of mission regarding my rehabilitation would tend to preclude telling his own stories. Perhaps I might convey the impression that I'm more open to suggestion when I have been softened up with tales of adventure. Whatever happens will have to be after class.

The morning class had been transferred to the AV Room in the Library because there were only twenty-four seats in my room. After the class had filled, I admitted six late registrations and one student had dropped for a total of twenty-nine. The topic of the course was supervision. It was required for several majors, so it was in demand. I tried to make the course as experiential as possible, but many of the students would have been happier if I had just lectured on some easy-to-memorize material that they could regurgitate on the exam with as little thought as possible.

When I returned, I found him gazing out the window.

"You should have come over to observe my class," I said. "The students were very excited about learning. It went very well."

"I cannot leave this room," he said.

"Why not?"

"I cannot say."

I took what he said for truth, and let go of my impulses to demand an explanation.

"I am happy that your class went well," he said.

"It didn't," I said. "I lied."

He turned toward me with an expression of confusion and hurt.

"Alright," I said, with some exasperation, "perhaps it was not a lie. It went normally. There were some students who were clearly with the program, and some others who seem to consider the requirement to attend class a great imposition on them."

"That is normal," he said. "It does not sound as though students have changed much since I taught here."

"Well," I said, "even though neither of us is in a position to argue authoritatively, I think we can establish some differences. I think that the purpose of education has changed along with the content."

"How so?" he said, giving the impression that he was eager for a discussion on the subject.

"Well," I began, "I think there are three major differences between higher education now, and what it was when you were teaching. First, students and their parents demand relevance. They are unwilling to study anything for which they cannot see a direct application."

"Application to what?" he inquired.

"To work," I said, "to their careers, to their ability

to earn money. A teacher today must persuade them that they will eventually make more money if they study a particular subject. They are looking expressly for return on investment, return, that is, in material gains."

"I concede," he said, "that may be a difference. In my day, most students accepted their study assignments without concerning themselves about why."

"Second," I continued, "students require many inducements to study. To most of them, grades are not indications of performance, they are more like paychecks. Despite their cry for relevance, few students take the long view of their studies. Like their parents, they are looking for quick returns by any means, and will take whatever shortcuts they can devise."

"I do not agree that your second point distinguishes your students from my students," he said. "I believe they all had hedonistic tendencies that it was our task to overcome. I think the nature of youth tends to immediacy. The job of the teacher is to set them on course for the distant future. It always has been thus."

"Perhaps you are right," I conceded. "I tell them that I am not the guy who hands out the medals at the Olympics. I'm just the guy holding the stopwatch at the time trials. I tell you what your time is, and it's up to you to determine whether or not you put in your best effort and whether or not you need to change your workout. The guy handing out the medals is your future boss. That's where your performance really matters. This is only practice."

His puzzled look prompted me to explain what a stopwatch was and its use in athletics. I think he finally got it.

"Third," I said, building for a grand finish, "young people today require so much constant stimulation, just to minimize boredom, that they literally cannot focus their attention on a classroom activity for more than a few minutes unless is has a high entertainment value."

"I'm not sure I follow you," he said, stroking his beard.

I spent the next half-hour or so explaining television, channel surfing, video games, and extreme sports like bungee-jumping.

"When you have to throw yourself off a bridge with a rubber band tied to your ankle to feel that you're alive," I concluded, "how will you respond to someone explaining cost accounting or poetry? Basically, when a teacher conducts a class, the students are comparing it to the forms of entertainment they experience every minute of every day. I have seen my own children surf through a hundred channels of programming, complaining that there is nothing to watch."

He did not respond immediately because he was lost in thought. I waited for him to digest what I had just told him.

"That could be a formidable problem," he said, finally. "It justifies the church's position on dancing and carousing. I never saw any harm in dancing and other forms of entertainment, but if this is what it leads to, then I must agree that such habits should never be allowed to form."

"Perhaps we are looking at it from the wrong point of view," I said. "Suppose for a moment that what most students and most parents of students believe is true, that the aim of higher education in the industrial world is to prepare people for jobs in corporations. If you were going to spend the rest of your life digging ditches and someone gave you four years to prepare for it, what would you do with those four years?"

"I am sorry," he said, "I have not the pleasure of understanding you."

"Most people who work in modern corporations are virtually slaves. They go to their jobs to do work that they would never choose to do on their own; they must do what they are told to do and when they are told to do it; and, they may not supplement their work with activities of their own choosing. Further, most corporations have no reservations about placing restrictions on your personal life, and about reserving the right to have you work whatever hours they choose."

"But people are paid for their work," he pointed out.

"But they are only paid what the company decides to pay them," I said. "Most employees cannot choose how much to be paid, and most surveys show that people don't think they are paid enough. In fact, people often go on strike over low pay."

"They can resign," he said.

"And do what?" I asked. "If you resign, you can either start your own company and be the slave driver, or your can work for some other company under the same conditions. The only other alternative is to be homeless."

"And your point is," he posed, "that if students know this as their fate, they will not be enthusiastic about learning because they suppose it to be no different from the work they will be doing for the rest of their lives. The final result is that school lengthens their toil."

"Exactly," I said, triumphantly.

He pondered this point of view for some time before saying "in my day, you prepared yourself for a lifetime of work, because that is God's plan for us. A life of toil is a life of devotion and ultimately of salvation."

"But," I offered, "this generation of students understands salvation as salvation from work. Heaven is a place where you can sit around all day and drink beer and play video games and do no work at all. Through marketing, they have been exposed to lifestyles where work seems to be either nonexistent or at least enjoyable, and success is defined as absence of work. And, they hold out great hopes that they can spend their lives in self-indulgence and enjoyment while being supported by some sort of magical income. I guess, in the final analysis, they define their lives materially, and the manner in which they spend their time is one of the material ends they pursue. They feel entitled to a certain amount of leisure time."

"So, what is to be done?" he asked. "Can students not be made to see that education has many advantages besides preparing one for work?"

"I don't know," I said. "I can only demonstrate my enthusiasm for learning as its own reward. Students are the ones who must ultimately decide what ends they are pursuing with learning and working. You can lead a horse to water, but he won't drink unless he decides he is thirsty. By the time they realize that they will never have lives of leisure, they will have lost all motivation to pursue anything more than basic subsistence. Because they are poorly educated, they will never be able to figure out why they are miserable."

"Yes," he said, slowly. He did not seem convinced, but I decided there was no need to press the point further.

He stood gazing silently out the window for some time while I prepared for the next class.

Finally, without turning from the window, he said, "you should consider moving to Fayette."

IV

By the time they looked upon the village of Fayette from the low hill that marked the southeast corner of the valley, Sarah had nearly put aside the tragedy that had befallen them. So spirited was the hopefulness and so vivid were the images recounted by Charles during the course of their journey that her grief had been all but succeeded by anticipation. The occasional relapse of memory brought tears to her eyes. But, her steadfast determination, the change of environment, the considerable challenge of the task at hand, and the conviction that they were pursuing a course laid out for them by providence all served to soften the affects substantially, making life almost bearable.

Charles had allowed very little occasion for his own grief. He had devoted the bulk of his energy to providing comfort to Sarah. He, too, was consumed with the excitement of this new adventure, and the thought of sharing it all with her energized and comforted him.

The journey to Fayette took four weeks this time. They were in no hurry, and Charles made sure that appropriate accommodations were made for Sarah that would minimize her hardships. The primary goal of reaching their destination before winter made traveling more difficult. If they were lucky, their furniture would arrive soon after they did. They trusted that the house would be ready. Charles spared no quarter in stressing his confidence in the Colonel. But when they passed the lot that the mechanic had indicated as the one chosen, all they could see was a partially dug basement. This was not an encouraging development.

Under Charles's instructions, the driver of the coach stopped in front of Mo's inn. It seemed particularly quiet to Charles; usually the Davis children would be about doing chores and would certainly come arunnin' to see who had just arrived in town. But, he supposed that everyone was involved in some activity elsewhere. As they were unloading the luggage, a man unknown to Charles opened the door of the inn and stepped outside.

"Hello," said Charles, heartily, "is Mo about?"

"I'm afraid yer too late," said the stranger, "Mo died more'n a month ago."

"Died!" exclaimed Charles, freezing his movement in shock.

"Yup. Martha's upstairs on her death bed, an' the kids what is left is over to the Maxon place."

"But I left the whole family in good health not three months ago," said Charles, his tone betraying a sense of responsibility as well as remorse. "What caused his death? Do you know?"

"They said it was the typhoid," said the stranger.

"What date exactly did he die?" asked Charles, almost demanding.

"Well, lessee," said the stranger, scratching his head. "it was on a Sunday, and... uh... I guess it was the fourteenth. That would be in October. He's buried up to the cemetery. His daughter come down with it too. She died two weeks after he did, but they ain't buried 'er yet. She's layin' up in her room 'cause they ain't got around t'makin' her coffin."

"Which daughter?" Charles inquired, with a tone of exasperation.

"It's Sarah," said the stranger. "She come down with the same thing as Mo. It's too bad too, 'cause she were only seventeen, an' cute as a button. Martha's got it too, an' it ain't gonna be long for her."

Charles turned to his Sarah. His expression told the story of his anguish. By now she knew from him all the details of the Davis children's illness. She also knew, without him telling her, that the child who died was not one of the two he treated. It was apparent to a physician's wife that Mo and his daughter could not have shown symptoms before Charles left for Ohio. Still, it was her turn to be strong, and to reassure him.

"There was nothing you could have done," she said softly to Charles.

He knew that as well as she, but he needed to hear it all the same. It was painfully clear to both of them the great need for a physician in this town.

After taking a moment to recover his presence of mind, Charles turned again to the stranger and introduced Sarah and himself.

"Name's Keaser," he said, pumping Charles's hand. "I'm helpin' out. I heard 'bout you, an' I'm bettin' that there's a lot of folks gonna be happy you come back. The Colonel tol' me that if'n you was to show up, I best take you over to Mr. Robertson's house. They got a room all ready. Don't go unpackin' yer trunks."

"Is the Colonel in town?" asked Charles, hopefully.

"Naw, he's up to West Union," said Keaser. "He should be back tonight."

With Keaser's help, their belongings were moved into storage in a room that had been previously occupied by workmen from the construction site. Another room was being used to house one of the workers who had been stricken with typhoid as well. Everybody who was not sick had cleared out of the inn except Keaser. The odor of death permeated the building. Charles went immediately to Mrs. Davis and began treating her. Encouraged by his previous success treating the children, he was reasonably sure that she and the construction worker would recover. The two weary travelers would have to travel a bit more to the Robertson house. They arrived just in time for supper.

James and Elizabeth Robertson were two of the most prominent citizens in the Westfield/Fayette greater metropolitan area. James's older brother, Samuel, was the husband of Elizabeth's older sister, Sabra. Both sisters were the oldest daughters of Colonel and Elizabeth Alexander, and their sibling husbands were key ingredients in the Colonel's plans to settle this portion of the wilderness. Samuel and Sabra Robertson were not as imposing in the community as their younger siblings. Samuel was content tilling the soil of his land on the eastside of the town he had platted, and, beyond his service on the college committee, was not highly motivated to be a civic figure. James had graciously and happily taken on the responsibility of the Methodist congregation and the local school, and, behind the Colonel, was the town's most recognizable patron.

James Robertson was the very picture of dignity and deference. His balding head was adorned by thatched, graying hair at its sides and supported, at its base, by a generous beard, without a moustache. The sagaciousness of his countenance distinguished him in a crowd as a patriarch and elder. He and his wife, Elizabeth, welcomed the weary travelers with Christian charity.

Elizabeth Robertson was the Alexander's second oldest daughter, after Sabra, and bore a stronger resemblance to the Colonel than she did to her mother. Her eyes were a bit more round in shape than her mother's, and carried a perpetual expression of gentle inquiry rather than the one of piercing scrutiny that so characterized her mother. Her face was flat and square like her father's, and she had his large, fleshy nose and ears. Her mouth was more full, and her lips more discernable than her mother's. Still, her appearance was plain and carried an air of gravity that recommended her as a devout Methodist. She inherited strength from both of her parents, which was tempered most amiably with her father's reserve.

Charles and Sarah were not the only guests at the Robertson house. The log schoolhouse, which had been recently built in close proximity to the residence, boasted of its first teacher and pupils. Because the settlers had little money to pay the teacher, he was "boarded round" among the patrons of the school, and the Robertsons had been first to volunteer to put him up.

Seventeen-year-old Jason Lee Paine was an eighth generation American whose great grandfather, Edward, had risen to the rank of brigadier general during the Revolutionary War, and had served in the New York State Legislature. Edward Paine moved west to Ohio in 1800, and founded the town of Painesville. Jason's grandfather, Joel Paine, was the sheriff of Cleveland, and was commissioned as brigadier general during the French and Indian War. Jason's father, Cortez Paine, was not interested in his civic and military heritage, and moved his family from Ohio to Wisconsin to Fayette seeking moral and religious solitude.

Jason reminded Sarah very much of Charles at that young age. He was exceedingly intelligent, gentle, and passionate in the pursuit of good causes. He was slight in posture, but well-proportioned, upright, and sturdy. His constant inquiries and insatiable curiosity would endear him to Charles in a bond that would last for the rest of their lives. But, just now, the development of their new friendship would have to wait. Charles and Sarah were not up to the task of maintaining conversation.

The elder Robertsons were not avid conversationalists at the dinner table. It was a natural consequence of having vivacious female children to keep the room filled with sound. Besides, they were not inclined to impose upon their guests, two of whom were preoccupied with their own anguish and fatigue. There would be ample time for discussion later. After a few cordialities, and a lengthy prayer of thanksgiving offered by James Robertson, they all sat to eat. The bulk of the dinner conversation was delivered by Jason, whose discourse expounded upon the great advantages of temperance. He stimulated some responses from the Robertson girls, but only occasional nods of approval from the elder Robertsons to whom this soliloquy was ponderous affirmation of the obvious.

As they all partook of the Lord's bounty,

Charles's thoughts drifted back to the happier scenes that took place the last time he was in town. He recalled Mo's elation with the improved condition of his children. He remembered the Colonel's unshakable confidence in what to him was an obvious omen of progress. The profusion of vitality and optimism that had issued from that inn, that had so infected him before, was utterly gone. The disparity of Mo's death was saddening, and it cast an appalling shadow on Charles. He imagined with horror and extreme sadness how Mo must have felt, as he sensed his life slipping away, knowing that the deliverer of his children was nowhere to be found in his own hour of need.

While Jason and the elder Robertson girls chattered among themselves about that which was important to them, the newcomers ate in virtual silence. Sarah devoted her attention almost entirely to the food on her plate and to her orderly manner of consuming it. As Charles watched her, a deep remorse, which had accompanied the revelation of the dreadful fate of the Davis family, began to impose itself more heavily upon him. It was a remorse founded more uniformly in self-doubt than in the normal regrets that attend loss and disappointment. He now feared that his enthusiasm for this move had outstripped the material basis for his expectations. At some level in his mind, he was aware that coming to Iowa was more a conveyance *from* something than *to* something. And now, he was beginning to have serious doubts about the soundness of his decision and the prospects for their future happiness and success. His greatest fear was that of disappointing Sarah; he had let her down too much as it was.

When supper was over, there was enough light left in the cloudless dusk to allow for a walk down to the river. The couple excused themselves from the table, and begged leave to take in the fresh autumn evening that they might be alone. The air was chilled, and Charles took care to make sure that Sarah was bundled up against the cold. He very much wanted to know her feelings, but could not find the courage to ask. So, they walked in silence.

Sarah was feeling more resolve than anything else. She was aware that Charles was shocked and disappointed over the loss of his friends, but she had resolved to take on her new life with an open mind. She did not consult her emotions closely for fear that they would excite feelings she would prefer to avoid. By the time they stood upon the riverbank gazing down into the dark water, she knew that he was expecting some sort of declaration from her. She was ready to give it.

"This is so very pleasant, Charles," she said, in a gentle voice. "I think I shall like living here. I think we shall be very happy here."

By the time they turned back toward the Robertsons' house, it was dark. When they opened the front door, the Colonel and Elizabeth Alexander were there to meet them. Almost instantaneously, Elizabeth began speaking as she moved swiftly and anxiously over to where they stood.

"Oh, Dr. Parker," she said, with great affectation, "it is so good to have you back. You must be Sarah. We received your letter with the tragic news. I can't say how sorry I was to read it. I am so glad to see you're arrived safe and sound."

As Elizabeth took Sarah's hand in earnest conciliation, the Colonel strode over to Charles and took his hand in a patented "Colonel Alexander" handshake.

"C.C.," he said, "I can't tell you how happy I am to see you again."

The force and conviction in the Colonel's tone conveyed a much deeper sentiment than the words themselves could express. The remorse that Charles had harbored so recently all but disappeared under the sincerity of these affirmations.

They were soon joined by Samuel and Sabra Robertson. As the women sat and began the long process of becoming acquainted, the men discussed business. The Colonel relayed more detail about the deaths of Mo and his daughter. Mo had not shown any signs of illness until well after Charles had left. After Mo's death, Martha was distraught beyond consolation at the untimely loss of her husband. It was not long before Sarah developed symptoms. Meary, the only Davis child to not fall victim to the illness, was obliged to look after her sister. That is when Keaser volunteered to help. Shortly after Sarah's death, Martha was stricken and the children were taken in by the Maxons.

James Robertson stated that Mo was the first of the newly formed Methodist congregation to be buried in what had become the town cemetery, to be built around Martha Alexander's grave. A cemetery association had not as yet been formed, and there had been no plans developed to provide for burials. Mr. Goodrich and Mr. West were kind enough to make the coffins, but that task had to be accomplished when their time afforded.

The Colonel also reiterated the importance of

having a physician in town. He revealed what had been previously unknown to Charles, that there was another physician in the area. His name was Aaron Brown, and he owned a farm about two miles from the village. He had informed the Colonel of his desire to give up medical practice as soon as a suitable replacement could be found. Dr. Brown's expression of disinterest, accompanied by the developments in the Davis case, discouraged the Colonel from attempting to sway him. Charles was assured in no uncertain terms of the appreciation felt by all concerned for his presence. Dr. Brown had been encouraged to run for state office, and he was leaning in that direction. The Colonel expressed his opinion that Aaron Brown would be a much greater asset to the community in that capacity.

When the Colonel felt he had established closure on the marketing portion of his present mission, he turned to discussing the practical issues of the house. The foundation was nearly ready, but the lumber had not yet been cut for the frame, lath, and siding. The Colonel expressed his deepest regret that problems with construction of the seminary caused in part by the weather and in part by the disruption of the outbreak of typhoid had distracted him from his obligation to his friend. He promised in the sincerest of terms to have all of the resources at his disposal set to the task.

It occurred to Charles that the Colonel had not been altogether confident that the new town physician would actually return to Iowa. After all, Charles had made no deposit, nor had he purchased any land. It would not have been the first time that good intentions were abandoned for one reason or another, and investments of this sort must be carefully weighed for their risk. But he was here now, and the Colonel would no longer consider this transaction a risky proposition.

It was agreed that the construction should be resolved before the furniture arrived, and that the couple would move into their new abode as soon as possible. Charles inquired about a place in town from which to conduct his practice. The silence and blank stares indicated that no thought had been given to building a clinic. Rather than argue the point, Charles quickly solicited for a large room to be added to the front of the two-room house as soon as possible in the spring. He also queried Sam Robertson about the possibility of buying the lot next door for expansion. After some discussion, they agreed on a price for the lot adjacent to the south. The house, the two lots, and the extra room were to be a package deal.

Before the Alexanders and the Robertsons departed, the weary travelers begged to be excused, for they were anxious to retire. With minimal preparations, they collapsed into bed and fell into a sound, reassured, and peaceful slumber.

The following day, the necessary lumber was delivered for the house, and the process of construction began. Within a week, one of the two main rooms was ready to be plastered. The plaster froze up overnight before it had cured, but two days later Charles and Sarah moved in anyway. The weather hampered further work, and their furniture had not yet arrived. But after a little more than a week, they could no longer, in good conscience, impose themselves on the kindness of the Robertsons. Arguments that a room made of green wood and uncured plaster would not provide sufficient warmth and protection were acknowledged but rejected.

So, the Robertsons were obliged to content themselves with lending the Parkers a few odd pieces of furniture. While the house was under construction, a bed had been made to order by Mr. West as soon as Sarah Davis' coffin had been completed. A small wood stove had been installed for heat and for cooking, but seasoned wood was not available so green would have to do. It was a difficult winter, but the still-grieving couple endured their hardship with faith and conviction.

Charles and Sarah joined the new Methodist congregation soon after their arrival, and Sarah spent much of her time working for the congregation. Charles operated out of the added room in their home, making house calls frequently. Soon he had a bustling practice.

By March, Sarah was pregnant, but still their furniture had not arrived. Several letters were written to the steamboat company, but all to no avail. The information they received was neither clear nor detailed, but it indicated that their shipment was placed in a warehouse in St. Louis to await the spring thaw on the upper Mississippi. Charles was obliged to accompany the Colonel to Dubuque on a business trip to see what might be done.

Finally, a steamboat arrived from Davenport with their furniture. Much of what arrived was damaged, and some was missing altogether, never to be recovered. Their loss exceeded eight hundred dollars. Charles took what was salvageable back to Fayette by wagon, and Sarah proceeded to organize the household for the family they were planning. Their second son, Daniel Mason

Parker, was born on the twenty-ninth day of the following October.

The new seminary was not progressing as well as might have been expected. As the year of 1855 drew to a close, the first floor was completed. But, a severe snowstorm in December and a long, bitter cold snap delayed construction for much of the winter. The pressing business of securing the sponsorship of the Iowa Conference of the Methodist Episcopal Church took the lion's share of the college committee's attention. The sponsorship was finally granted, but only conditionally. The Iowa Conference, having grown to unmanageable proportions, was contemplating reorganization. Such sponsorships were not binding on newly created organizational entities assuming jurisdiction.

When the Upper Iowa Conference was convened in Maquoketa in 1856, it created a Committee of Education to decide upon such issues. The committee readily accepted the seminaries at Fayette and at Mount Vernon to the great relief of the illuminaries in both institutions. This acceptance was accompanied by visions of revenues intended to help with westward expansion and with the establishment of congregations in northeastern Iowa. Expectations proved to be frustrated by the financial difficulties that would plague the Fayette institution for much of its existence.

The Colonel had already sunk $8,500 into the development of the seminary, and his son-in-law, Samuel Robertson, contributed $6,000 on top of the ten acres he had donated for the school grounds. Even so, it was clear to all that much more would be needed.

In March, the college committee officially

became the Board of Trustees, and set to work on its Articles of Incorporation. Even though Colonel Alexander was a key member of the original college committee, it was thought best that he not officially be named to the Board of Trustees. The Colonel's attitude toward religion and toward the church was widely known to the Methodist ministers of Northeast Iowa. Most of them had experienced it directly. In order to secure the support of the Upper Iowa Conference, the Board was loaded with ministers and lay citizens whose religious integrity could not be doubted. Everyone, including the Colonel, recognized both the political importance and the pragmatic inconsequence of this action. The Colonel's interest in the progress of the institution, both financially and personally, assured his rightful place among the decision-makers. Charles was prevailed upon to join the faculty as Lecturer on Anatomy and Physiology, a position he readily accepted. This would inaugurate his lifelong commitment to the university and to all of its concerns.

The Articles of Incorporation reflected the values of its founders. The new school would accept students of both sexes and of all backgrounds, and would strive to furnish a thorough and liberal education for their minds as well as religious elevation for their souls. According to the specific desires and recommendations of the Colonel, the Board retained ownership of the school, which included the power to transfer assets, transact school business, and to select the faculty.

With the Articles completed, the next step was to procure a faculty. In August, twenty-five-year-old William Poor from Troy, New York, who had taken his degree from Union College and who had been teaching science in other seminaries, was chosen principal. His salary would be $550 per year. The Reverend Poor was presently residing in Independence with his family. His father, David, was appointed steward. David Poor then proceeded to hire his wife Julia, William's brother, Reverend Clark Poor, Clark's wife Elizabeth, William's sister Clarissa, William's fiancée, Louise Rice, and one other faculty member who was not related to the Poor family. Charles remarked to the Colonel that the steward must have run out of relatives.

Growing expenses demanded payment. With no tuition to provide revenue, the Board sent its business agent, the Reverend Eber Byam, east to mortgage fifteen hundred acres of the Colonel's land. In October, he reported to the Board that Gustavus Austin of Vermont had bought the mortgage for $12,066.

The arrival of the bell, which had been ordered at a cost of $462.60 by the steward from a foundry of his acquaintance in New York, inspired a fund raising event to accompany its first ringing. Citizens of the area, impressed not only by the clarity and spiritual authority of the bell's tone but also by the nearly complete three-story stone structure, contributed enough to pay for the bell with money to spare. Reverend Byam took the spare money to Dubuque for the purchase of groceries, crockery, and furniture in anticipation of the much-desired opening of the school.

One year had passed since Charles and Sarah had taken their first walk to the river together. Their young son, Danny, was healthy and happy, and was the spitting image of his father. Charles was becoming familiar with the countryside, finding the shortest routes to his patient's homes. People were moving into the area at a steady pace, though it seemed to the Colonel that local growth did not match that of the southern portion of the state.

The signs of progress were inescapable. The past year had seen the opening of Maxon & Griffith's store and Budlong & Norton's store as well as the Stock Hotel. Mo's inn had been sold to a man named Allen Payne, who cared not a whit for the building's tragic past. It would no longer serve as an inn; the new owner was interested only in a private residence. The house would remain in his family for some time. Besides, the ill-fated inn was not equipped to compete with the new hotel, which was owned by the Volga Hotel Stock Company. The Stock Hotel was designed for the boom anticipated to accompany the opening of the school. The number of saloons and questionable resorts was held to a minimum by the stalwart Methodists who refused to patronize such places, and Fayette was able to avoid some of the problems with ruffians and outlaws that plagued other frontier towns. Still, there were enough laggards, cads, and drunks to rankle the pious, the moral, and the sober.

The town Christmas celebration for the year of 1856 was held in the Stock Hotel. It was the only facility large enough to accommodate all the people expected to participate in the social event of the year. Christmas had long been understood as a resolution of the rituals of pagan feasting and jubilee with the rituals of Christian devotion. Everyone was welcome in the hope that some may seek to mend the error of their ways and join the congregation.

Services for the devout of the congregation had been held daily in the seminary chapel since the summer. The chapel was one of the first areas of the new building to be completed for just such a purpose. Hope was rampant that sufficient growth in the congregation and in its revenues would eventually pay for the building of a church. Unfortunately, those who would have been principal donors for such a project had pledged their philanthropic funds for the seminary, and no one disagreed as to the importance of that priority. The church could wait if it must.

The official services dissolved into a social hour, and the Colonel herded Charles into a secluded corner of the large room. Charles had been somewhat surprised to see the Colonel participating in the devotionals with everyone else, but assumed that he had made the concession for Elizabeth. Her wishes were long known, and difficult to deny.

"I need to talk to you about something important," said the Colonel. When he was sure that he had Charles's undivided attention, and that they were out of earshot of the rest of the celebrants, he began an uncharacteristically rambling and fragmented discourse.

After hemming and hawing for a bit, the Colonel finally gathered the courage to come to the point. "I saw something last night," he said.

Charles waited patiently for further explanation. When it did not appear to be forthcoming, he said, "What did you see?"

"I wish I knew," said the Colonel, with a completely uncharacteristic element of bewilderment in his tone. "I wish I knew."

Charles continued his patient receptiveness, but the Colonel just stood there. Charles considered posing a structured set of inquiries to ascertain the nature of this sighting, but finally decided not to pursue that tact. The Colonel had initiated the conversation, and had imposed a sense of gravity into it, therefore the Colonel, and no one else, should set its course.

"Have you ever seen anything, C.C.?" said the Colonel, finally. "Have you ever seen anything you could not explain?"

Charles thought for a moment, and decided that his answer should be oriented more toward the Colonel's personal needs than toward the demands of rational positivism. "I have seen many things I cannot explain," he said, with an air of truth.

The Colonel focused all of his intensity on Charles. "Have you ever seen someone before you who was not there?" he asked in earnest.

"I cannot say that I have, actually," said Charles, realizing that his answer would not help the situation. As he began to search his store of medical knowledge for information on hallucinations, the Colonel formulated his own explanation.

"Last night it was Christmas Eve," said the Colonel. "I went to check on the seminary. I wanted to make sure all was in order." Then he let out a great sigh, and continued. "I was thinking about what it would have been like to go to college. I never had the chance of it, you know. I was thinking about the students sitting in their classes and reciting their lessons, then I saw a man. He was there, but he wasn't really there. He was motioning to me. What does it mean?"

Charles considered responding with possibilities, but was stayed by the Colonel's peculiar bent. Having posed the question, he did not seem to be actually looking for the answer. That he already had it for himself was confirmed in his next statement.

"It was Our Lord, Jesus Christ," he said, very soberly. "He was beckoning me to His Church. Right there, on the ground of the seminary I have put so much of myself into, He was calling me to Him."

"I take it," said Charles, "that you are sure of what you saw."

The Colonel straightened up to his full height in a mode of defiance. "I saw Our Savior standing in front of me clear as I ever saw a buck in front of my rifle," he said, with conviction.

Charles knew that when the Colonel used any reference to hunting or shooting, he was serious.

The Colonel looked at Charles with an anxious blend of conviction and perplexity, and asked, "what should I do?"

Charles smiled, and in a very gentle voice he said, "You should join the congregation and be baptized."

"Baptized?" asked the Colonel, as if the ramifications of his predicament were becoming more plain.

"Yes," said Charles. "I cannot think of anything that would please Elizabeth more. Besides, you may be the only member of the Upper Iowa Conference who has seen Him. You cannot let that go to waste."

"Yes," said the Colonel, turning to look at his wife, who was standing with a group of people across the hall. "Yes, you are right. I will speak to the minister directly."

"Colonel," said Charles, with a tone of caution, "some people may doubt the truth of your vision. Do not let them sway you. You must do what you know is right."

The Colonel narrowed in on his confidant with an expression that suggested a glorious transformation, a conversion from hesitation to determination. Not a further word was spoken. The Colonel shook Charles's hand, conveying gratitude and respect, then he turned in the direction of the minister.

The following week, the members of the congregation, meeting in the chapel for their regular services, were surprised to see a large and unexpected figure in their midst. The Colonel did not explain his presence to them until his fourth successive visit. He then explained what he had seen and expressed his desire to be baptized. His wish was granted, and he was formally initiated into the faith on the first day of January of the year 1857 along with several other new members.

Elizabeth could not have been more pleased, and she placed great strain on the muscles in her face, which had not been used for smiling for as long as anyone could remember. Thereafter, the Colonel was often seen on the grounds of "his college," and was frequently in attendance at services.

Fayette Seminary of the Upper Iowa Conference opened on the seventh day of January in the year 1857 with one hundred seventy-four students, all younger than college age.

As was the tradition, literary societies were established: the Philomathean Society for men in October of 1857, and the Aonia Society for women the following month. The tradition originated with secret societies formed by Thirteenth Century students in the University of Paris to study the banned works of Aristotle. However, the reclassification of the works of Aristotle from the forbidden to the required served to remove a good deal of the original curiosity about their contents. By the Nineteenth Century, most literary societies excited more hopeful anticipation from the faculty than devotion to learning from the students. Still, those established at Upper Iowa were hotbeds of lively debate and intense rivalry. By the Twentieth Century, fraternities, sororities, and athletic teams would replace the societies.

The University rules were uncomplicated, and would have been easily anticipated by any incoming student. No games of chance were allowed; no swearing or spitting; students were not allowed to take leave of their rooms or of the college overnight, nor were they allowed to be away during the Sabbath without permission; students were not allowed to visit taverns, grocers, or other public places for the purposes of pleasure or entertainment; no drinking of spirits or liquors, or using tobacco in any form; students must strictly observe the Sabbath, and were not allowed to collect in the rooms of other students without express permission; faculty members were to have access to students' rooms at all times. Dancing was not specifically mentioned in the rules, but was understood to be forbidden, and anyone caught dancing would be instantly dismissed.

The students' life was entirely governed by the bell that so gloriously rang them into consciousness every morning at five. The student who rang the bell was granted tuition credit, but ringing the bell was not his only job. He hoed potatoes in the garden on the east side of campus from four to five. Then he would lay his hoe down, walk to the building, and tug on the bell cord on the first floor which extended down from the tower. Following that, he would return to hoeing. He rang the bell nineteen times each day, calling students to services, to meals, to class, and to bed.

As with any such undertaking, small troubles sprang up during the course of the institution's development as tulips from the soil. Everyone had expected some difficulties, but the range and degree of them raised certain eyebrows. Initially, it became apparent that the steward had hired too many local girls for the domestic chores. Some had to be dismissed. In February, Steward Poor and Reverend Byam requested their salaries in advance because they each had overextended their credit, and were experiencing financial embarrassment. By March, several members of the Board were becoming impatient with the steward's inefficient management practices. Principle William Poor was asked if he would continue in his present position if his father were dismissed. He declared that he would not, so the matter was tabled.

By June, the situation with the steward had not improved. The Executive Committee of the Board asked the full Board to request the steward's resignation. In July, the Board acted on that request, and James Robertson demanded a hearing. Charges against the steward were listed and witnesses testified. Finally, the decision was made. Reverend Byam was forgiven his oversights and relieved of all censure, but the steward,

David Poor, was relieved of his duties. In August, the entire Poor family had departed Fayette, leaving only three full time faculty to teach the classes.

The summer term was completely disrupted, and the introduction of college level classes in the fall seemed to be in jeopardy. Professor Nathan Cornell was prevailed upon to act temporarily in the capacity of president, and given one month to hire a faculty. The good professor had anticipated this turn of events, and had already begun contacting qualified teachers of his acquaintance. By the time the Reverend Lucius Halen Bugbee had arrived to assume the presidency, the new faculty was in place. Great confidence was placed in this deeply religious and highly structured patriarch to resolve the issues and to set the new school upon its proper course.

The Financial Panic of 1857 added great weight to the struggles of the fledgling institution. It was as though every dollar in the State of Iowa was locked away. Years later, Jason Paine would write that the only businesses to thrive during that period would be the sheriff and the courts. Faculty were obliged to work as common laborers during the summer to supplement their incomes.

Fayette Seminary completed its first collegiate term in December, and changed the name of the institution to Fayette Seminary and Collegiate Institute. This would be a temporary situation though, because the college would be constructed on College Hill as soon as the debts held by the seminary were discharged.

The resolution of the seminary's debt did not loom largely on the horizon. Reverend Byam resigned his position as Business Agent for the board in December, citing present financial difficulties as his reason. The current debt stood in excess of thirty-one thousand dollars. Even so, the school had all that was needed to conduct the business of higher education. In the now completed "Sem" were a chapel, a music room, quarters for faculty and administrators, a dining hall, recitation rooms, a library, a parlor, a museum, and dormitories for the students.

Before the year of 1858 imposed itself on the western world, Charles found that his ability to concern himself with the affairs of his classroom and with activities of the seminary was limited by the demands of his practice. The influx of settlers had inflated his workload to the point where he could no longer handle it alone. Providence always provides what is truly needed to those who have given themselves over to its courses in good faith, although the solution provided does not always materialize in the most desired form.

Dixon Alexander was a gruff, outspoken, impatient, misanthropic sort of fellow; the formal opposite of Charles. But, he was a good physician, and he was there. Dixon was born in De Kalb County, New York in 1822, and took his medical training in Castleton Medical College in Vermont. Like the Parkers, the Alexanders had lost a child before coming to Fayette, and like the Parkers, they were seeking a new beginning.

Dr. Parker and Dr. Alexander set up their office in a new suite of rooms added to rear of the Parker home for the practice of medicine and surgery. Together, they would entail the institution of health care in Westfield Township of Fayette County for the next three decades.

They charged a standard one-dollar fee for a treatment, and between twenty-five and seventy-five cents for continuous treatments for the same ailment. Flour, sheep, and other commodities were accepted on account, but the books that Charles meticulously kept would show far more charges than collections.

The first of the late February's days to show a break in winter's icy grip brought sad news to the Parker household. It came in the form of a letter from Sarah's brother, William. Sarah's mother had died on the fifth of that month. The news was not unexpected, and in many ways it provided relief to know that her suffering had ended. William expressed the family's desire to see their sister again, and his hopes that she could attend the funeral, which might be delayed for some period of time as a result of winter's conditions.

Sarah explained her feelings to Charles, who readily accepted her wishes and immediately made arrangements to accommodate them. They set off with their infant son, Danny, for Ohio within the week.

It was good for Sarah to see her brothers and sisters again. She missed them very much. Her many friends in their new home just did not provide the same sort of comfort that can be had in a family. They were happy to see her as well, and all of them were taken by the antics and the other symptoms of intelligence displayed by her young son.

After the family business had been settled, Charles and Sarah were approached by her youngest brother, Jimmy. Jimmy was a cheerful, enthusiastic young man with sandy brown hair and the family's characteristic blue eyes. He was five and a half feet tall, which made him a bit taller than Charles. He had that month embarked upon his twenty-first year. Having discharged the responsibility for taking care of their mother, he was ready to seek his own way in the world. His fancy had been captured by their stories of life and opportunity on the frontier, and he wished to accompany his sister and her husband back to Iowa to live. Charles had a great liking for the boy, and the proposal was gladly accepted.

One thing though, could they alter their usual route through Chicago and travel through Springfield instead? Jimmy had a close friend from his days in Clermont Academy who was living there, and he wished to see him again. Jimmy's friend was remembered by the older couple, but only as a little boy. However, Charles was not one to turn down the opportunity for an adventure, so he readily agreed.

The end of April found the whole party on the road to Springfield. Jimmy had written ahead regarding their plans, and they were able to meet with his friend several times while they were in town. He worked in a law office as a clerk, and had many interesting stories to tell of unusual cases and of local politics.

Their visit over, the travelers set off for Davenport by coach, stopping for the night in the town of Petersburg. The following morning, as they were preparing to continue their journey, they were obliged to receive a visitor, who had specifically requested an audience with Charles. The stranger seemed agitated as he arranged himself for a discussion, yet he exuded a calm and measured demeanor.

Of more than mild curiosity to a physiologist

were the man's features. His whole being was one of the most remarkable for its deviation from average that Charles had ever seen. His jaw was angular, to the point of being square, expanding upward to a broad forehead. The whole of his face was framed by two large, fleshy ears, and dominated by his large, shaggy brow which protruded from the forehead to a greater degree than Charles could remember seeing before. That portion of his face extending from the prominent brow to the scalp seemed rather younger than the portion from the brow to the chin. His eyes were remarkable in themselves. They were deep set and wide apart, but they reflected a perceptive understanding and a gentle nature. They were captivating and disarming, and they contradicted the appearance of the body to an extreme. He appeared to be at least fifty years of age, but he could be older. His tall, skinny frame and his awkward movements might suggest frailty to the casual observer. But, to an anatomist, the uncommon strength residing in those limbs was unmistakable.

"My name is Abe Lincoln," said the stranger, in a high-pitched, almost squeaky, voice. "I am an attorney, and I could use your help. I understand that you are a expert in forensic medicine."

"I have made a study of that subject," said Charles, "but I do not know that I am an expert."

"I need you to be an expert," said Abe, his voice forceful and hinting of agitation.

"I teach anatomy and physiology in Fayette Seminary and Collegiate Institute," said Charles, dryly. "I am a practicing surgeon."

"Ah, that is good," said Abe. "I am working on a

case that is of supreme importance to me, and which has presented me with some very perplexing problems. Will you serve as my medical witness?"

Charles thought for a moment. He had Sarah and Danny to consider. "How long will this take?" he asked.

"We are scheduled to begin on May fifth," said Abe. "I anticipate a day or two for jury selection, and one day for the trial. I expect to be finished by the sixth or seventh."

That was less than a week away, and Jimmy was available to help Sarah. Charles agreed.

"Then," said Abe, "you must not report our conversations to anyone else. Are you in agreement?"

"Yes," said Charles.

"Good," said Abe, who then relayed the details of the case.

Some time ago, he had received a letter from an old friend. It was not just any friend, but it was from a family to whom Abe felt he owed his start in adult life. When he first came to New Salem he was befriended by a man named Jack Armstrong. Charles would learn from Abe's legal assistant, William Walker, that the friendship grew from a wrestling match in which the young Abe prevailed. As most honorable men on the frontier would do, Jack Armstrong respected and appreciated the man who had bested him in a fair fight. Abe would spend many nights in the Armstrong cabin, and would always remember, with the highest regard, the kindness he had been shown.

The letter was written by Jack's widow, Hannah, who was following through with her departed husband's last wish. Because she was illiterate, Hannah dictated the letter to a neighbor, who wrote it for her. It seems their son, Duff, a boy Abe had held on his lap in earlier, happier times, had been mixed up in some bad business. He was accused of murder. They needed Abe's help.

In August of the previous year, there had been an altercation in a place nearby called Walker's Grove. An assortment of young men had been drinking heavily and enjoying racing their horses on a summer evening. Jim Metzger, a large, powerful, hardworking father of three children, was taking advantage of one of his rare opportunities for a respite from the responsibilities of life. As he sought out a sutler's wagon, where he might procure another drink, he spied a young man of his acquaintance sleeping on a bench. The young man was twenty-four-year-old William "Duff" Armstrong. Seeing an opportunity for a bit of sport, Metzger caught Armstrong by the legs and pulled him violently from the bench. Armstrong, who was much smaller than his tormentor, made a token show of retaliation, and then they had a drink together. Shortly after that incident, Metzger visited similar mischief on another young man by the name of Jim Norris.

According to witnesses, an hour later, about midnight, Metzger was attacked by the two younger, smaller men. It was said that Norris came at him from behind and hit him with a neck-yoke, a three-foot piece of frame from a wagon. At the same instant, Armstrong was said to have hit Metzger from the front with a slung-shot, a lead weight fixed to a cord and swung at the target.

"Witnesses claim," said Abe, "that they saw Duff use the slung-shot, but I think it was too dark for them to see much of anything. They say the moon was up, but I have my doubts. I have been able to establish that Duff did not own a slung-shot, and that the one found at the scene was owned by a fellow who claims to have been asleep under a wagon when this was all going on."

"Metzger rode home," continued Abe, "but his wife says that he fell off his horse on the way home. He had a bad bruise on his right eye and another one on the back of his head. He died the next day. Dr. Stephenson testified before the grand jury that the skull was fractured in two places, in the back and in the front, near the corner of the right eye. I spoke with Dr. Stephenson, and he told me that he was reluctant to be as positive about his conclusions as the prosecutor would like him to be. Still, he is the prosecutor's witness, and that's why I need you. All I need to do is to create doubt in the jury's mind about which blow caused the death. Norris has already been convicted of murder for his role. I think it's possible that Metzger's death could have been caused by injuries he received from falling off his horse. What is your opinion?"

With that question, Abe handed to Charles a copy of the grand jury indictment. Charles took the papers and began reading them without comment. After reading them, he spoke in his most authoritative voice.

"It is entirely possible that Mr. Metzger died of wounds he could have received from falling off his horse," he said. "There are several possibilities as to what circumstances were the cause of death, and nothing here points reliably to any one of them."

"Say he did not fall off his horse," Abe posed. "Is it possible that the fracture above the eye could have been caused by the blow to the back of the head, the skull then being fractured in two places by one blow?"

Charles thought for a moment. "Yes, that is possible," he conceded.

"And that would be your testimony?" asked Abe, anxiously.

"Yes," answered Charles, with a tone of resolution.

Abe's features relaxed somewhat as he sat back in his chair. "That is very good," he said. "I am very glad to hear that."

After a moment or so of silence, Abe spoke. "This case has perplexed me greatly," he confided, with sadness in his voice. "I feel my responsibility toward the family most acutely, and I must continue. But it is not a case the sort of which I would readily agree to argue in court."

Charles took that statement to mean that Abe believed his friend's son to probably have committed the crime of which he was accused. Abe did not seem to be the sort of lawyer who would knowingly defend the guilty unless there was some extenuating reason. If there was anything obvious to one who beheld Abe Lincoln, aside from his unusual physical features, it was the pureness of his integrity. Since Charles did not know what was true and what was not, he determined to provide an accounting of his best scientific analysis of the circumstances and leave to those upon whom the responsibility fell to make the decision. The circumstances of the case entreated for mercy at least as strongly as for condemnation.

Abe related his plans and presumptions regarding

the upcoming series of events. He would not request a subpoena for Charles until the last possible moment to avoid alerting the prosecution that he intended to make an issue of the medical evidence. Charles should remain at the inn in Petersburg until he received his subpoena, and then he should remove to Beardstown where the trial would be held. Once on the stand, Charles should respond directly to questions, and should be as honest in his responses as possible. And with that, the busy Mr. Lincoln concluded his business with an admonishment to not discuss any particulars with anyone, and then he left.

When he had gone, Charles explained the situation to Sarah and to Jimmy without revealing any details of the case. Jimmy was excited about the prospect of watching the trial, but Charles knew from her composed and indifferent manner that Sarah was something less than enamored with another week's delay. Still, she would not complain, and she was content that they would at least be together.

At length, the summons arrived. Charles was concerned when he discovered that the middle initial of his name was incorrect on the legal form. He was not an expert in such things, but it seemed to him that this could be a problem. Since he was to travel to Beardstown directly, he decided to inform Mr. Lincoln as soon as they arrived.

Their journey was uneventful, and they found suitable lodgings even as the town was beginning to fill with people arrived for the trial. Before they had completely settled in their quarters, Abe appeared at the door to their room to check in on them.

"They have gotten my middle initial wrong," said

Charles, thrusting the document toward the lanky attorney.

Abe took the paper from Charles and squinted at it. "So they have," he said. "I told the clerk 'Charles C. Parker,' and he must have heard it as 'Charles E. Parker.' That is understandable, but I would not worry about it. He misspelled Stephenson's name altogether. It seems that the medical witnesses are misnamed alike."

He smiled as he handed the paper back to Charles. "When they ask you to state your name, say that you are Charles Parker. No one will make an issue of it. Now, we should get down to business. You are a teacher of anatomy; you now have an eager pupil."

Mr. Lincoln pressed past Charles and seated himself at the small table in the center of the room. He reached into a bag he had been carrying and produced a human skull. "I borrowed this from a druggist of my acquaintance," he said, and for the next two hours, he questioned Charles closely about the anatomical particulars and about the possible causes for the injuries suffered by the deceased. Mr. Lincoln asked intelligent questions and took copious notes. Charles was very impressed with the lawyer's quick study, with his logical mind, and with his attention to detail. He could well have been a scientist.

Selecting the jury took two full days. It was an intricate game played by the opposing attorneys. The prosecution was pressing for older men and the defense for younger, assuming that younger men would be more understanding of the situation and sympathetic toward the accused.

Finally, on May 7th, the court convened for the

trial. Hannah Armstrong and her other sons sat near Duff and Mr. Lincoln, who surprised everyone by wearing a pure white suit. This unusual attire naturally drew everyone's attention to him, making him the central figure in the room. Sarah had elected to remain at the hotel with Danny, and perhaps take advantage of a fine spring day with a stroll. At Mr. Lincoln's suggestion, Charles and Jimmy sat in that section of the gallery more closely associated with the prosecutor's table. It was unlikely that anyone there would know who he was until he was called, but this way Charles would not give the impression that he was on the "side" of the defense. The prosecutor in the case was Hugh Fullerton, who had led the prosecution in the Norris trial. The judge in the case was to be James Harriott, of the Twenty-first Judicial Circuit, who had also presided over the Norris trial.

As the murmuring in the courtroom began to settle for the beginning of the trial, Mr. Lincoln sat motionless at the defense table with his head back, staring at some point on the ceiling. He was oblivious to that which occurred around him, apparently lost in thought. His attention was brought to bear on his surroundings when the judge entered the room.

At the judge's behest, Mr. Fullerton began explaining his case to the jury. With that completed, witnesses for the prosecution were called in a steady and rapid succession. Dr. Stephenson explained the nature of the wounds and his conclusion as to the cause of death. It was still before noon when the prosecution's star witness, Charles Allen, took the stand to tell his story. The circumstances of that fateful night were related pretty much as Mr. Lincoln had explained to Charles, except for the claim that the moonlight was bright in a cloudless sky. The prosecutor had several men stand and reenact the scene for the jury. Confident that he had made his case, Mr. Fullerton concluded, and the judge called a recess for lunch.

Making his way back to his original seat after lunch, Charles overheard Mr. Lincoln telling Hannah Armstrong that her boy would be cleared before sundown. When the court had reconvened, Mr. Lincoln took the floor to make his defense.

Mr. Lincoln's opening remarks stressed his client's innocence, and cited two reasons for it. First, Duff Armstrong did not use a weapon; he attacked Metzger with his bare fists. Second, the blow delivered by Norris from behind happened some minutes before Duff hit Metzger, and the two assailants did not act in concert. The unfortunate Duff was guilty only of losing his temper. And what man would not be angry at having been abused in so humiliating a manner as he had been by Metzger. Norris, who suffered similar abuse, was angry enough to assault his foe from behind with a three-foot club. Duff should be admired for his courage in confronting such a large and powerful bully face to face.

When his opening remarks were concluded, Mr. Lincoln called his character witnesses. Sure Duff was rowdy, they said, but so are all of us. Duff never did anything that had brought on legal charges. He was a good son of good pioneer parents. The next set of witnesses were questioned in detail about where they were standing, about what time it happened, about what they had seen and not seen. It happened about eleven o'clock. No one had seen or heard of the existence of a slung-shot in the camp that night.

Mr. Lincoln then called Nelson Watkins. Watkins admitted that the slung-shot held in evidence was his. As proof, he described how he had fashioned it, and Mr. Lincoln cut it open to show the jury. Its unusual construction was exactly as Watkins had described. Watkins went on to claim that he had taken it to the camp that night, but that he had not lent it to anyone. As far as he knew, Duff never had it. When he laid himself down under a wagon to sleep, he had placed it up on the frame underneath. He had forgotten to retrieve it when he awoke, and it must have dropped off the next morning when the wagon was moved. That is how it came to be found at the scene several days after the fight. Watkins was dismissed with little challenge from the prosecution.

Finally, Charles was called to the stand. As he rose from his seat in the audience, he removed the skull that Mr. Lincoln had entrusted to him from its bag. All eyes in the courtroom rested on the skull as Charles proceeded to the witness stand. He swore an oath to tell the truth, and then stated his name as Mr. Lincoln had suggested. When Charles was seated for his testimony, Mr. Lincoln began his line of questioning.

The first order of business was to establish his credentials as an expert witness. When Charles had finished reciting the particulars of his career, he could not help thinking that it must sound far more impressive to the strangers in the courtroom than it actually was. With that finished, he held the skull aloft for the jury to view. Mr. Lincoln began to explain the basics of cranial anatomy asking from Charles only occasional acknowledgement of the truth of his assertions. He pointed to each anatomical feature, identified it by the appropriate scientific name, and explained its relationships with other features. The spry attorney maneuvered the course of his dissertation with such skill that, not knowing any better, Charles might have taken him for a surgeon. He wished his students in Fayette had learned their lessons half this well.

"If a blow were to be struck," said Mr. Lincoln to Charles, with a bit of dramatic flair, "on one side of the cranium sufficient to cause an injury, could a similar injury be caused by that same blow in a different spot? Say, on the opposite side?"

"Of course," Charles replied. "Any rigid structure can transfer the energy applied to it in one point to other points in the structure. In fact, multiple injuries could result from a single blow of sufficient force."

"Could a blow delivered here, causing a fracture in the parietal bone above the lambdoid suture," continued Mr. Lincoln, pointing to the rear of the skull, "also cause a fracture here?" Mr. Lincoln turned the skull for the jury to see, and moved his finger along a line from the lower part of the frontal bone to the superciliary arch near the corner of the right eye socket.

"If the blow was sufficient in force and if it was struck at the proper angle," said Charles, confidently, "yes, two such fractures could readily be the result."

"Now," said Mr. Lincoln, as he strode across the room with his hands clasped behind his back, "suppose for the sake of argument that the blow to the back of Jim Metzger's head was not strong enough to produce a fracture in the frontal bone. It is a matter of record that Mrs. Metzger has told us that he fell at least twice from his horse on the way home. Is it possible that the fracture in the frontal bone above the superciliary arch, as recorded by the medical examiner, was caused by one of those falls?"

"Yes," said Charles, "that is possible. It is likely that he fell as a result of losing consciousness, which would be expected from the sort of wound received on the back of the head. Given that the back of the horse is at least five or six feet from the ground, and even if he were lying prone in the saddle, Mr. Metzger could have sustained the injury to his frontal bone in a fall from the back of the horse if he hit his head upon the ground. In fact, when a person falls from a horse as the result of unconsciousness, it is usually the head that strikes the ground first with the full weight of the body propelling it downward."

"Thank you, Dr. Parker," said Mr. Lincoln, with a slight smile on his face that the jury could not see. "You have been most helpful in this matter."

The prosecutor did not have any questions for Charles, and he was dismissed from the witness stand.

As Charles was making his way to his seat, Mr. Lincoln called Charles Allen to the stand, which sent a wave of commotion through the room. Mr. Allen had given his elaborate testimony in favor of the prosecution, and no one could imagine what Mr. Lincoln had in mind by recalling him to testify for the defense.

The line of questioning taken by Mr. Lincoln did not seem to be challenging any of Mr. Allen's previous testimony. In fact, he seemed to be looking for verification of it. Many of the questions were of the type one might expect to be asked at a social event upon being introduced to a stranger. Where do you live? How often do you go to Walker's Grove? And so on. At one point, the exchange was focused entirely on the position of the moon in the sky when the event took place. The repetition of questions establishing that fact was becoming tedious.

Finally, Mr. Lincoln narrowed to his objective by asking specific questions that would establish an ability to actually see what happened, and what he actually saw. How far away were you standing? How did the accused strike his blow? And so on. But, the questions rapidly returned to the subject of the position and brightness of the moon. Mr. Allen insisted that the moon was nearly overhead and very bright.

Abruptly, Mr. Lincoln ceased his questioning and turned to walk slowly back to the table where Duff Armstrong sat. From a briefcase, he retrieved three small books. He handed one of them to the prosecutor, and one to Judge Harriott. The judge noted that the book was Jayne's Almanac from 1857. Mr. Lincoln asked him to turn to the page for August.

Returning to the witness, Mr. Lincoln again asked him if he was certain about the position and brightness of the moon. Yes he was. Was he familiar with the term "moonset"? The witness supposed he was. Mr. Lincoln explained that astronomers used the term to indicate that the entire moon had disappeared below the horizon.

Holding the almanac up, Mr. Lincoln explained that it contained the exact time of moonset in central Illinois for every day of the year. According to the almanac, on the day in question, the moon set at three minutes past midnight. Therefore, at eleven o'clock, the moon was near the horizon and not overhead.

With that revelation, the crowd of spectators burst into laughter. Charles noted that several of the jurors were also laughing. He did not need to be an expert in the law to see that the case was definitely going in Mr. Lincoln's favor.

The judge called for order as Mr. Lincoln handed the book he was holding to the jury foreman, who looked at it and passed it down the line.

The spectators were active but mostly quiet as the jurors inspected the almanac. Charles Allen looked bewildered. His previously reserved and confident demeanor had been unraveled. Sensing defeat in a case that he had been assured of winning, Mr. Fullerton called a clerk over and instructed him to find any other almanacs that might be in the courthouse. The man returned shortly and handed the prosecutor two that he had found—one was Goudy's and the other was Ayer's. Even though each almanac was calculated for a different latitude, they still agreed within minutes on the time of moonset.

Mr. Lincoln seated himself at the defense table without speaking another word. Mr. Fullerton rose to cross-examine the witness. Mr. Allen was forced to admit that he did not take any specific notice of the position of the moon in the sky. Yes, he was certain that there was enough moonlight to see what transpired; in fact, he thought the moon was high in the sky because it was so bright.

By late afternoon, all testimony had been heard and the stage was set for closing arguments. Following custom, Mr. Fullerton went first, delivering his summary of the prosecution's case and its relative merits. He stressed statements made by witnesses, and proposed several possible ways the accused could have procured a slung-shot. He countered Charles's testimony by citing that of Dr. Stephenson. He pointed out that all the witnesses attested to the sufficient level of light, and that the consistencies in their independent testimony could not be denied. Satisfied that he had made his best case, Mr. Fullerton sat down.

Mr. Lincoln did not stir immediately following Mr. Fullerton's conclusion. He sat quite still. When a certain amount of tension began to accumulate in the room, he rose slowly from his seat, stretching to his full height in the manner of a sunflower reaching for the heavens. His white suit sliced through the gray room as though it were reflecting a divine light beaming down upon his slender frame, as though he were being revealed to a sorry world in want of divine glory.

As he moved around the table from his seat, his awkward and ungainly manner of moving invoked a sensation of embarrassment in the observer. One could not help but to feel sorry for him. His odd shape and gangly limbs seemed to work against him as he moved. Still not having spoken, Mr. Lincoln removed his coat in a slow and deliberate manner. He finally began to speak as he removed his vest, revealing a knitted suspender, which fell from his shoulder to rest on his arm without being replaced. The shrill and squeaking quality of his voice on beginning his soliloquy gave the impression of a forced abstinence from speaking; these could have been the utterances of a voice held silent for decades, waiting for the right moment to deliver the most consequential of messages.

He began speaking directly to the jury with his hands clasped behind his back. As he spoke, he brought his hands around to the front using them more and more frequently in gestures to emphasize points. As time passed, his awkwardness and his shrillness melted away. His discourse evolved into an harmonic expression—a unified stream of word and motion.

The wily lawyer spent a good portion of his short summation on a careful and calculated analysis of the facts that he had attempted to establish in the case. But the audience was fixed on his allusions to the undeserved tragedy that had befallen the hapless family of the accused. Every soul in the room was entranced by the performance. There was scarcely a heart within the sound of his voice that was not touched. He told the story of his friendship with Jack Armstrong, and what it had meant to a poor, friendless boy. He told how the generous Armstrong family had provided him with food, clothing and shelter when he was struggling to survive. He told of the many happy evenings spent in the Armstrong home holding young Duff on his knee and telling him stories. He told of the hardships Hannah faced as a recent widow with a family to raise. He told all of this with an eloquence that would extract tears in its own right by virtue of its perfection. After less than an hour's time, Mr. Lincoln concluded with a plea for the life of the son of his old friends and benefactors. His appeal for acquittal would be remembered more for its pathos than for its rehearsal of the evidence.

Charles was moved beyond any words he could use to describe his feelings. He could only imagine how the aura of energy surrounding this display of greatness affected the jury.

Mr. Lincoln retrieved a small piece of paper from the defense table, and handed it to the judge. Mr. Fullerton joined him at the bench and the three had a short conference. When the two lawyers had returned to their respective tables, the judge recited his instructions to the jury, reading in part from the paper that Mr. Lincoln had given him.

If there was reasonable doubt that the defendant delivered the fatal blow, or that he acted in concert with Norris, they were to acquit. When the judge had finished, the jury was escorted from the room, and the interested parties began their tedious wait for a decision.

Charles waited to see if Mr. Lincoln had anything further for him. He was, at present, engaged with Hannah Armstrong. As Charles stood by with Jimmy, he noticed Judge Harriott motioning to him. They moved through the crowd toward the judge, who by now had removed his robe.

"Dr. Parker," he said, "I want to thank you for your testimony. It was most enlightening. If there is an acquittal in this case, and I suspect there will be, it should be more the result of your testimony than of Abe Lincoln's courtroom antics. Notwithstanding the appeal of an impassioned speech, I think you have truly raised a reasonable doubt. It is a fine public service you have provided, sir, and I thank you."

"It has been my honor and duty to provide it," said Charles, aware that his chest was expanding ever so slightly with pride.

As they parted from the judge, they were

surprised to see Mr. Lincoln standing directly behind them.

"Will you remove to your hotel?" he asked. Given an affirmative, he added, "then I shall accompany you there."

Mr. Lincoln did not speak further, and seemed to be bearing the weight of the earth upon him. They were joined by all of the Armstrong family with the exception of Hannah, who decided to take a walk by herself.

Outside the courthouse, they were accosted by a young man named Abram Byers, who wanted to take Mr. Lincoln's photograph. Mr. Lincoln politely refused, but the young man was insistent. Finally, the beleaguered lawyer gave in. After giving instructions for contacting him should they receive word that the jury was ready, he separated from the party, which continued on to the hotel lobby.

Once inside the hotel, Charles made his way to his room to check on Sarah and Danny, while Jimmy remained in the lobby with the Armstrong boys with whom he had struck a friendship. After about half an hour, Mr. Lincoln appeared, fresh from his sitting. He seemed to be in a better mood.

An hour following the seclusion of the jury found Jimmy pounding on Charles and Sarah's door. The jury was back for a reading of the verdict. Charles made his apologies to Sarah, but he had to see this thing through. The Armstrong party and Mr. Lincoln had preceded them to the courthouse, so they hurried to catch up.

Jimmy and Charles had just entered the door when they heard the jury foreman read the verdict. "We the jury acquit the defendant from all charges preferred against him in the indictment."

There were a few hoorahs from Duff's brothers, but Duff himself could only smile. From his height of less than five and a half feet, he looked up at the face of the six-foot-four Lincoln with the deepest of gratitude, and shook his hand. Hannah Armstrong was not in the room, having chosen to remain in the solitude of the pasture behind the courthouse. Mr. Lincoln sent a man to tell her the news. It was over.

The journey back to Fayette was filled with discussion of the trial. Jimmy recounted every minute detail to his sister, Sarah, with multiple variations. He spoke with admiration and pride of the part his brother-in-law had played, and Charles was deeply flattered. But the greater portion of the discussion was devoted to Mr. Lincoln's unforgettable performance. Charles was compelled to agree that he had never before heard anything of the like. All were arrived in Fayette with vaulted spirits; Charles was eager to return to his former duties, Sarah was hoping to increase the number of their family, and Jimmy looked forward to beginning his new life as a student in the new college of Fayette.

By July, the college hill project was officially abandoned, and the Seminary would be transformed into an institution of higher education. New articles of incorporation were adopted to reflect the seminary's new status, and the name was changed to Upper Iowa University. Reverend Dr. Bugbee was sworn in as the first president, and Charles was elected to the Board of Trustees for the first of his many years of service on that board. The desires of the founders had finally come to pass, even if everything was not to their complete satisfaction.

Despite the crop failure of 1858, which compounded problems persisting from the financial panic of the previous year, five sophomores and ten freshmen were added to the eighty-eight gentlemen and fifty-four ladies who were enrolled in the Normal and Preparatory departments for the 1858-59 school year.

One student wrote in his diary the following reflection on the beginning of the new school year:

The bell held its tongue pretty much throughout vacation, but today, Thursday, it revives. Signs of life, young life, are manifest around the premises up there. Spruce looking boys, with portly trunks and satchels filled out like an Alderman's pocket, are wending thitherward and jaunty little bonnets with pretty faces inside. Here the rollicking colts are to be broken to harness through the day and turned out afterward to graze on the village common. Dear old Seminary! It was under your cavedropping roofs that we acclimated in the coldest weather known to the oldest inhabitants.

Here we sang our first morning hymn of praise beyond the giant Mississippi. Here we ate our first bacon in the Steward's Hall. How baby laughed and crowed and rattled down the tottish stools and dodged the corners of the tables--how the wind, the sleet, the snow, the hail and thunder and lightning altogether shook the window of our room. How it friz and thew and friz again till our ideas of the "Italian climate of Iowa" set forth in documents, left us in possession of the shivering fact that it was all an egregious fallacy. How we explored the nooks and crannies of the temple of Science and clambered over fallen plaster and rubbish, snuffing the fresh paint and mortar.

That fall, Charles inaugurated the first chemistry class. One day, he came to class with large circles of dirt on the knees of his trousers. Stares from the students compelled him to explain.

"As I came up through the woods from Lima last evening," he said, "I caught sight of a likely young sapling and decided to bring it home with me. I had no spade. The only tool I had with me was a pocketknife. By hard work with knife and hand, by cutting and pulling, I finally got it out of the ground. I have just set it down by the west gate."

He had decided that the seminary grounds needed a little something. The elm sapling became the spark of an idea. Yes, he thought, this ground could use some trees. He determined to bring them in one by one, collecting them as he made his rounds. Pines, he thought. There should be more pines. A pine grove would set the grounds off nicely from the surrounding deciduous forest. It would take more than twenty years for him to see the project through.

By 1859, Sarah's younger brother, William Lakin, had come west to seek his fortune. He had been practicing law in Ohio for seven years, and he was ready for a change. Excited by the wagon teams assembling quickly among the herds of cattle in the town for the express purpose of charging off in search of gold, Will recruited a team of his own. Sarah was furious with him for luring Charles on a wild goose chase to Pike's Peak. To avoid her wrath, Will fled back to Point Pleasant. There may perhaps have been other incentives for that dodge, because he married his long time sweetheart,

Caroline Thompson, soon after his return to Ohio. He would not be away long. Will soon returned with his bride to make Fayette his home, and to become one of its most prominent citizens.

On August first of that year, Charles Lucius Parker was born healthy and happy to two very proud parents. Charles began to think of buying a larger house, but he was not sure where he would find the money. A number of people owed him debts, but he was not of a mind to collect from them until they were able to pay. Between his obligations to the college and the ever-expanding demand for his services in the area surrounding Fayette, he had little time to think about money in any case.

Back in 1851, West Union was selected county seat by special election. That had always chafed with the Colonel, who considered it a fluke because Fayette did not exist at the time of the election, and Westfield was little more than a sawmill. He and others hoped Fayette might one day win that honor and the advantages that accompanied it as soon as people realized that Fayette was the better city.

Dixon Alexander, now enjoying a thriving medical partnership with Charles, decided to take action himself. He gathered 1,349 signatures on a petition to hold a referendum on the issue. Should West Union remain County Seat, or should said seat be removed to Fayette? The Court ordered an election, and it was held on April 2, 1860. Fayette lost 1,221 to 1,304. The chance for the Colonel's dream passed, and he would not see it rise again.

By the fall term of 1860, the Collegiate

Department had an enrollment of fifty-five male students, and the Female Collegiate Department boasted of forty-eight. Reverend Bugbee had resigned the previous summer claiming a successful administration. The books reflected otherwise. Most members of the faculty held promissory notes instead of the salary they were due. The mortgage secured on the Colonel's fifteen hundred acres had inflated to $17,000. Colonel Alexander, obliged to settle the debt honorably and loath to shift the responsibility to the institution, reached an agreement with G. A. Austin to resolve the mortgage in exchange for over four thousand acres, half his holdings. The Colonel was never heard to utter a single word of regret over that turn of events.

Faith in the progress of the new university was given a substantial boost by the arrival of a tall and imposing Methodist minister whose personal power and majesty rivaled that of Heaven itself. He was Yale-educated Reverend William Brush, and there was no doubt among those of his acquaintance that whatever needed to be accomplished, he would find a way to do it. He assumed the presidency of the college at a time when he was most needed, and he did not disappoint.

Convinced that the pastoral approach was superior to the isolation of the ivory tower, Reverend Brush set off periodically through the surrounding countryside in a wagon drawn by a brace of matched, white mules. He made an impressive spectacle as he visited each farmhouse, reinforcing the faith and soliciting contributions for God's work. Reverend Brush's mission included the counseling and recruiting of young people whose lives and service to God would be improved through higher education. Of this latter, the Reverend served as his own excellent example.

Charles added to his other duties the supervising of the construction of a garden in southeast corner of campus. Here, students planted, tended, and harvested potatoes, turnips, and other vegetables for their own consumption.

The pragmatic approach to smoothing the imperfections of life adopted by the Methodists was attended by the faithful, and was understandably in the heart of the new institution. For a certain few however, the allurements of the contemplative life beckoned from their ancient Greek origins. Lest one be accused of embracing the pagan ways, the dear delight of philosophy must be savored in relative secrecy, concealed, at least in part, by a facade of piety and devout religious study.

Late in March of 1861, Charles received word that his father, Reverend Daniel Parker, had died on the twenty-second. It was decided that Charles would travel alone to the funeral, and would return as quickly as possible. Sarah, for reasons of her own, was reluctant to participate in his family's affairs. Besides, the burden of traveling with an infant and a toddler was not something she was ready to endure. Dixon Alexander and his wife, and their many other friends, would look after them until his return. Priscilla had many children in Ohio to care for her, and her oldest son, James, had already assumed much of that role.

After the arrangements had been made, Charles set off. He did not experience his usual delight in traveling. In fact, the entire trip was enshrouded in a melancholy that he had not known before. The flood of memories of his father, seen in the light of his own adult experiences, had new meaning for him and compelled him to reassess his own sense of family. Charles returned to Fayette with a deepened erudition, and with a renewed feeling of responsibility. It seemed as though the nation itself was following that same course of reassessment.

The optimism held by those immersed in the affairs of the new university was gradually being overshadowed by troubling developments outside the community. Occasional rumblings were heard, especially from the east and from the south, which were disquieting to say the least. Iowa was not suffering under the politics of slavery as it was being felt in Kansas and Missouri. Still, the disturbance was imposing itself more and more on this peaceful corner of the frontier. As if the violence and the bloodshed were not distressing enough, some were saying there would be war.

V

"What do you mean move to Fayette?" I asked, somewhat as a teenager would object to cleaning out the garage. "I can't just pick up and move here. My wife couldn't find a job."

"She can't do laundry or hire out her cleaning services?" was his reply.

Now it was my turn to give him the look. "Let me bring you up to date with the modern world," I said, mindful not to sound too much like a scolding parent. "Women today have the same opportunities for professional work as men do. My wife is the administrator of a hundred-bed skilled nursing and rehabilitation center. She's the captain of her ship, and she makes a good deal more money than I do. I can only afford to teach here because she makes good money."

"Is that true?" he asked, incredulous.

"Well," I said, "it's all true except that I suppose I could work here without her salary if it was absolutely necessary. But she is not the sort of person who would be contented to confine herself to traditional wifely duties, and I am not the sort of person who would suggest that she try. These are the peak years of her career, and I can't let my failures interfere with her best chance of success."

"What failures are those?" he inquired.

I was not sure how I wished to respond. "That's not something I want to discuss," I said, finally. "You have things you do not want to discuss, and I have things

I do not want to discuss. Let's just say that I have been less than successful in holding down a job."

His features relaxed, and he became quite pensive. "And you do not think you need any help?" he finally asked, gently.

I thought for a moment. "It's not as simple as you suggest," I replied. "I could list reasons in each case why those who decided to fire me were wrong, and I could tell you what I did, or refused to do, that encouraged them to make that decision. But if I did that, I would not have addressed the point."

"Oh," he said, "and what is the point?"

"The point is my integrity. I have done and said things that I know are right, but that are not popular with those who control organizations. What would you help me do, abandon my integrity and do what I know is wrong to curry favor with those who lie, cheat, and steal as a rule?"

"I see your point," he said. "I too have faced such decisions. Still, there is always room for compromise."

"Perhaps there is," I said, "but, as you should know, I have little tolerance for fraud, hypocrisy, and incompetence. My life is too short for me to be wasting my time sucking up to ambitious pretenders."

He appeared to be considering my position.

After a moment, I said, "there is one thing on which I would like to hear your opinion. This has to do with something I have thought about since childhood. You know how most Christians blame Judas for betraying Jesus, and condemn the Jews for crucifying Him? How Jesus had His moment of doubt, but He decided to allow unpleasant things to happen anyway because it was His destiny?"

"Yes," he said, slowly, not sure if this conversation was progressing in an appropriate direction.

"Suppose that Judas had not betrayed Jesus. Suppose that Jesus had not been crucified. How would the prophecy be fulfilled? How then would there be Christianity today?"

His face took on a puzzled look.

"I have never felt," I continued, "that I've ever had a choice in my life. Now, I'm not saying that I'm a prophet by anyone's definition, but I am saying that each time something bad has happened to me, something important happened as a result of it. I was fired in New York because I represented a higher standard of scholarship than my colleagues could live up to. Then, we moved to Iowa. When we came here, we had no idea what Barbara would do. Now, she has the best career opportunity of her life, something she can really do well and take pride in doing it. She would never have had that opportunity in New York."

"I see," he said, without a great deal of conviction in his voice.

"I was fired in Dubuque," I continued, "but I think there has to be some reason for it other than to cover up the incompetent and self-serving actions of certain administrators. Every failure has been a setup for something important ahead. If I had not been fired, then I would not be here to do whatever it is I'm supposed to do."

"What do you suppose that might be?" he asked.

"How should I know?" I cried, throwing my hands up in the air. "What are you doing here? At any time in your life were you ever visited by a ghost who said 'I'm here to help you?'"

"No," he admitted, "I cannot say that I was."

"Are you a figment of my imagination, then?" I yelled.

"That is for you to decide," he said, softly.

This was going nowhere.

"I am taking you on good faith," I said, finally, more calmly. "I do not need to know why. I guess all I need to know is what to do next."

"You asked my opinion on this," he said. "I think that providence finds its path more readily in the lives of some than it does in the lives of others. Some are more inclined to heed its prodding than others. If you are guided by providence, then you should do what you have always done. Then, you should accept whatever help you are given, and make of it what you can."

"I need to do some work," I said. "I need to make up exams."

I wheeled my chair over to the computer, and went to work. I was not angry, but I was agitated enough to be unable to continue the conversation. As I worked, he wandered over to the south window and stood gazing outside. I could not help but to consider that nothing is ever as easy as I wished it would be.

The next morning, I confronted him.

"You did that to me, didn't you?" said I, trying not to sound as diverted as I actually was.

"I am sorry," he replied, turning from his position at the window. "I have not the pleasure of understanding you."

"You know what I'm taking about," I said, trying

to keep a straight face. "I went up to Grandview Cemetery to find your grave. I must have walked past your monument half a dozen times without seeing it. It's not like it isn't obvious. It's the tallest one out there, and it's right on the road. But you didn't let me see it, did you? I had to go to the town library and look it up in the cemetery record. You made me work for it."

"Was it worth it?" he asked, with a slight grin on his face. "I've never seen it."

"I suppose it was," I answered. "At least I got some exercise."

"Everything worthwhile requires effort."

"You gunky!" I said. Then, in response to his puzzled look, "it's a term of critical endearment used by a comedian named Bill Cosby. Don't make me explain it, just take it like a man. You know what it means."

"Fair enough," he said, and turned back toward the window.

For a time, nothing of consequence happened. I was still chafing over our earlier discussion, and I was not inclined to pursue any topic that might lead in the same direction. We were like Rodolfo and Marcello in *La Bohème*, pretending to do our work while trying to ignore the real issue. His work consisted mostly of staring out the window. This activity was punctuated by stints on the Internet. If he was on a mission to correct my many flaws, he did not seem to be in any hurry to do so.

It might have been irritating having him there constantly but for two things. First, I am an experienced husband and father, which is to say that I am highly skilled at tuning people out. Second, his presence was more enjoyable than it was irritating, particularly when he was not pressing me to mend my evil ways. I suppose this characterization of his motive is unfair. After all, he was there to help me. Whether it was appropriate or misguided, well, that's open to debate. His presence had implications that I was not completely willing to face.

That period represented the end of the fall semester, with all of its normal demands. The students parading in and out of my office did not see him at all, and he seemed to be content to watch and listen without comment. I felt guilty leaving him alone for the ten days or so that separated the end of the fall semester from the beginning of the interim session. But, I was not going to travel all that way just to keep him from being bored. That's his problem, and I had work to do at home. Besides, he knew how to use the computer. Still, I felt guilty.

When I came back after New Year's Day, which marked the turn of the new year, the new decade, the new century, and the new millennium, he was still there.

"What course are you teaching?" he asked, as I leafed through my files for materials.

"Business ethics," was my answer.

"Business ethics, you say?"

"You know how in your time ethics was an issue of religion?"

"Yes."

"Today ethics is an issue of economics. It has less to do with what sort of life one should live, and more to do with how the highest profit can be made legally."

"And you teach this?"

"Not really. I am of the old school. I think that

living a virtuous life is more important than acquiring material wealth. But then, I'm a dinosaur."

"At least we are in agreement," he said, thoughtfully.

"We agree that I'm a dinosaur?"

"No," he said, patiently, "we agree that living a good life is more important than having wealth."

"Then you are a dinosaur too," said I.

"Yes," he said, with a smile, "I suppose you could readily say that I am."

"I try to encourage students to think about who they are and what they want," I said. "I try to get them to think for themselves so they don't become victims of the predators who want to take their money and their integrity."

He nodded, approvingly.

"They have to figure out where to draw their line," I added.

"What line?" he inquired.

"Their line of integrity," I responded. "Everybody draws that line somewhere. In order to live in modern society, you have to prostitute yourself; you have to trade away your time and your energy and your talent in exchange for money and for your share of industrial output. Some people are willing to do whatever it takes to get money and power, no matter who gets hurt. Other people will risk losing all their material wealth and status before they do something they know is wrong. People with integrity draw a line beyond which they will not go. To cross that line is to lose your integrity. My line is up close, which is one reason I get fired so often."

"I understand," was his brief reply.

"Do you?" I asked, accusingly. "Then let me ask you a hypothetical question. Where should a counselor draw the line? Suppose—this is hypothetical, mind you—that you were sent to help someone who did not ask for help. How far should you be willing to go to help that person do something he doesn't particularly want to do? Who decides what is best, the counselor or the counseled?"

"Are you addressing a particular action?" he asked.

"You know very well what I'm talking about," I answered, abruptly. "You did it to me again."

"To what are you referring?"

"How is it," I asked, with an animated tone, "that last month, when I went to turn in my book orders, that I turned left coming out of the library instead of turning right to go through the center of campus as I usually do? How is it that a 'For Sale' sign that I must have driven past dozens of times suddenly registered itself in my consciousness? How is it that the owner just happened to be there to ask me if I wanted to see inside the place? How is it that my wife, on hearing my brief description of the house, was ready to buy it sight unseen? How is it that the house just happened to be in a price range we could afford, but still not require any major expenses to fix? Tell me how all of those coincidences came about?"

He was pensive for a moment. "Are you saying you bought a house?"

"You know very well what I'm saying, you gunky!"

"Which house is it?" he inquired, as though I had not accused him of anything.

"Yeah," I said, "like you don't know. It's the house on the corner of Washington and Madison, just across from the library."

"On the southwest corner?"

"That's the only house on that intersection."

"Well, it was not always that way. That particular one was Alex Winston's house."

"Who?"

"Alex Winston. He was a very good friend of mine. Yes, I know just where it is. That is a very nice house, indeed. You say Barbara likes it?"

I folded my arms and glared at him. "She thinks it's charming," I answered, flatly. "She can't wait to spend her weekends up here."

"How do you like it?" he asked, with that disarming manner of his.

"It's nice!" I said, sharply, with my hands on my hips.

"And, when will you be moving?" he asked, with an unmistakable glee in his tone.

"We're still keeping our house in Dubuque," I replied, "so we won't be moving much of our furniture."

"Can you afford to do that?" he asked, with genuine concern.

"Actually," I said, "the mortgage payment is less than a monthly car payment. The total for the two houses in Iowa is less than what we paid for one house in New York."

He was thoughtful, but did not say anything.

"You know we can't move here," I said. "Barbara has to live near her work. She has to be available for emergencies."

"Will you be living there?" he asked, hopefully.

"I'll be staying there when the occasion demands it," I said, "when the weather is bad or there is some special event."

This latter comment seemed to remove some of his cheer, but he did not say anything.

"I'll probably be staying there quite a bit," I admitted. "Barbara does not come home until late, and she's in bed early to be up the next day. It's hardly worth the three hours and the hundred fifty miles just to see her for five minutes while she falls asleep in the recliner with the cat in her lap. Besides, if I have work to do, those three hours come in handy. It is a nice house."

His mood seemed to elevate a bit. "I used to sit on the front porch with Alex," he said. "We would watch them build the new library and drink lemonade. You know that library was a gift from Andrew Carnegie. The Carnegie Foundation did not usually make donations to colleges or to college libraries, but my friend David Henderson managed to arrange a donation of twenty-five thousand dollars. As I recall, the note written to President Benton by Mr. Carnegie himself said that any school that can make so much of a Scotsman deserves it."

"Alex Winston was Scottish?" I asked.

"No, no," he said, "David Henderson was Scottish. He was the first Speaker of the House from west of the Mississippi, and one of our most illustrious students. It is for him that the library was named."

"Who was Alex Winston?" I inquired. I may as well know something about the house.

"Alex?" he posed, rhetorically. "Alex was originally from New York. He moved out to Wisconsin with his parents when he was still a lad. He and his wife, Erva, came to Fayette long before I did. He owned a farm outside of town as well as his house and his business downtown. He was a mechanic and wagon builder. He built the house you bought after he retired and sold his business. He had a workshop in the basement that he used to repair wagons and carriages occasionally for something to keep himself busy. He was very active in the church and on the school board."

There was an emotional pause.

"I was invited to dine there many times after I lost Sarah. Alex and Erva were a great comfort to me, and I treasured their friendship."

Just as his sentiments were getting the better of him, he caught himself.

"At one time," he said, forcing cheer into his voice, "I owned two of the four lots upon which sits that very house. Yes, in the late sixties, I was a big land speculator. That whole block—it was called Jones Block—was platted for townhouses, which were to be built for all the people we thought would flock to the university. James Robertson designed lots about twenty feet wide and one hundred feet deep. In the end, I sold what I had to Jimmy Lakin, and made no profit. As I recall, Jimmy neglected to file a deed. Poor Alex had to buy one lot twice, once from Jimmy and once from Charlie Herrick."

"Tell me," he said, after a pause, "has the house changed?"

"I don't know what it looked like before," I said, "but there doesn't seem to be any major modifications. The porch has been rebuilt, and most of the inside was paneled, but the dining room seems to be the same as it was with new wallpaper. The floor in the dining room is definitely original."

"Then the elegant colonnade remains, separating the parlor from the drawing room," he said.

"No colonnade," I said. "The living room is just one large room. There is a bathroom in the back of the living room that was definitely added."

"Near the back stairs?"

"There is only one staircase, and that is by the front door."

"Oh. There used to be a stair case leading to the hired girl's quarters that ascended from the back of the drawing room."

This last statement drifted off into what must have been a flood of memories. I determined to ask him for more details on the house later, but now it was time for class. At least the enrollment allowed the use of my room, and I did not need to travel far.

The class met for thirteen days in January between twelve thirty and four in the afternoon. The class meeting time, of my choosing, provided for weather delays in either my coming or going. We would not close escrow on the new house for another week, and it would be some time after that before it would be ready to occupy.

As usual, and to the great chagrin of my students, I held the class to its fully allotted time. Two students who had taken my class the previous semester were mindful, as I had requested of them, to alert me when it was four, else I would have run overtime.

He had abandoned his post at the window to stand

in the office doorway, watching and listening to the proceedings. When, at last, I flopped into my chair to rest, he was ready with an academic question.

"You made a comment that intrigued me," he said. "You stated that there is no such thing as a moral dilemma. Would you please explain?"

"You were actually listening," I said. "I am flattered. To answer your question, it refers to an idea that Socrates proposed. Doing wrong things hurts you in some way. People would not do things if they knew they would be hurt as a result of it. People who behave immorally, do so out of ignorance. In other words, they do it without understanding the real consequences. Dilemmas can only exist for people who are ignorant, people who do not know themselves well enough to know the most appropriate course of action. Socrates was big on complete self-knowledge, and most people don't have that."

"I thought a dilemma was a predicament that forces one to choose among undesirable alternatives," he said.

"Ok," I said, "give me an example."

"Well," he mused, "let me think for a moment. Very well, how about a case where a doctor knows that a patient is going to die soon, but he does not want to hurt the family. Or, better still, he does not want to tell the patient because he believes the news will make the condition worse."

"What is the dilemma?" I asked, confidently.

"Why the dilemma is whether or not to tell the patient," he answered, a bit impatiently.

"Let me restate the dilemma," I offered, "and you

tell me if I have it right. The dilemma is whether to tell the truth and risk injury to the patient, or to not tell the truth and minimize that risk."

"That is it," he said.

"Very well," I said, "we can assume that telling the truth will potentially injure the patient. So, who is injured by not telling the truth?"

He hesitated for a moment, and then said, "I suppose the doctor is hurt."

"How so?"

"He is hurt because he has lied, and he believes that telling a lie is a sin," he said, defiantly. "Telling the truth is moral and telling lies is not."

"If he really believes that, then why would he even consider telling a lie?"

"Because it might injure the patient."

"Then he believes that injury to the patient is a more important sin to avoid than telling a lie."

He knit his brow while considering my last statement. "You are very crafty," he finally said.

"A professional hazard," said I. "Your dilemma is resolved easily when the doctor determines which value is more important, always telling the truth or taking care of patients. When he knows for certain which is more important, there will be no dilemma. If he knew himself well enough in the first place, there would have been no question."

"Suppose there was a law," he hypothesized, "that required the doctor to tell the truth?"

"It is the same problem," I pointed out. "All that is required is for the doctor to know which is more important. Would you injure your patient to avoid going to jail?"

"That is the line of integrity, I suppose, to which you alluded before."

"Indeed it is," I answered. "When most people think they have a dilemma, what they really have is a conflict between their closely held personal values and the rationale they are using to justify their behavior. People think of themselves as moral because they follow the rules, but they find many rules with which they disagree. Then, they are required to rationalize their choices."

"But being moral is more than just following rules," he said.

"There, I disagree with you," I said. "Let me explain. *Moral* is a word derived from the Latin word for custom. Morals are sets of customary rules that we set up for ourselves and for others to follow so we can live together. Being moral means nothing more than meeting a behavioral standard that is accepted in your society. What you may be referring to is called an ethic. The word *ethic* comes from the Greek word for character. Your ethic is your spiritual definition of life and what's important in life. That's what defines your character. You may think it is immoral to lie. That is, lying is a violation of the rules. But, your ethic may lead you to lie to avoid injury to a patient because a patient's well-being is something that means more to you than rules."

"I am not understanding your argument," he said. "Being moral is what the Bible teaches. You must be moral in order for your soul to reside in Heaven."

"Would you agree," I posed, "that there is a difference between those who behave according to God's law reluctantly in order to gain salvation as a reward, and those who do not believe in or care about salvation but happily behave exactly the same way because they believe it is the right thing to do?"

After a moment's reflection, he conceded "yes, there is a difference."

"All right," I said, "then you have recognized the difference between being moral and following an ethic. Being moral from a Biblical point of view is still merely following rules. Of course, they are assumed to be God's rules, and if you really believe that they are absolute, then there is nothing more to discuss. If there is a set of rules established and enforced by an all-powerful, all-seeing, and all-knowing God, then the argument is over. However, if you are willing to grant that the rules in the Bible are set there by men for the purpose of social control, then we can continue the discussion."

"I will need an example," he said, unconvinced.

"Thou shalt not kill," I said. "Not only do people go right on killing other people, but a lot of them say that God told them to do it and use the Bible for reference. If that is not an example of people writing the scriptures to suit their own needs, then I don't know what is."

He was still not convinced, but he finally said, "let me hear the remainder of your argument."

I considered momentarily whether to continue with the discussion. He came from a religious tradition that allowed little flexibility for disagreement on the issue of Natural Law. But, he said continue, so I did.

"There are at least three types of rules that we feel obligated to follow," I began. "The first type seems to be universal because it is a set of rules that are based on what we all have in common as human beings. We all want to live unmolested. We all want the opportunity to prosper and be healthy. We all want the right to make free choices. We all want to keep the stuff that we make or earn. So, all human societies have rules against murder, rape, incest, assault, and theft. I, personally, have never heard anyone stand up in public and argue against these rules. No one says there should be more murder, rape, and theft."

"The second type of rule that all societies have," I continued, "is based on environmental conditions. If food is scarce, then we have rules regarding distribution of food, or we have rules limiting the number of children you can have. If there are certain dangers in the environment, then we have rules about eating shellfish or about driving on the right side of the road. If people from other societies come over and steal our women, then we might have rules that require women to be tattooed, or to wear disks in their mouths to stretch them out and make them unattractive to the other men. If there are too few men or too few women, then we may have rules to allow for polygamy. Out west, it was a capital crime to steal a man's horse because he could die in that environment without it. In other environments, horses are not considered to be something that one needs to have at all. These kinds of rules change when the environmental conditions change, and they are not universal."

"The third type is a set of rules that all societies have that are put in place to solve specific social problems. These rules are constantly in dispute because people have different ideas about what a social problem is and how to solve it. For example, how many laws did you have that restricted your use of drugs?"

"Why none," he answered. "We use drugs to cure illness. Why would anyone pass laws to restrict their use?"

"Precisely," I said. "Back then, using drugs was not considered a problem. Today, there are many rules in place that regulate the use of drugs and many social debates over those rules. That is because in your day, drug use was not considered a social problem, and today it is."

"I do not understand why that would be the case," he puzzled. "Why is the use of drugs considered to be a social problem?"

"That is simple," I answered. "Drug use is considered a problem today because people who take too many of the wrong kind of drugs do not spend a lot of time working; plus, they steal to pay for their drug habit. The drugs that are outlawed interfere with productivity, and productivity is today's moral bottom line. Some drugs are regulated by the government because too many people are swindled by those who sell them. Another example: what about dancing? How did your generation feel about dancing?"

"Oh, well," he said, "dancing is a sinful waste of time, and it is strictly forbidden. The rules here at the university did not even mention dancing because everyone knows of its evil consequences. No one who claims to be educated would advocate dancing."

"That's not the case now," I said. "In your time, dancing was considered a social problem. Now, it is considered a desirable social activity. People even pay for dance lessons."

A smile crept over his face. "You know, I never saw all that much harm in dancing. There was a group of students of my acquaintance who would hire a quarry sled and a team of oxen to steal away to Lima and dance. They would have hired a wagon, but wagons were too expensive. Coming back, they began to worry that the slow oxen were not going to bring them home in time. One boy would run out ahead of the sled and hide in the brush. When the oxen approached, he would jump out and frighten them and the oxen would run at a faster pace. Eventually, they would slow down and the process had to be repeated."

The image of students pulling this stunt struck me as particularly funny, and I began to laugh. It was infectious, because he began to laugh as well.

When I had gained some degree of control, I said, "I wish they would put that kind of ingenuity into their studies."

That set us off again.

The next morning, he was much more pensive; I would even say melancholy. I sensed that he had something particular on his mind, though I had no idea what it could be. By this time, I was cognizant that there were certain subjects which brought to him painful memories, none more particularly painful than those of the passing of his wife, Sarah. As usual, I let him conduct our interaction.

He took a deliberate stroll around the room, obviously aware that my attention was upon him, and came to a stop in front of a poster on my wall.

"Who was Joshua Lawrence Chamberlain?" he asked.

We had discussed Chamberlain previously, but I do not think that his question represented the issue he intended to pursue.

"He was a Civil War hero," I said, not knowing precisely what sort of answer he wanted.

"What is it about him that you admire, such that you keep his photograph?" he asked.

"Well," said I, "that's a long story if you do not know anything about him."

"I have time," said he.

"I'm not sure I have the time," I said, "but I suppose I can give you the brief summary. He lived in Maine, and studied at Bowdoin College. He was appointed a professor at Bowdoin about the same year that you came to Iowa. He taught logic, rhetoric, natural theology, and oratory. In the summer of 1862, he contemplated joining the Army, but the college refused to grant him leave. He was, however, given a two-year sabbatical to study in Europe. It was a great honor, which the college president thought Chamberlain could not possibly turn down. He accepted the leave and then went to see the Governor of Maine, who commissioned him as a Lieutenant Colonel in the 20th Maine Infantry, which was just forming. The faculty at Bowdoin pointed out to the Governor that Chamberlain was not qualified for military service, but because the Union needed regiments, their appeal was ignored."

"The 20th of Maine was mustered just in time to be sent against Marye's Heights at Fredericksburg. Chamberlain's regiment was cut to pieces, and he was almost killed when he wandered into the enemy's line by mistake. He managed to bluff his way out of that one.

His big moment of truth came on the second day at Gettysburg. His regiment was assigned the extreme left flank on Little Round Top and was under heavy attack. Most of his men were out of ammunition when he pulled off a maneuver that analysts and historians agree saved the Union from certain defeat. He was awarded the Medal of Honor for that. He was so seriously wounded outside of Petersburg that his obituary was actually printed in the paper. Grant, after being told that the wound was mortal, promoted him to General on the field. Chamberlain recovered and distinguished himself again at Five Forks. He was put in charge of the troops receiving Lee's surrender at Appomattox Courthouse. It was Joshua Lawrence Chamberlain who ordered the Union soldiers to salute the surrendering Southerners. After that, he became governor of Maine and president of Bowdoin College."

"But that is not why you admire him," he said.

I was taken back by his insightful comment. There was no point in asking how he knew, so I went ahead with my story.

"I admire him for a number of reasons," I said. "He was said to have had the soul of a lion and the heart of a woman. Just before Gettysburg some mutineers from the 2nd Maine were assigned to his regiment. They were extremely angry that they were not allowed to go home with the rest of their regiment whose enlistments were up. Chamberlain was given instructions to shoot them if they did not cooperate. He sent the guards away, fed them, and invited them to join his regiment and avoid court martial. All but one or two accepted. In order to keep the peace during the election crisis of 1880, he stood on the steps of the Capitol Building in Maine and defied a mob that was bent on killing him. They went away peacefully. He implemented progressive ideas both when he was Governor and when he was President of Bowdoin. He was roundly criticized. He offered to resign from Bowdoin when the faculty and students objected to his suggestions, but the Board of Trustees refused to accept his resignation. He stood in the face of every mortal challenge and stared it down with determination, with faith, and with dignity. He did what he knew was right regardless of the consequences. He was the sort of man Aristotle would refer to as virtuous. He was the sort of man I wish I were."

"He had integrity, then."

"Yes, he did. And, he also understood what leadership is all about. He spoke at the Academy of Music in Philadelphia on Lincoln's birthday in 1909. He said 'great crises in human affairs call out the great in men. But true greatness is not in nor of the single self; it is of that larger personality, that shared and sharing life with others, in which, each giving of his best for their betterment, we are greater than ourselves; and self-surrender for the sake of that great belonging, is the true nobility.'"

"And this is also your view?"

"Yes, it is. Leadership is not all about getting followers to do what the leader wants them to do; it's not about what the leader does at all. It is all about the common and infinitesimally small elements by which the masses are moved. Leadership is not created by the leader. It is the leader who is created by leadership."

"I do not know that you and he are all that

different," he said.

I did not know if he was attempting to flatter me or if he was simply making what he considered an objective observation. I was by no means convinced that Chamberlain and I were equals on any footing.

He stood gazing at the portrait of the young general for some time. Finally, he said, "have you ever fought in a war?"

"No," I responded. "At the beginning of the Vietnam War, I joined the Navy to avoid being drafted into the Army, and they stationed me at the Naval Facility in Argentia, Newfoundland. You could say that I went to Canada to avoid the draft."

He did not understand the joke. It was not much of a joke anyway.

"I never saw any combat," I said. "I understand that you were the regimental surgeon for the 12th Iowa."

"That is correct," he said, flatly, still staring at Chamberlain.

"What was it like?"

At that question, he turned to me with a hardness in his eyes that I had not seen before. "It was insanity!" he said, with uncharacteristic force.

I was surprised by his tone, and decided not to press him further on the issue. As always, he would tell me what he cared for me to know.

"That was a difficult time for all colleges," he said, after a pause. "I can fully appreciate the protest registered by his faculty. At this institution, President Brush was just getting things in hand when the call came from President Lincoln for more volunteers. He could see what was coming when the first war meeting was held in the Chapel in April of 1861. The first man to enlist was Jacob Abernethy who had been among the first students in the University. Nineteen students enlisted that day, as did my brother-in-law, Jimmy Lakin. There was a big parade for them in West Union, and Nellie Washburn presented them with a flag that she and the other students had made."

"President Brush was concerned at losing a tenth of our student body," he continued, "but he did not become fully alarmed until students began conducting military drills on the campus green and took to calling themselves the University Recruits. I do not think they were seriously considering joining the Army until after the disappointing loss at Bull Run. Until then, many people thought it would be a short war not requiring an army larger than the one we had."

"Just after the term began in September, two of our best students, William Warner and David Henderson, petitioned President Brush to make an announcement after services in the Chapel. They said it was a trifling matter to throw Dr. Brush off his guard. Then they proceeded to make impassioned and highly persuasive appeals to students to postpone their studies and fight for our country. I, myself, was moved to consider joining the group."

"Twenty-three students signed up that day. Only one later reneged. That was Jason Paine, a young man I had known from my first week in Fayette. He was close to completing the full course of study in the preparatory and collegiate departments, and he would become the first student in the University to do so. Besides, he had recently married, and his wife was dead set against his going. It was a difficult decision for him, and he suffered a great deal of abuse for it. But in the end, it was probably for the best. He was of a sickly constitution, and would likely have been one of the casualties of disease. His contributions to society in his later years would far outweigh any he may have made in the war."

"President Brush realized that not only was he losing the enrolled students, but at this early hour in the term he would be obligated to return some amount of their tuition. He finally took action to stave off the pending disaster to the college. He appealed to the students' parents to forbid their enlistments, claiming that educated men make better soldiers than boys who drop their books and run off to fight, but to no avail. He was thwarted at all sides. The Preceptress, Elizabeth Sorin, maintained that their act was noble and patriotic, and she carried the support of most of the other women who admired such behavior in men. Warner and Henderson had discovered that if they raised the right number of recruits, they could be elected officers, which I suppose encouraged them on to carry out their plans."

"In the end, Dr. Brush conceded, and delivered a speech in honor of the new Company and its officers. Elizabeth Sorin, as was the tradition, presented a flag that the ladies had sown to Henry Grannis, who the ladies elected to be the color bearer. I was not there, but students who were there relayed to me that the event moved them deeply."

"The company was staying at Gray's Hotel, the one that was previously called the Stock Hotel, and would be later called the Fayette House. On the morning of the 16th day of October, they formed their ranks and marched up to the 'Sem'. They formed a single line such that well-wishers could pass them all by and deliver their farewells. The band played 'The Girl I Left Behind' and the students paraded in their best military fashion around the green. Finally, they marched up the hill to the cemetery and clambered into wagons as the bell tolled their departure. The crowd stood right here in front of the 'Sem' and watched them until they disappeared over College Hill. The ladies waved handkerchiefs, the tears flowed in streams, and it began to snow. It was a scene I shall never forget."

"I had resolved to join them previously," he confided. "I told Sarah of my decision, and immediately wrote to the Governor. I followed the troop to Dubuque, and was granted a commission as regimental surgeon. Sarah was not enthusiastic about my decision, but I was able to convince her that I could at least look after Jimmy. We decided that the best course of action was to remove to Ohio, and for her to stay with her family there. There was no one left in Fayette to help her and our two boys. They were precocious children at that age, and I was reluctant to leave them with anyone but family. I was able to arrange for Mr. Mott's folks to take care of our house while we were gone. Mr. Mott was a baker and confectioner, and his family was relieved to be able to find a place for his folks to stay. So, when our arrangements were complete, I packed a few belongings and took Sarah and the boys to Ohio."

He struggled for a moment to retain his composure. "All in all, that was a very difficult time for us."

Dr. Charles Coleman Parker, circa 1888

Sarah Lakin Parker, circa 1888

VI

Most of the University Recruits were sworn into the service of the State of Iowa on October 3rd of the year 1861. Their solemn oath was administered by the Reverend Eber Byam, member of the Board of Trustees of Upper Iowa University. On that date, and to no one's surprise, William Warner was elected Captain, and David B. Henderson was elected First Lieutenant. By order of Governor Kirkwood, the company was to quarter in Fayette until further notice. The officers and men divided their time between drilling and recruiting. Later recruits were sworn in by Sarah's younger brother, William Lakin, Esq., who was serving as a magistrate by this time.

Fayette, Fayette Co., Iowa
Oct. 12th/61

To His Excellency
The Governor of Iowa
Sir,
I desire hereby to make application for appointment as Surgeon to one of the regiments of volunteers now being formed in this state - Would prefer the twelfth - I have not yet been able to go before the Board of Examiners, but hope to pass examination at their next meeting. I forward you today, in addition to the

*enclosed petition, separate letters from Judge Williams,
Dr. Levi Fuller, Hon. Reuban Noble, & Jesse Clement. I
take the liberty also to refer to Dr. R.J. Patterson,
Superintendent, Iowa Hospital for the Insane at Mt.
Pleasant, to Hon. Oran Faville, and to Rev. E.C. Byam
whom I understand to be acting as one of your special
aids.*

With great respect,

*C.C. Parker
To S.J. Kirkwood
        Governor, Iowa*

Charles explained to Sarah that his duty and
obligation was to serve his country in any way he could.
He held the full weight of the recent activities of the
University Recruits hard as evidence of his charge.
Someone must take care of these brave lads. The tidal
wave of moral sensibility and the call to action that swept
the nation on both sides of the Mason-Dixon line was
rolling through the western frontier, and was difficult to
deny. Secretly though, he longed for adventure, and
looked forward to seeing new places and to meeting new
people. He had not been able to wander far since his trip
to Pikes Peak, and the countryside surrounding Fayette
offered little variety and only as much as his schedule of
medical rounds would permit. Sarah did not object, but
Charles knew she was less than delighted with his
decision. He would make it up to her somehow.
        Company C of the 12th Iowa, the University

Recruits, was officially mustered into the service of the U.S. government at Dubuque on October 24th, the same day President Brush made his second visit that month, this time accompanied by Elizabeth Sorin and Reverend Webb of the Board of Trustees. Charles would not make his trip to Dubuque to see about his commission until the 31st, the same day Governor Kirkwood was finally able to manage his long-promised visit.

The former UIU students were quartered, along with several other companies, at Camp Union, a dry, level, sandy plateau near the river, three miles north of the Dubuque Depot. The buildings were not designed for winter, and living in them was very uncomfortable. The barracks were twenty by fifty feet, and had no doors or flooring. Sleeping was supposed to be accomplished on two twelve-foot-wide platforms, one over the other, which ran the length of the building. These straw covered platforms could each accommodate fifty men if they slept with their heads together in the center and did not mind the knees and elbows of their comrades. Their discomforts, though, were easily overlooked after a full day of drilling.

The idle hours found the former students organizing the members of the Philomathean and Zethegathean Literary Societies into the *Union Branch*. This effort was so successful that soon the by-laws and the constitution for the *Soldier's Debating Society* were formalized. Besides the comfort of familiarity reminiscent of their recently quitted institution, the activity provided a stimulating distraction for otherwise bored young men.

On the 30th of October, the new regiment was

introduced to its commanding officer, Colonel Joseph Jackson Woods, a West Point graduate and highly recommended personage. It was a good day for ceremonies on account of the bad weather, which always made drilling worse than usual.

Respite from drill was not often and not advisable. The men and most of their officers knew very little of military training. Drill master Major Brodtbeck's patience was sorely tried by clumsy and inept efforts to march the Swill Drill. He favored Swill over Casey's revised tactics. Captain Warner was biased in favor of the more modern approach taken by Casey.

After a month or so, the raw recruits of the 12th began to settle into army life. Their world was consumed with drilling and parades and sham battles with the 13th, with army food, mail, and sundries from home. As is the lot of most soldiers, the glory of the sendoff soon wore away into a tedium the only merit of which was its consistency. They had no real idea of what was in store for them. Soon the discomforts of camp life would be trivialized by the horrors of battle.

Dubuque, Iowa, Nov. 4th 1861

N.B. Baker
Adjt. Gen.

Sir,
Yours of the 25th ult. directed to Fayette &
containing Commission as Surgeon of 12th Inf. Regt.
Volunteer Militia of State of Iowa is received.
I hereby respectfully signify my acceptance of the
appointment.
I will endeavor to be ready to report myself for
duty on the fifteenth inst.

With great respect,

Your Obt. Servant,
C.C. Parker

P.S. Enclosed find oath

Priscilla Malloy Parker's Journal - 1861

*Nov. 11th C.C. came home from Iowa with his family, his
wife & two little boys, one two years & a half old & one
five years. How joyful to see them, his wife & children
well, but he is in very slender health, been gone six
years. Went away on the 12th arrived in Dubuque on the
morning of the 15th reported himself & was
commissioned as Surgeon of the 12th Iowa Regiment
Volunteer Infantry. Since ordered to St. Louis. They are
there last accounts.*

Charles found Camp Union to generally meet with his satisfaction, but of course he did not share the barracks, the meals cooked and eaten outside in the cold rain, or the drilling with the men. He wrote about the Camp in his report for the month of November, 1861 to N.B. Baker, the Adjutant General of the State of Iowa. "Encampment at Camp Union, situated about two miles north of the city of Dubuque, Iowa on Lake Peosta—a most healthy and delightful site, being upon a commanding height in a beautiful grove of oaks. The weather remained very pleasant—golden days of an Iowa autumn till the 20th of November when a severe storm of rain and snow came from the West—after which time it continued variable till the 27th when the regiment moved south."

The same report reflected the problems he was facing. Even though the hospital was located in camp, "the regiment has not yet been provided with any means for the transportation of the sick or wounded. The regiment has not yet been furnished by the Department with any medicines or hospital stores." In the column of the report that was used to address the adequacy of appliances for the comfort of the sick, he wrote, "None have been furnished of an amount worth mentioning."

Many of the men would later write that it was the worst camp they experienced in the entire war. Matters were not helped by continual revision of orders to leave for St. Louis. The on again-off again nature of the decision making and the cold temperatures roused the tempers of the recruits. Their destructive rumbles with the inadequate barracks prompted officers to march the men into the City of Dubuque and to quarter them in public buildings. Company C spent the night of November 27th in City Hall.

Finally, on Thanksgiving Day, they were ferried across the Mississippi to the Illinois Central Railroad Station in Dunlieth where they boarded for the thirty-hour trip to St. Louis and Benton Barracks. It took four days to make the journey, most of which was spent standing on docks in the cold rain waiting for transportation.

In his report for the month of December, 1861, Charles recorded the number of sick and the number of deaths (which was four in the Regiment), primarily from pneumonia and rubella. The boys who grew up in rural areas had not developed any tolerance for the common city diseases. He included in the report his impressions of Camp Benton.

At Camp Benton near St. Louis, Mo., during all of the month of December have occupied 2 different situations in the Camp - moving twice since first arrival. The Barracks are over crowded - they are imperfect in ventilation and insufficiently lighted. That portion of the Camp last occupied by the 12th Iowa is flat & imperfectly drained. The weather has been generally fair and warmer than usual for December. The climate of St. Louis is well known. Until the 10th of December there was no Regimental Hospital. At that time, one was established 1/2 mile out side the Camp. It is a large, new brick house and as well adapted to the purpose, accommodating 25 patients. The hospital contains 1 Hospital Steward, 1 Matron, and 8 male nurses. There is

*no means for transporting the sick or wounded.
Requisition was made but we were told we must wait
until "Regiments in the field are supplied." We have
depended chiefly upon the City Ambulances. Regarding
sufficiency of medicines and stores, nothing more but
something less than the regular standard supply table for
field services---medicines supplied are generally of good
quality---In great need of expectorants. Appliances are
tolerably well supplied by or through Aid Societies of
Iowa, Sanitary Commission, and Aid Societies of St.
Louis. A large number of our sick are sent to the General
Hospital. In that case the date of the return to duty or
death is not reported to the Regimental Surgeon. The
figures in this report are not entirely accurate.*

Life at Benton Barracks was somewhat different than it had been at Camp Union in Dubuque. At first, there was much less drilling. Ironically, drilling had become the most desired activity. When the men were issued their first weapons, the great pride they took in their new Enfield .577 caliber rifles had them looking forward to any excuse to carry and display them.

There were reports of skirmishes in the nearby countryside, of casualties and prisoners. A soldier was stabbed in the home of a Sessionist near the camp. There were also rumors of guards being poisoned by women offering them food. These events served to motivate the men further to pay attention to their drilling.

Attempts in Company C to revive the debating society floundered. There were arguments over dues, but that was not the real issue. The men were making the transition from the idealized life of a student who contemplates poetry and theology to the abject pragmatism of a soldier who contemplates killing and dying. The activities so central in importance to the student were trivial distractions to the soldier.

The highlight of that period of encampment was certainly their first payday. The Army did not yet have the necessary bureaucracy in place to carry out such a large task with any efficiency. After great difficulties it finally came to pass. Young men, many of whom had never had such a large sum all at once, were savoring their sudden increase in worth. Many did not show up for drill the next morning, having been waylaid by over indulgences.

Disease played havoc with the soldiers in camp. There was nothing so discouraging to young men who looked forward to a principled and providential fight as being thwarted by illness. Worst of all was the tragedy of death visited upon men who never had the chance to see the field of battle. If one is to die, at least let it come on a field of honor and not in the dreary confines of a hospital. Captain William Warner, the commander of Company C, came down with a severe attack of congestive fever. On January 24th, Charles was able to arrange a fifteen-day leave for him to go home to Iowa to recover. He would miss the regiment's first engagements. David Henderson took over as company commander just as they received their orders to march.

On January 26th, Charles sat himself at his makeshift desk to make his monthly report in a manuscript that he intended to send to the Adjutant General. He could not find any of the State of Iowa forms he used previously, which were abundantly available at Dubuque but not at St. Louis. It would be imprudent, he thought, to wait until the end of the month since the regiment had received orders and was leaving the following morning. They were likely to be on the march for some time, and he did not know when he would have a better chance to perform his obligation.

The 12th Regt. after much exposure to cold at Dunlieth & traveling 2 nights and one day arrived opposite St. Louis on the morning of 1st December. The men stood nearly all day upon the river bank in a cold wind. In the evening were marched to Benton Barracks the streets being excessively dusty were quartered in an unfinished building which had been begun & has since been finished & used as a stable - There were no stoves and no means of warming the Quarters. There was a very limited supply of straw - the weather continues cold - & snow fell the 2nd day after arrival in camp - after remaining in this stable a week or more were ordered into Barracks which had recently been used as a convalescent hospital - The officers & men were diligent in renovating the new quarters but after occupying them a week or two were ordered to remove to barracks less perfectly ventilated & in a part of the camp less thoroughly drained - Coal stoves were in use in the barracks & many of them smoked - Two companies were crowded into each apartment originally intended for but one. All these causes conspired to develop & aggravate catarrhal affections - So nearly universal were coughs, colds, and sore throats that it was thought by many to be an epidemic of influenza.

The camp was at the same time full of contagion of Measles & the 12th did not long escape its attack. A larger number were liable to it from having been recruited in the frontier than if taken from an older & more densely populated State - This disease ordinarily considered a mild affection has under these circumstances proven dreadfully fatal - The mortality resulting in almost all cases from the after consequences, either upon the lungs or bowels --

After being in Camp Benton a week or more without any hospital accommodations at all a new brick building capable of accommodating 25 to 30 patients outside the lines has been assigned as regimental hospital. On the 10th of December the worst cases were selected and taken there. After it became full, those most seriously sick were taken to a different General Hospital in the city while the mild and middling cases were retained for treatment in the Barracks. The Regimental Hospital, while at first scantily furnished was soon well provided for by the aid societies of Iowa and by the aid societies of St. Louis acting in concert with the Sanitary Commission & Surgeon Gen. Hughes. Many faithful friends have visited our sick and contributed to their comfort.

The general hospitals under the supervision of the Sanitary Commission are also excellently managed institutions having all the advantages that money can purchase & a benevolent skill can apply ---

Charles stopped writing and thought about that last paragraph. It did not relay the full weight of the message he intended to communicate. It could most certainly be improved, so he lined through it and continued.

We have had a faithful Corps of nurses and our Hospital Steward, J. C. Hubbs & his wife as Matron have been indefatigable in their labors. Assistant Surgeon Finley has been very efficient though laboring under circumstances of great difficulty. We are supplied with good articles of medicine but the variety of articles is limited and some that would have been specially serviceable were not furnished. At first, we all labored under an erroneous prejudice against the general Hospitals, & kept our patients out of them as long as possible. They are indeed, under the supervision of the Sanitary Commission, excellently managed institutions, having all the advantages that money can purchase or Benevolent skill can apply.

We now have no new cases of Measles. Some of our men are having mumps and a few have pneumonia. But the general improvement in health is my great satisfaction. Our men under marching orders and well armed are in good spirits save the sadness at the loss of so many comrades. Our Reg. Hospital is now broken up and packed for transportation, the sick being all sent to General Hospital by orders of the Commanding General.

It will be seen by the following list that we have

lost 23 men up to the 13th instant, all but three of whom have died from the affects of Measles or at least have had Measles since coming to Camp Benton.

Many of our men are now have manifested general improvement - marching orders have good effect.

Name | Company | Place of death | Complaint | Date of Death

Charles never had the opportunity to finish or to send the report.

No one was sorry to leave Benton. The disease-ridden quarters saw nothing positive except the new equipment and the payday. The payday was more important than anyone knew. Many of the soldiers in the 12th Regiment would not receive pay again until November. They were on their way to Cairo to join General Grant. The journey was made almost entirely by train. They reached Cairo about noon on the 28th, and Company C boarded the steamboat, *City of Memphis*, about two and a half hours later. They were assigned space on the middle and upper decks, and from that viewpoint determined that they were fortunate indeed to not have been camped in the town. It was an exceedingly muddy place on the banks of the Ohio.

They set sail after dark, and stopped for the night at Paducah. The next morning, they proceeded on to Smithland, where they disembarked in a mixture of rain and snow. It took two full days to unload the equipment and supplies, so camp was not set until the third day. A suspected case of smallpox among the troops prompted

Charles to widely administer a potion thought to prevent the disease.

Groups of soldiers organized themselves into messes to expedite cooking. Each member of the mess coughed up twenty-five cents to pay a selected soldier to do the cooking. It was not just convenient, but those hired for cooking had better than average skill at it. Even though it was against regulations to do so, most soldiers went "jayhawking" and gathered up any edible animals they could find.

At four in the morning on February 5th, drums signaled the order to strike camp. They were on their first campaign at last. Charles boarded the steamboat *Illinois* with the 12th Iowa, and all were conveyed up the Tennessee River to Barley's Ferry, about four miles downstream from Fort Henry, where they were unloaded the following morning. The assembly into attack formation was severely hampered by the flood conditions brought on by heavy rains. These were the same flood conditions that would make the defense of Fort Henry from the river side all but impossible. The soldiers listened to the booming of cannons from the gunboats attacking the fort while they awaited further orders.

When the order to march came, Charles rode on his horse alongside the troops of his regiment. It was a narrow and winding road upon which they traveled. After about seven miles of slogging through the snow and mud, they stopped for the night. At that time, all were informed that the fort had surrendered, and it had been completely a naval victory. There was some degree of disappointment, and several expressed the fear that the Secesh would give up before they had the chance to shoot any of them.

The next day, the 12th marched to the earthen works outside the fort where they would stay the night. Except for food, there were plenty of supplies and tents left by the retreating Confederates. The following day found most of the University Recruits carrying supplies up to the new camp from the boats because the ground was too muddy for wagons. Others were sent back for supplies left at the original landing place. On their way, they took great license with the abandoned private property that happened to be in their way, eating whatever chickens and hogs could be found. Pillaging was so widespread among the troops that General Grant became alarmed. He issued another general order calling for restraint. He felt this was needed to further their cause.

Having taken Fort Henry with very few casualties, General Grant intended to move immediately on Fort Donelson and take it as well. Delay was not advisable because the rebels were digging in and building up their troop strength. But a scouting trip to within a mile of the rebel lines convinced him that Donelson would not be so easy, and that he must wait for the gunboats which were so effective at Fort Henry to move up. He was obliged to pause, thus allowing his troops to move as much of the captured supplies and equipment as they could out of danger from the rising flood waters. There was more to gain from waiting anyway. Besides the captured supplies, there were ten thousand Federal reinforcements on their way.

The evening of February 11th brought word that the 12th Iowa would march to Fort Donelson first thing in the morning with three days' rations in their haversacks. Charles took the opportunity to write to Sarah.

The snow is drifting lightly though the roof of my cabin & falling sometimes on the paper. It will be warm soon. I must close & retire to rest so as to rise early & get ready for our march. My horse is a noble fellow & carries me gallantly but all the poor brutes suffer in this weather & mud without shelter & without hay or nearly so. Ours have had a very little. They had none for two weeks. You express fears that I do not have any good things to eat. We have never suffered for quantity but sometimes I think I would love a taste of your nice cooking. We have just to day finished the bottle of Catsup that was in my trunk. It was very nice on some cold corned beef we had.

I hardly know where to send this to reach you. I suppose you have gone to Lebanon by this time. I think I will send it to Cincinnati however & if you are gone the friends will forward it to you. Our sick list is not so large to day as yesterday. We will have to leave quite a number behind us however.

My own health is improving to day. I have felt quite well all day. The pay master does not come round. I fear we will get no pay till May. It will be rather tough if we don't. I am out of postage stamps. If you have any to spare, send me a few in your next. I cannot get them here.

Skirmishes and accidents provided ample work for the 12th Iowa surgeon beyond his usual allotment of measles and diarrhea. Most wounds were of a nature that was consistent with his experience as a frontier doctor. Despite his great skill as a surgeon, and his extensive experience coping with the perils on the frontier, he was ill-prepared for what was about to come.

The 12th Iowa was assigned to Smith's 1st Division, and placed on the Union left directly in front of the fort, facing General Buckner's Confederate troops. From their position, they could hear the booming from the gunboats and the shore batteries trading fire. The gunboats would not carry the day this time, and the ground troops would be called upon to do the lion's share of the fighting. In front of the 12th, Buckner's troops were spread thin, but very effectively entrenched on the high ground. Batteries were entrenched in such a way as to inflict the most amount of killing. Also protecting the defenders' positions were felled trees, cut so that their branches, sharpened into points, would hamper any attack.

The thinness of their line encouraged the rebels to make liberal use of canister and grapeshot to repel the attackers. No part of the Confederate line could be attacked without heavy losses. Consequently, when the fighting started, the casualties mounted quickly and incessantly.

Saturday morning, the 15th of February, Charles and his assistant, Finley, along with several nurses, were assigned to a crude log cabin a fair distance to the rear of the line. The dirt floor cabin was hastily converted to a field hospital in anticipation of the coming assault. They placed planks on sawhorses and lashed them together to make an operating table. There was room only enough for one table, and there was little in the way of supplies, equipment, or medicine—most of what they needed was sitting in the various camps and boats behind them waiting to be brought forward.

Soon, it became apparent that it did not matter; no amount of preparation would have been enough. The first casualty was brought in as skirmishers began to test the enemy's defenses. It was a young man who had been struck in the thigh by a *Minié* ball, which had passed entirely through his leg. He was not from the 12th Iowa, but regimental jurisdiction had given way to pragmatic necessity. Besides it would never have occurred to Charles to refuse succor to anyone in need, even if he were the enemy.

The young man was brought in on a stretcher and hastily dumped onto the operating table for Charles to apply his treatment. While the man was unceremoniously deposited on the table screaming in pain, Charles noticed that his leg was wobbly, indicating a possible broken bone. Before cutting off the man's trouser leg and removing the tourniquet, Charles felt the leg gently to see where the break was located, and how it should be set. It was with a great horror that he discovered there was no bone to speak of at all within a span of two inches on either side of the entry wound. The thighbone had been completely shattered by the ball, and most of the fragments had exited with the projectile. There was literally nothing to set, and no possible way for the bone to heal itself.

Charles stood shocked by the ramifications of the

situation before him. The man was so young. He would be obliged to live his entire life with only one leg. That would be a serious impediment to his ability to secure his livelihood. It was likely that he would not be able to maintain a home and support a family, certainly not as a farmer or a laborer. In all probability, he was fated to be destitute the rest of his life. If that were not grievous enough, as this man lay upon the table, his whole life altered for the worse; there was some corresponding tragedy on the opposing side of the line of battle. It was calamity beyond belief. The inhumanity of it all began to creep over Charles like a vine over a tree—at first imposing, and then suffocating.

Charles was paralyzed with sudden clarity—with the realization that this was not simply a noble activity conducted in the name of an abstract principle of right and wrong; it was the ripping and tearing of human flesh and of human life. Those idealistic young lads who had embarked upon a divinely inspired mission to rid the world of evil were themselves spawning evil more insidious by a thousand fold. Those splendid legions which had displayed their finest civilized discipline so gloriously on the parade ground were, in application, no better than the mindless, savage, wild beast rending its victim limb from limb.

Momentarily, Charles's sense of duty and professionalism regained him. He steeled himself and set to work applying the only treatment possible—removing the leg. Charles applied ether to dull the pain, and then began cutting with his surgical knife. There was no need to use the bone saw except to trim the jagged edges of the upper portion. Once the leg had been removed, and he held it in his hands, Charles looked around for a suitable place to put it. The one room cabin was too small to accommodate such a grisly artifact with any degree of comfort, so, with some difficulty, he threw the severed limb out of an open window situated behind him.

Within minutes, another casualty was brought in. Then another, and another. Many of these poor fellows had the same affliction as the first. The grape shot and the shrapnel indiscriminately shattered arms, legs, heads, and torsos. For some, the bone was intact, but the major artery of the limb was severed. There was no way to stop the bleeding except with a tourniquet. And by the time the bleeding stopped, the blood-starved limb would be dead anyway. Sound medical procedure digressed into little more than cutting and hacking that was more suitable to the butcher than to the surgeon. The need for amputation was so frequent that soon the only decision to be made was where to begin cutting. In a very short time the ether ran out, and Charles was forced to cut limbs off of screaming, writhing, pitiable souls who moments before this were vibrant young men. The best of them were the unconscious ones, who were unaware of what was happening to them. Assistance was limited to holding the hapless victims still while the procedure was repeated over and over again.

Charles was forced to disengage his sentiments. He willed himself into a mechanical pattern of cutting and throwing the limbs out the window, and he did not allow himself to see that what he was doing involved human beings. He could have been laying bricks or shucking corn. His work was accomplished with surprisingly little forethought or reflection. It occurred to him that there would be an ultimate accounting for this state of mind, and that its toll upon him would not be denied. But contemplation of that sort could not be allowed to interfere. Denying himself the most basic feeling, Charles carried out his task in a state of semi-consciousness.

It could have been hours or just a few minutes that passed when something tugged at his awareness and brought him reluctantly back to full consciousness. That last arm he had thrown through the open window had slid back into the room. Charles just stood looking at it, not quite able to grasp its meaning in his present state of mind. His routine had been interrupted, and he was going to have to adjust. This would take some time.

"They must be up to the window," said Finley, as he stooped over to pick up the limb. With a hearty fling, he tossed it out beyond the pile.

Charles stood for a moment more, until his reason told him that he had neither the time nor the energy to do what Finley had just done with every new severed limb. He mechanically walked out the front door and around to the dreadful stack of limbs behind the building. The brush surrounding the cabin had contained the column of flesh and bone, and prevented it from spreading out. Without considering that the grisly pile was larger than he was, he pushed what he could to the side to make room for more. It could have been cordwood or bales of hay; it did not matter. It was just a pile of refuse that needed to be moved. He would not allow for this to be anything more. He would worry about it later, he thought, as he returned to his grim task.

The succession of bodies demanding to be cut

into pieces finally began to give way to multitudes of lesser wounds. When the last of the amputees was removed from the table, Charles made his rounds in the tents set up outside the small cabin where slight and mortal wounds were thrown together as equals. Some of the men were lying out in the open, under trees. The Steward told Charles that more tents were being brought up from the store of equipment at their last landing. Charles was suddenly aware that he had no idea how much time had passed. It might have been hours. It might have been weeks.

The corruption of time spent in such occupation redefined the life it so preciously contained. It seemed to Charles not that this was a dream, but that it was the only verity and all the rest of his life had been the dream. He could barely remember a life before this moment, and he forced himself to rationalize the dream-life into credible memories.

As he walked, Charles noticed that his clothing was weighing him down. His apron and uniform pants were so soaked with blood that gravity was literally pulling them from his body. He reached under his apron to tighten his belt when he noticed that he had been leaving a trail of blood, draining in a stream from his clothing. He watched with an unsettled detachment as the stream began to form a pool at his feet where he stood. My trousers should lighten up presently, he thought to himself.

During his rounds, he witnessed a variety of wounds that his wildest imagination could not have conjured. There were eyes shot out, noses missing, and men with only half of their faces intact. Men were still alive who had their entrails piled indiscriminately on their stomachs by whomever had dropped them off. There were men who were missing entire sections of their heads. Some had holes in their bodies large enough to see through to the cot underneath. Charles did what he could. It was not much, in light of what needed to be done.

Charles was surprised to see David Henderson in one of the tents. He had been wounded in the throat, and his wound had been dressed by one of the nurses. It was not a serious wound, but it was not a scratch either.

"I was brought here by my brother, William," said David, with great difficulty. "Look at my coat."

David held up the coat he had been wearing. The ball had ripped a hole in the top of the right shoulder and passed under his chin, cutting his throat nearly to the windpipe.

"You were lucky," said Charles, as he inspected the wound.

"Luckier than you know," David croaked. "I was hit in the leg by some grape shot. It was too far gone to take the leg, but it still hurts like the devil."

"Let me have a look at it," said Charles, mechanically.

David loosened his trousers, and dropped them far enough for Charles to see the massive contusion made by the lemon-sized iron ball.

Charles examined the wound. "You are lucky it did not break the bone."

David just nodded.

Darkness brought on a lull in the fighting, and a corresponding lull in the procession of wounded. The bitter cold complicated treatment, but at least it was not snowing. Charles estimated over two hundred wounded in his charge. He thought to make a count for his report, but the rapid changes in the population from death and from transfer for various reasons indicated a degree of futility that stayed him from carrying it out. By the time he finished the count, it would be wrong.

Late in the evening, Finley convinced Charles to seek out his bed for badly needed rest.

"You do not look well," said Finley. "You do no one any good in this condition. Go to bed! There are nurses to see to them. Most of them are sleeping anyway."

Charles was not in a state of mind that made him capable of forming protest. He briefly considered the situation, and then carried out Finley's instructions as though they were orders. There was no medicine to give them. All of the surgery that could possibly help had been applied. There was nothing anyone could do for them except to sit with them and to hold their hands as they suffer. Many were unconscious, and many more would not be comforted.

Charles found his tent, and laid himself down, but he could not sleep. He felt numb all over, but not from the cold. The bottoms of his pant legs were heavy with frozen blood, and he worried about staining the blanket on his cot. It was too cold to wash them or to remove them.

He sat up again. He was having difficulty organizing his thoughts. He did not have the will to address the most obvious questions, and he did not have the energy to suppress the obvious answers. He longed more than ever to be with Sarah.

Charles had not fully understood until now how much he depended on Sarah for emotional support. At this time in his life when he needed her most, he was not even sure where she was. There had been no mail since the beginning of the campaign. He thought to write her, but what would he say? How could he explain what he was feeling? He felt vulnerable and alone, and he wished with all his will that this thing would be over.

It was just as well that he could not bring himself to write to her. Even if he found a way the express his feelings, he would not want to place their burden upon her. It was bad enough that he should bear them. He resolved to spare her from the horrors that replayed themselves in his mind like endless photographs on a corridor wall. He also resolved that he would never leave her again.

He rose from his cot, unable to rest. He may as well attend to the wounded. It was their suffering that had become his, and whatever he would do for them he would do for himself. In their mutual agony, they would be forever bonded.

Word came the next morning that the rebels had surrendered. It was said that Grant had demanded and received an unconditional surrender because that is what his initials stood for: Unconditional Surrender. The celebrations were ongoing—whoops and hoorahs filled the air for some time. It was a sorely needed victory for the Union after the disasters at Bull Run and Wilson's Creek.

Charles was happy that the battle had been won, but he did not feel much jubilation. His former lighthearted faith in the justness of the war and his expectations for glorious adventure had faded to the point of extinction. He could, however, manage a smile for the excited young lads of the 12th, some from Company C, who were full of stories about their part in the battle. They had lost one man dead, and twelve were wounded, whom they were visiting.

They spoke in low and revered tones about the fate of the 2nd Iowa, many of whose wounded were also in the tents outside the rude cabin that passed for a hospital. The 2nd had lead Lauman's Brigade, and was the first regiment to plant their flag on the enemy's breastworks at a cost of forty killed and one hundred sixty wounded. These were the boys, along with boys from the 7th Iowa and the 25th and 52nd Indiana, that Charles found on his operating table after their encounters with grapeshot and canister.

As Charles listened to their boasting about the musket balls thick as hail and about the number of rebels they had killed, he was struck by the matter-of-factness they employed in the telling of it. He was surprised to see that the grim reality of wounds and death had not affected them as it had him. He wondered idly if it might be a result of the manner of their education. This thought led to the realization that he could not even begin to imagine himself in his classroom teaching the basics of anatomy and physiology. He would never regain the optimism toward the nobility of human endeavor that had so marked his persona as a teacher. He could not bring himself to pretend that this never happened. There would always be this cloud, this specter of limbless, faceless, lifeless boys who should have nothing to be concerned about more serious than passing exams and raising families. He began to seriously doubt that he could ever teach again.

Later Sunday afternoon, Colonel Woods came to visit the hospital. He showed the report he intended to submit commending Charles and Assistant Surgeon Finley for their bravery and efficiency. When Colonel Woods had a glimpse of the pile of limbs behind that cabin, he was visibly shaken and had trouble speaking for some moments. He took Charles's hand in earnest.

"The tales I have heard of the doings in this hospital have not been exaggerated, sir," he said. "Your country cannot offer you enough in the way of gratitude."

Charles graciously acknowledged the outpouring of affection, but he could not help but feel a bit hypocritical. Any one of these poor lads deserved the nation's honor much more than he.

This would be only the first of a long procession of honors and acknowledgments. The battlefield of Fort Donelson would receive dozens of delegations and notable personages. Governor Kirkwood of Iowa visited in late February. Although logistics did not allow for him to visit the 12th, he wrote a glowing letter of commendation to Colonel Woods. The Iowa State Legislature passed a resolution thanking its regiments for their bravery and gallant conduct.

Many of the delegations came specifically to help with the more than two thousand wounded in the battle. Some of the boys were taken home by their families, some were transferred to permanent hospitals, some died of infections and other complications, and some were released for duty. David Henderson went back to his home in Iowa to recover.

Just as the plight of the wounded seemed to be under control, a massive outbreak of dysentery swept through the camp. Some thought it was because of the high sulfur content in the water; others blamed a continuous diet of salted meat. It was probably a combination of diet and cold, wet weather. Charles did not give it much thought because he became one of the afflicted. He continued with his duties as much as possible, but found himself too weak to contribute much.

Grant was alarmed. The epidemic was so widespread that he felt his ability to wage war was compromised. He sent troops out into the countryside to find beef, but there was little to be found. Government contractors had cattle, but no way to deliver them. With some effort, a better quality of food was procured. Aid societies sent much needed medicine and fresh fruit and vegetables by train. Meanwhile, orders to march had been issued and received.

On March 7th, the 12th Iowa marched from Donelson to Metal Landing on the Tennessee River, where they would remain until the 13th. Charles went with them on horseback, though he was not strong enough for the trip. He would not allow himself to be left behind. They boarded the steamer *John Warner*, and were taken upstream, past multitudes of curious southerners, eventually to Savannah. There, they had three days to rest. The weather was bad, but sleeping in town was preferable to conditions on the boat. On March 18th, they proceeded upriver to Pittsburg Landing with many other boats to prepare to march on Corinth.

Charles found time to write again to Sarah.

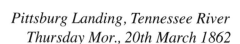

Pittsburg Landing, Tennessee River
Thursday Mor., 20th March 1862

My Dear Wife,
        *I wrote you yesterday that I was not well & that if
I did not improve rapidly, I should try to get leave of
absence & come home. But I feel so much better to day
that I feel quite encouraged. I kept about all day
yesterday & attended to business without lying down at
all & feel as though I can do so to day without much
fatigue, but I will be as careful as I can. We are all going
into camp to day - I have not yet been up to the ground
but those who have say it is a very nice place. I am glad
for I think it is the confinement to the boat that made me
sick more than any thing else. It is very doubtful whether
I could get leave of absence any way unless I get sick
enough to go to the hospital. So you will hardly expect to
see me until this expedition has gone through with the
present campaign - I feel distressed at not getting any
pay, and not being able to send you any money - I know
you must need some badly. I hope however you will not
really suffer for want of it. As to starvation I know you
are in no danger, but I know you need some new clothing
for yourself & the children & money to pay your
expenses from place to place. But I will not borrow
trouble if I can help it & hope all will come out right &
that we may be able to get pay before long. I am very
uneasy however at not hearing from you for so long. I
have no letter since the one you wrote at Mrs.
Thompson's on the 2nd inst. and then dear little Charley
was sick and you seemed so uneasy about him. If I could
know that you are all well again I should feel quite*

content. I do not know where you are or where to direct my letters. I have sent several to Lebanon. I will venture to send this one there also supposing it will be forwarded to you should you not be there. I suppose some of my letters are miscarried almost as a matter of course. I try to write as many as I can in hopes that you will get at least half of them. Jimmy had a slight chill yesterday followed by some fever. I gave him some medicine and he seems better this morning - If he is going to be sick it would make me more unwilling to go home now that we have just got together. I think however a few doses of Quinine will set him all right.

I can give you no news of general character. We get no mails and hear nothing but extravagant and unreliable rumors.

Charley Byam came on board to see me yesterday. He belongs to the 6th Iowa Regt. & they are encamped about 5 or six miles in advance of us.

Charley is a fine looking young man and has the appearance of being more steady than formerly. I got him some coffee & crackers - the best we had - for supper - I also talked encouragingly to him giving him good advice which he seemed to appreciate. He hurried back to his camp for fear of being out after the proper time - He seems to be ambitious & has a little prospect of promotion - I was glad to see him on his father's account at any rate. I wrote not long since something in reference to your going back to Fayette wishing you to act entirely as your own judgement & choice may dictate - provided I can send you the means of carrying out your choice in either case. If I cannot do that of course you must do as you can until I get money. I wrote to Vines to send you a few dollars if possible but I have not heard from him since Christmas. My impression is that if Will & Carrie go to Fayette you had perhaps better go with them if practicable & I think also if you do all go that the sooner after the first of April perhaps the better. That however is only in case Mr. Mott's folks should leave the house. Otherwise it would be much better to wait till may or june. I wanted you to make more of a visit at Hygiene also. Do just as you think proper. I miss you all, affectionately

your husband C.C. Parker

P.S. It is still possible that I may start home in a few days but you need not expect me unless you see me.

Writing the letter flooded Charles with reminiscence of a life that seemed so far away as to be an illusion. He thought about Aaron Mott, whose parents now resided in the Parker house in Fayette. Aaron was a farmer who had found a new path in life as a confectioner. He was a good and gentle man, and he and his wife were faithful members of the church. He offered to look after the house. Charles thought it was a good idea to have someone living there, so Aaron's parents were nominated.

He thought also of Daniel Vines. Daniel had been one of the old time residents of Fayette. He began his career as a carpenter, but his interest in writing and reporting the news gradually overtook this occupation. He was an active citizen who took an interest in the welfare of members of the community. He especially liked the Parkers, and seemed to understand Charles's reluctance to collect from his debtors and his constant need for unobtrusive assistance. Charles could depend upon Vines for unconditional support when he needed it. Daniel considered his support of Charles an important investment in the welfare of the community, and was always sensitive to issues of dignity.

Ever-present in his mind was anxiety over Sarah and her well being. He was not comfortable at all with her situation, and with not knowing where she was. But he had faith that her friends would look after her and the boys. Sarah was exceptionally close to Carrie's mother. The Parker family might have helped more, but Sarah seemed particularly reluctant to impose upon them. Charles suspected that there was not much affection on her part, and he was not going to insist. Besides, after the death of his father, his mother was not able to provide for guests.

He longed to see Sarah. He had not expected this perpetual ache he was experiencing. There were times when he felt like picking up, leaving all this madness, and going to find her. It was the sort of fantasy those imprisoned by obligation and duty often dream of. In fact, he would not leave without permission under any circumstances. The hope of gaining permission for a leave was real, even though he did not think it likely.

Everyone's impression was that once Grant was on the warpath, he would hold to it like a bulldog. Thus oriented, Grant would protect the means needed for the campaign at all cost. His troops respected him for this even if it meant their own inconvenience. Charles particularly felt respect for the General because he was notably a man of integrity. All were disheartened by the politics at the top between Halleck, McClellan, and Grant that resulted in a lot of inappropriate shuffling of command. Unfortunately, those who cared the most were powerless to interfere.

Charles also began to feel some reluctance to return to Fayette. He was not sure why he had that feeling, but he noted that it took the form of a nagging dread. Perhaps it was his reluctance to return to the classroom; perhaps it was just his illness. In any event, he could not imagine doing things in the same way he had done before. He just could not imagine it. He knew everyone in Fayette would be deeply disappointed if he did not teach again, and he was loath to disappoint them. It would be much easier to act pursuant to his own desire if he could start over fresh in a new place.

He thought about posing the idea of relocating to Sarah, but he had run out of room in this letter and had to write the postscript in the margin. He would think about it some more before writing it down. Sarah's brother, Will, was not likely to leave Fayette because he had found some success there, and Carrie had indicated an interest in teaching art in the university. It was difficult to tell what Jimmy would do. Charles suspected that he would follow his big sister and his favorite brother-in-law wherever they went.

A few days later, Charles wrote again. His anxiety had reached panic proportions, but he would not burden Sarah with that.

Pittsburg Landing Tennessee River
Sunday afternoon 23d March 1862

My Dear Wife,

*I have written to you quite frequently of late
fearing that you do not get all the letters, for certain it is
I get none from you. I do not know whether the mails
going toward you are any more regular than those
coming from you or not. I hope however you get at least
a part of my letters. I have no word from you since the 2d
of March & feel great anxiety about you & the children. I
try to believe however that you are all alive & well &
with your friends at Lebanon or Xenia. I suppose of
course communication between us will be more & more
difficult as I go further into the enemy's country. So let us
try to not feel disappointed if letters do not come to either
of us regularly. I have no news to communicate to day.
We are very pleasantly encamped about 1/6 mile from the
river on good dry ground. The weather has been
generally cold & unpleasant. A few scattering snow
flakes floating in the wind to day. We now and then see a
peach tree in bloom, or a red-bud spreading its judas like
blossoms but these few manifestations of spring even
seem premature while such cold winds are blowing.*

*Well now I have been interrupted in my writing
for about an hour by the coming of Jimmy & Jim Patrick
& Charley Byam & a friend of his all happening in to see
me at about the same time. The camp of the 3d is about
one mile from ours & the camp of the 6th (Chas. Byam's
Regt.) about 4 or 5 miles. It was a very pleasant
interruption though it has disconcerted my plans & may
shorten my letter. I wrote to you a few days ago that*

Jimmy was sick. He had a chill followed by some fever but he soon got over it & seems very well & cheerful to day. I wrote you also that I was not well. I am now better again though not very strong - I manage to keep up pretty well though I can't say I feel first rate yet. I said something about trying to get leave of absence to come home two or three weeks. If I had such a leave now I think I should use it provided I could find a paymaster & get some money on the road home. But I think there is scarcely any probability of any body getting leave of absence just now, nor much prospect of getting money soon so I do not allow myself to think about it, but go along attending to my duties as well & as cheerfully as I can, and then we are so much more pleasantly situated in camp than we were on the boat that I am almost content. We are on the West side of the River about 10 miles above Savannah.

I suppose that sooner or later - probably in a few days - we will take up the line of march either towards Corinth, Miss. or towards Memphis, Tenn. There is a considerable force at this point - I should think about thirty thousand encamped - Some more arriving & also a considerable force back at Savannah. There has been a good deal of rain of late & the roads are almost impassible for baggage trains & heavy artillery wagons. I suppose this is the principle reason why we move so slowly. Nobody who has not seen such things attempted can form any idea of the difficulty of moving an army under such circumstances. But no doubt we will have better weather, drier roads & marching orders before long, and if so you must not think at all strange if you do not get letters regularly - We have no late letters from our

friends - no late papers & no news of any kind. Such
privations are harder for me to bear than any other I
meet - although I would sometimes like a little different
food ---

There now I had another tent full of company &
interruption and now it is night. I will try again. I feel
pretty well or would if I had not eaten too much supper
like a fool that I always am when good things are set
before me. We had some very nice sugar-cured ham &
boiled potatoes - the first for some weeks - then we had
another rarity: light bread and butter & some plum
butter which was sent from Iowa to Lieut Col Coulter -
and a cup of black tea - We have had nothing but poor
coffee for a month - It was all very good but I indulged
too freely & have some pains in consequence - If I could
have you cook me some milk with flour or a soft egg with
a bit of bread & tea I should soon get well - but I will try
to be more careful next time. I am thank full for the
appetite but I find I dare not indulge it ---

Lieut Col Coulter is quite feeble indeed with the
chronic diarrhea & ought by all means to go home. He
made application upon my certificate - some days ago for
leave to go home but it has not yet been granted - It is
almost impossible to get such favors at such a time as
this ---

Lieut Leroy Templeton is complaining of
rheumatism & the boys say he intends to resign & go
home immediately. He is always frightened at a little
sickness & is especially afraid of rheumatism - He is now
the only commissioned officer with the company & if he
should resign somebody else must be appointed - The
boys say there is a good deal of electioneering among

them to day - Swank & Abernethy have each some ambitions in that direction. They are looking for Lieut. Brown back soon. But Capt. Newcomb some of them think will never come back to command the company. They all say Col Williams conducts himself very well since the trial and restoration to his command.

We had preaching this afternoon for the first time since we left St Louis our Chaplain having been at home sick most of that time. There is prayer meeting this evening in the tent next to mine. I can hear nearly all the exercises as I write - Religion is almost as a matter of course rather in the back ground in the army. But so far as sobriety & general morality are concerned I think our regiment excels any other with which we have become acquainted - How I should love to be with you and our dear boys to night - & how I wish this accursed war was properly and honorably at an end. That we might all be permitted to return to our peaceful homes. I do not however feel inclined to resign unless ill health should compel me to. But I should like to have my pay up to this time & leave to go home to see you & rest a week or two & no doubt I could get it if there were not so many hundred applications of the same kind - The general health in the regiment is again improving rapidly ---

Love to all the good friends & kisses to the children. Heaven's blessing on you all - I embrace & kiss you - Good night.

As ever your own C.C. Parker

That last part about resigning just sort of popped out. It had been a part of the conversation at dinner. Charles was not conscious of having such thoughts, but the rash of resignations and rumors of others must have planted the idea. Certainly he could do no good if he were in poor health, or worse, dead from disease. A resignation is no worse for the army than a death. A soldier must do his duty, but he must also take care to not become a burden to his comrades. Still, a resignation is the equivalent of an admission of failure. Everyone, to some degree, regards a resignation as at best weakness, or at worst downright cowardice. Charles was determined to come to the end of his life, whenever that may be, and look back knowing that he had always done the right thing.

But what is the right thing? Should a man abandon his family and all of its obligations to fight for his country? Is that more noble than forsaking the country to maintain his obligations to his family? Which is the greater good? What would become of Sarah and the boys if he were to die in this God-forsaken place?

Charles thought of Jason Paine—he pictured him as that intelligent, sensitive young schoolteacher with whom they shared the Robertson house upon their arrival in Fayette so many years ago. Jason had demonstrated his capabilities often and consistently as a student in the university. When the fervor of patriotism swept the community, Jason was among those to pledge his support. But later, having thought the better of it, and reluctant to interrupt the life he was just forging with his new wife, he chose not to join the regiment. Oh, how he was disparaged for making that choice. Besides the taunts and jeers directed at him, a parody of the Book of Chronicles was written and circulated on campus last September specifically to humiliate him. Jason was given the designation of "Moses" and was characterized as "decidedly weak" and an "able-bodied coward."

Charles reflected on the amount of strength it must take for an individual to knowingly defy a group of his peers who are so strongly charged with zeal. Jason did what he knew was right despite the taunts and jeers. Perhaps he set an example of courage rather than of cowardice.

Charles ached to hear news from Sarah. He would almost give up the chance for a leave just to have some news. When he was working, it was not much of a problem. But when he was idle, his homesickness seemed worse than his other afflictions. Fortunately, a number of circumstances conspired to increase his workload. Diarrhea was so prevalent that the men took to calling it the "Tennessee quickstep." It was another week before he sat down to write Sarah again. Writing to her was almost more difficult than not writing to her.

Pittsburg Landing Tenn
March 31st 1862

My Dear Wife

I have only time to write a few lines to say that my health is still improving. I am very busy because my assistant has been too sick for two days to do any work. I have had it all to do besides having to perform the duties of Brigade Surgeon on account of the sickness of Dr. Marsh who acted in that capacity before. The next oldest by rank that is by date of commission always has to take the place of the one that fails above him in the army. But my asst. is better to day & I have got a good deal of the extra work past through so that I hope to have a little more time in a day or two.

We have been at Pittsburg Landing over a week & there are no indications of a forward movement as yet. Do not know when we may move however - We have a very pleasant camp & pass the time quite pleasantly. The weather is now warm & fine. The peach trees are in bloom and other indications of Spring. Jimmy called & took dinner with me to day. He seems quite well. I had little time to spend with him. He showed me a letter from Will & one also from one of the Geabit Cousins. She writes a good letter. I infer from it that you are in Lebanon although I have not heard so positively. The last letter I had from you was written at Cincinnati - The prospect of my coming home before the close of this campaign grows smaller - I hope however the war may soon come to a favorable termination so that I can come home as well as for a great many other important reasons ---

If Will does not conclude to go to Fayette to

spend the summer I think perhaps you had as well stay in Ohio - that is if you prefer it. I wish you to have your own choice but at any rate you can't go till I can send you some money - I hear nothing lately about the paymaster

This evening Dr. Lake of West Union called on me & brought a letter from Will ---

Dr. Lake is just appointed & come on as surgeon to the 7th Iowa Regt in place of Dr. Witter of Mt. Vernon who died recently. L.C. Noble also of West Union is appointed Major in the 14th Iowa & will be here soon if he is not already. I understand that Capt Newcomb of Co F 3d Iowa has resigned. I do not know that it is true. Well I shall not resign just now at any rate & perhaps not at all. But really I would much rather be at home. My position is a laborious one & difficult to fill. But at present I must stand up to it manfully & hope to come through all right.

Will is quite undecided what to do & talks some of settling in Burlington - I think we will none of us choose to live very much longer in Fayette but it won't do to entirely sacrifice our little home there and other interests. I am willing to go to any good place but of course am anxious to find the best, that is I mean one where we will feel satisfied to spend our days - I do not want to make more than one more move - & I think I want you to have your choice also although I confess it is hard for me to yield my judgement in such matters. Kiss the dear boys for their Pa. Oh how I should love to see them and you too my darling. I embrace & kiss you & pray Heaven's blessing on you & all our friends.

As ever C.C. Parker

Pittsburg Landing Tenn Apr 2d 1862

My Dear Wife

I wrote you a short letter a few days ago and soon after, I recd yours of the 23d by which I was glad to learn of your safe arrival with the little boys at Lebanon & were enjoying your visit so much with your good friends. I hope you are still having a delightful time. But your good Aunt is so feeble & will work so hard. I fear the children will be so noisy and troublesome to her & Uncle - you must not stay too long.

I saw Jimmy yesterday. He is quite well & showed me a letter he had recd of you and Aunt of the same date as mine. I have no news to communicate to you different from last date. We are still here in large force & no particular indication of a forward movement. As to my health I cannot give a very flattering account and yet I am not sick - neither am I quite well. I remain rather thin and feeble though able to attend with tolerable promptness to my duties. I do not however gain as I should like to. I have tried to get a leave of absence for 30 days but failed. I now think some of offering my resignation soon if I should not feel better - But there are difficulties & doubts in the way as to what my real duty is, and then it is quite doubtful whether a resignation would be received if offered on the eve of an expected expedition so I will work away a while yet and watch the signs of the times.

I recd a letter from Mother, same date as yours. She was still at Milford & would remain there 2 weeks longer. She expects you to make her a visit after she goes home -- As to your going to Fayette don't be in a hurry unless Will & Carry determine positively to go - I cannot

*tell what I may do yet so hold on in Ohio till I can write
more definitely. The weather has been fine for a few days.
We had a hard shower this morning & it is now quite
cool. It is late bed time & I am getting cold without a fire
so I must close. Love to all & kisses to the boys & you.*
Your own C.C. Parker

*Apr. 3d. This bright morning finds us all alive and some
of us well. I do not feel first rate but I am up & at my
post. I snatch a moment to finish and mail this. Our
regiment is ordered out on a grand review or rather our
Brigade & I don't know but the whole division - The
whole camp is astir with preparations. The weather is
delightful & probably the review will be interesting to
witness. But I shall not go. I shall work what I must and
rest all I can get to. I think I shall have a quiet time when
the most of the others are gone - I think that I shall
tender my resignation before very long but cannot tell
positively - I will try to do what seems to be my duty
looking to Divine aid for wisdom to direct my steps.*
C.C.P.

*Pittsburg Landing Tenn
April 4th 1862*

My Dear Wife
    It is night again after a day of april showers & a little sprinkle of hail. The evening is pleasant however and stirring news coming in just now, the camp is all astir. There has been some skirmishing this afternoon among the pickets & we have orders to provide two days rations & 40 rounds of ammunition and to be ready to move at a moment's notice. Of course we may not move at all but again we may be off in the morning. I suppose we are about 18 miles from the main body of the rebels at Corinth. Their skirmishers are of course nearer to us & may attack us. But we have pretty good reason to suppose not. News just now comes that one of our batteries was out in a field practicing when 3 rebel regiments came up and fired. The battery returned the fire pursued and took 40 or 50 prisoners ----
    We have a large force, so large that I cannot have much idea of the number. The camp extends many miles. Our position is at present - that is our regiment - in the right wing. So many are coming in & interrupting me I can't write worth a cent. I hope you will not feel any unnecessary uneasiness about me. Our regt may not move at all & if it does most likely I will have to remain behind with the sick as we have quite a number in camp. But of course if there is to be a fight I prefer to go out with the men & be on hand to dress their wounds. My health is improving again. I am sorry I have alarmed you by writing that I was not well as I know you are by your letter of the 27th which came yesterday. True I am not very stout & I think the service is rather too hard for me

to continue long and as soon as I can get round to it, that is get my books & reports all straight, all the public property in my hands inventoried & turned over to my successor as I would have to do etc. etc., that I will offer my resignation. Then perchance it may be excepted & perchance not. I have no doubt however but it will be accomplished in course of time - All these proceedings take time. It takes a week or more for any paper to go up to head quarters & come back with an answer. But I may get so much better as to not care about resigning. The prospect of a battle always improves the health of the men in the regiment - except a few cowards - and may be it will make me strong also - You continue to say that I promised you that if I was sick at all I would resign & come home immediately. Now I do not remember making any such promise. I assured you that if my health should fail that in all probability I could resign when necessary & so I hope to do yet. I ought not to throw up my commission for any slight or trivial or temporary cause - But I will try to do right if I can, if I can know what right is - I had rather fail and die even from home & friends than to fail in doing my duty & go home to enjoy their sweet society with a stain upon my honor or a blot upon my conscience. May Heaven help us to know our whole duty & give us the strength to do it. I kiss you & the dear Boys and go to rest. Good night

Affectionately your husband
C.C. Parker

Pittsburg Landing Tenn
April 5th 1862

My Dear Wife

I commenced a letter to you last night & finished it this morning in which I told you we were ordered to be ready to march at a moment's notice on account of some skirmishing yesterday etc. Well that's about all it amounted to. It is now night again & all things remain about as they were. The secesh made some kind of mistake when they ran into our lines yesterday. We have heard nothing from them to day.

I have felt better to day than any day before for a long time - indeed have felt quite well but not very strong. I still think however I shall probably put in my resignation before a great while unless I should get perfectly well & hardy. But at any rate you must not look for me very soon because it takes a good while to get any such thing through. Jimmy called to see me this evening with J. Swank. We walked together down to the Steamboat Landing - there are now about 15 steamboats lying here & the wharf looks business like. Most of the boats contain commissary stores forage etc. though some are transports & two are hospitals. 3 or 4 new regiments have arrived here within 24 hours, among them the Iowa 15th & Iowa 16th & Wisconsin 18th ----

It is said that one hundred and ten thousand rations are issued daily at this post. If this be true it is an indication of a very large force indeed but I doubt it.

Jimmy as I wrote you this morning had some thought of trying to get a cadetship at West Point. But this evening he says he has declined trying in favor of a young man by the name of Thompson and by so doing has some hopes of securing a commission as Lieutenant in his present Company. For Capt Newcomb has resigned & Templeton is about to do so. Lieut Brown will probably be promoted Capt. and Jimmy & Swank appear to stand about the best chance for appointment as the 2 Lieutenants - I hope they may both succeed. Jimmy is a good boy and I think would fill the place with sufficient ability to do him self credit & the cause good service. Such things however go so much by political favor that it is hard telling how they may turn. Abernethy of course is an aspirant but I think he is not as popular as Jimmy either with the men or with the officers ----

It may be also that Templeton's resignation will be withheld yet for he is recovering & when ever he feels well he - like me - feels like putting it through to the end & when sick thinks he had better make tracks for home - Well I will stop for the night & perhaps add a few lines in the morning if there should be anything of interest. How much I should love to be with you to night & our dear little boys and with the good kind friends where you are. I did think a few days ago I should get leave of absence & visit you while you are at Lebanon and Xenia for I very much want to see the towns & see whether either of them would suit me for a location. But any furlough is denied and it is not probable that I can now come home before you will have left there - I hope you will complete a good and satisfactory visit but I am always afraid the children will prove burdensome to friends especially to those who are not accustomed to have them around.

Good night - C.C. Parker

"There," thought Charles, "it is done." He was decided upon submitting his resignation for health reasons, and upon removing from Fayette as soon as he could choose a new location and settle his affairs. Jimmy no longer needed his brother-in-law to look after him, and whatever General Grant was cooking up, he could do it without one feeble surgeon. Dixon Alexander would take care of the citizens of Fayette as he has been doing in Charles's absence, and in time a new doctor would move there. Charles knew Sarah would be happy with his decision for it was clear from her letters that she was very worried about his health. He would mail this letter in the morning.

He never had the chance.

The rebel regiments that had been engaged on the 4th were not wayward stragglers, but advance troops of Confederate General Albert Sidney Johnson's army of forty thousand soldiers. They had marched up from Corinth to surprise Grant with his back to the river. They were scheduled to attack on the 4th, but muddy conditions slowed their progress over the narrow roads. The showers that Charles had mentioned in his letter turned the wagon tracks into knee deep mud. The attack was postponed until Saturday morning, the 5th. Some of the gunfire to which Charles had referred came from rebel soldiers testing their gunpowder to see if it was dry enough for battle. Many of the rebels had just been issued their weapons, and for some, the weapons they got were older than they were. They had all been shown the regulation procedure for loading, and many felt the need to practice their marksmanship on small animals and birds. They were green, and they did not understand that the plan had been to surprise the Yankees. They were itching for a fight, and took the opportunity to warm up their rebel yell.

By 4:30 in the afternoon of the 5th, the rebel troops were still not in position. Beauregard told Johnson that because of the noisy troops they had lost the element of surprise and they may as well have gone back to Corinth and draw Grant away from his supplies. Polk disagreed and suggested that the troops would be demoralized if they did not have a fight. Johnson agreed with Polk, and set the attack for daylight on Sunday the 6th.

Charles was up early on Sunday morning, as was his habit. His mind was preoccupied with the decisions he had made and the best way to execute them. There was nothing out of the ordinary at first. The boys of the 12th were up and had begun their day. Food was cooking, and some had gone to the creek to bathe. Abruptly they heard the booming of cannons and the rattle of musketry in the distance, at least four or five miles off. They were not alarmed because they had heard these sounds two days previous and nothing had come of it.

Word came that an attack was underway, and those caught cooking and washing were obliged to give up their endeavors and fall in. Once formed, they started for the front on the double-quick. On their way, they met hundreds of green troops high-tailing it for the rear. Many of them shouted things like "Go back! For God's sake, go back! The whole rebel army's up there. You'll all be killed!"

Charles assembled his staff quickly. Because they

were expecting to march, they had been using the camp hospital set up along the Hamburg Road, about two miles to the south of the 12th Iowa's encampment, to house those sick enough to need hospitalization. For the less infirm, there were plenty of tents in camp. Charles also knew of a log house across the ravine that divided the bluff between the north and south fork of the Eastern Corinth Road. The house could be seen if one looked directly south from the road alongside the camp. He was not sure at this point whether or not it would be needed, but he decided to keep it in mind.

Charles set to his task with the cool professionalism of a seasoned veteran. All his weariness, all his thoughts of resignation, and all his homesickness had been swept away, soon to be replaced by a steady stream of wounded. He was ready for them this time.

The wounded were slow in coming. The steadily retreating Union troops on the western edge of the field were forced to leave most of their wounded behind where they fell. The battlefield was wide, and there was a great deal of confusion on the roads crisscrossing the densely wooded land. Most of the wounded who were recovered were taken to the hospital or to the landing. The surgeons from the 2nd, 14th, and 7th Iowa Regiments, camped just west of the 12th, decided to move out to the line of battle instead of waiting in camp. Charles followed suit with his staff. When he was confident the camp was set to receive the minor casualties, Charles, with Dr. Finley and several of the nurses, set off in a wagon to find the regiment.

General Grant would later describe the ground as "undulating." Ravines and ridges shaped the countryside, which made the task of finding and evacuating the wounded all the more difficult. What was not swampy from the heavy spring rains was wooded. Where the trees were not thick, there was considerable underbrush. Aside from a few scattered fields, which tended to draw the combatants, the roads were the only reliable avenues for the ambulances. Wagons had to be parked, and the wounded carried some distance to them.

The medical staff of the 12th took the same road that their troops had taken previously. They, too, encountered the stream of soldiers in retreat. Inquiries about the location of the 12th were of no use. Those who were aware that an inquiry was being made had looks of such fright and anguish that it seemed pointless to press them for information they would just as soon forget. The sounds of battle were spread across the breadth of the landscape in front of them. Finally, a courier, in response to their appeal, shouted "straight ahead!" as he galloped past.

Meanwhile, the 12th Iowa, under Colonel Tuttle, was forming a line with three of his other regiments along an old road in what had been a wide gap in the center of the Union line. Prentiss' Division had been among the first to be overrun, and they were now holed up with Tuttle's regiments, which came up from the rear. For the next eight hours, they stubbornly held the rebel advance. That sunken road, from where no man of the 12th would budge without orders, became known as the Hornet's Nest. They were being pressed to the extreme by the Confederates with twelve full-scale attacks in all. They never did give way by frontal assault. It was not until the rebels had surrounded them that they withdrew.

Their action helped prevent a catastrophe for the Union that first day of battle.

Charles located himself and his staff some distance behind the 12th, which was posted on the sunken road about two miles southwest of their camp. The wagon could not be moved any closer without being in the battle, and it was not advisable to be too close. They were close enough, however, to help remove the wounded, which would avoid pulling riflemen off the line away from the fighting for any length of time. Fortunately, the number of wounded was minimal because of the tactical advantages of their position on the sunken road. When one of the men was wounded, Charles would assess the degree of severity and either send or accompany the man back to the hospital, which was down the road about a half mile to their left.

Late that afternoon, while Charles was en route to the hospital with two wounded soldiers from the 8th, it became apparent to the field officers that the Confederates had flanked the sunken road on both sides. Colonel Woods gave the order to retreat. Finley and the nurses, being back some distance, had the advantage of a head start. Finley blurted out "Look there!" To their right, they could see attackers who were definitely not Union forces pressing down a ridge toward them. They did not wait for orders to evacuate.

The 12th was nearly surrounded, but Colonel Woods was determined to break through. They had some success at first, but to no avail. They were surrounded and captured along with the 8th, the 14th, and the rest of Prentiss' Division. Colonel Woods was badly wounded in the leg and hand, and was taken along with his troops by the rebels.

Charles was just preparing to unload the wounded from his wagon, when word came that the rebels were closing. He jumped back on the seat and took off for the landing. Since his wagon was full, he could do no more. Even if the hospital was captured, the wounded there were in no danger from anything more serious than neglect.

Hamburg Road was blocked by the enemy advance, so Charles was obliged to take the road down the bluff from the hospital to the Upper Landing. When he reached the landing, he saw hoards of stragglers cowering between the river and the bluff. There were thousands of them, and no amount of chiding or threatening by the officers made any difference. Some were trying to convince the boatmen to take them on board; others were just sitting, staring blankly into space. The screams of the wounded and the dying did not help to relieve their fears. In fact, a few were motivated enough to make rafts out of driftwood to make the crossing.

Grant let them stay where they were. Nelson asked permission to shoot them down if they did not fight, but Grant thought it better that they not be forced. He knew that fear is contagious, and he did not want them to infect those troops who were still willing to fight. Besides, he probably saw them as a rebuke upon himself for not being sufficiently prepared for this attack, and for having green troops in the front while the veterans, like the boys of the 12th, were camped in the rear. He suspected that, under different circumstances, most of these raw and scared boys would show their gallantry in battle. In the next few days, he would prove to be right.

Charles made his way back toward the camp. The road he was traveling ran the complete length of the Upper Landing, and then crossed a small bridge at the north end to rise sharply to the bluff again. It circled around to the River Road, which joined the Eastern Corinth Road. There were no signs indicating the names of the roads, but his sense of direction and his powers of observation, sharpened by years of finding his way on the frontier, led him to familiar territory. By the time he reached the Corinth Road, he knew exactly where he was, and proceeded to the log house. There, he saw that several other surgeons had the same idea, and they all seemed to be converging on the only structure in the vicinity at once.

He helped the others set up the operating tables—this house accommodated three—and helped move unneeded furniture outside. Remembering their experience at Ft. Donelson, they removed the window coverings, so that they could discard amputated limbs. There was not as much brush around this house, so the pile would have room to spread on its own. They knew, from reports from the field, that there would be many more casualties than they had seen at Donelson.

Charles unloaded the two men from his wagon at the log hospital, and then returned to the 12th Iowa encampment. Before Finley and the others returned with the news they bore—they were coming on foot—Charles was accosted by David Henderson. David had returned to the unit from his respite in Iowa, but did not arrive early enough on the 6th to join them when the long drum roll called them into action that morning. Not content with being idle, David organized the others, who stayed behind for a variety of legitimate reasons, into a squad. They had been loading the regiment's equipment into wagons to take it to the river in case the rebels pushed as far as their camp. David was worried about his older brother Thomas, and when he saw Charles, decided to enlist the doctor's help in finding his brother.

David had learned from one of the wounded men recently brought in from the front that Thomas was either dead or wounded. The soldier from Company A thought he had seen Thomas take a ball in the chest, but he could not be sure. He had taken his own wound at the same time. The soldier told David where he had last seen Thomas lying near the sunken road.

Charles and David took off for the front in the wagon, not knowing what was transpiring ahead of them at the time. Tuttle was already out with most of his men, but two of his regiments, including the 12th, did not apparently get the word and were trapped by the encircling Confederate forces. Charles and David were moving toward the center of the line where the 12th Iowa was engaged, when suddenly there was a burst of gunfire in front of them, but out of sight. Union troops came running out of the brush.

"Go back!" cried one of the officers. "The rebels got us surrounded. You can't get through there. Go back!"

Charles brought the wagon about and ran with the troops for some distance, until they crossed a line of batteries set up in haste to halt the rebel attack. Some of the guns were huge siege cannons, and they dwarfed the standard field cannons that were mixed in with them. It was not long after the retreating party crossed this line that the order to fire brought tremendous explosions and clouds of blue smoke. When they slowed, Charles asked the officer about the 12th.

"I think they had to surrender with Prentiss and the others," he said, breathless. "We held 'em off as long as we could, but they finally broke through behind us. We were damn lucky to get out."

"What about the wounded?" asked Charles, in earnest.

"Can't get to 'em," said the officer. "The rebs hold the field. What you see here is all that got out."

With mixed feelings of relief at not having been captured, and sorrow for the loss of so many of their friends, the two turned back toward the log hospital. David was anxious to see if Thomas was taken there. But Thomas was not to be found in the mass of wounded gathering outside the log house, so David urged Charles to take him back to camp to look for him there. The other surgeons had things well in hand, so Charles agreed. He was worried about his own staff, and wanted to see if they had returned.

By the time they entered camp, almost all the firing from behind them had stopped. Only the shelling of rebel-held ground by the gunboats could be heard in the distance. Two rounds would be fired every fifteen minutes all night long. They could see the log house just across the ravine, and the batteries that had been set up within yards of it and were pointed toward the woods beyond.

Finley was in camp by this time, and while he related the details to Charles of their narrow escape,

David looked around for Thomas. Finding no success in his search, David entreated Charles to go back. But the latter suggested that it would be unwise to venture into enemy held territory to find him. David was insistent, and pressed Charles to accompany him in a search for Thomas. Charles reluctantly agreed.

It was nearly dark when they set out in the wagon again. The batteries had indeed halted the rebels, and Beauregard was content to wait until morning to finish off Grant. David was armed, but Charles was not. They proceeded slowly and with great caution until they came to a point, about a mile from camp, where they decided to leave the wagon and proceed on foot. David took the lead, while Charles dragged a stretcher in case they found wounded.

It began to rain. Peals of thunder blocked out the punctual shelling from the gunboats. Near the spot where the 12th had surrendered, they were surprised to hear voices. A Confederate regiment was camped there. The two searchers stopped still in their tracks. Charles was almost certain that the rebels had heard them, but they did not seem to be interested in investigating. Perhaps they were too tired; perhaps they did not think that any Union troops would be stupid enough to be foraging around out here in the darkness and the rain; perhaps they thought it was exactly as it was—a detail out to recover casualties. In any event, no one came to see who was there, and the two turned about and made their way back to the wagon as quickly and as quietly as possible.

The road seemed to be clear ahead of them, so they moved the wagon forward to within a quarter mile of the sunken road in front of the peach orchard where much of the fighting had taken place. They were ever-alert to signs of the enemy, but the enemy had scattered, looking for food and shelter and protection from the constant shelling from the river. The violence of the storm was increasing. Charles decided to take a chance and proceeded to where he knew that the 12th Iowa was positioned on the road.

The two were guided by the moaning of the wounded. Flashes of lightening lit up small streams of red liquid as the rain washed the blood of the dead and the dying toward the creek. As they approached the field, Charles was appalled to see the extent of the bodies. It was as if the field was carpeted with them. Of greater horror was the sight of hogs feeding on the corpses; the whole scene was surrealistically illuminated by the storm. Charles felt the impulse to chase away the hogs, but there were so many. Gunfire would alert the enemy to their presence.

David sought out the landmarks the soldier from Company A had indicated, and there he found Thomas's body. David knelt and wept for his fallen brother.

After a short time, David asked Charles to help him take Thomas back on the wagon. Charles implored that they could better serve the wounded. David reluctantly agreed and they buried Thomas there, at the foot of a sapling tree. Charles cut the tree with his pocketknife as a marker, and later made a cane from the piece he had kept. That cane would stay in the Parker family home as a reminder of the suffering endured by all.

After saying a prayer over Thomas's grave, Charles insisted that they use the wagon to bring back at least one wounded soldier. David agreed.

They loaded the first wounded soldier they encountered. He was shot through both legs, but he would live with treatment, if one can call amputation treatment. While Charles applied a tourniquet, they could hear cries for water from parched and dying lips. Charles longed to help them, but he was forced to content himself with just this one.

They loaded the unconscious man into the wagon with great exertion. Charles pleaded with David to recover one more, and David agreed. They loaded up another, which was all the wagon would hold, and made their way as quietly as possible back to the log house. Upon their arrival at the hospital, Charles and David unloaded the two wounded soldiers. Charles then instructed David to return to camp with the wagon and direct the nurses to the battlefield where they would find more wounded. The more severe wounds were to be brought to the hospital, and the lesser wounds were to be treated by Finley in camp. Their recovery efforts lasted all night and into the next day.

With the care of the wounded in camp thus arranged, Charles joined the several other surgeons who were working in shifts, hacking and sawing as though they were meat packers. The stream of wounded was slight, but steady, and held through the night. There was no formal system in place for collecting the wounded or the dead aside from what the surgeons and their staffs were able to do. Efforts to find wounded were piecemeal, and when they were found many of them had to be carried some distance. Some were fetched by comrades, who like Charles and David, had been searching the battlefield.

It must have been about midnight when Charles heard a commotion just outside the building. He left the table he was working at to the other surgeons to see what was the matter. The Steward from the 14th Iowa was arguing with a young officer who was insisting upon using the building for General Grant's headquarters.

General Grant had spent the previous night in a fine home nine miles downstream, and had been there eating breakfast when he heard the first sounds of the attack. But now, he did not want to be off the field until the battle was decided, and he needed a place to stay. If the truth were known, the General had originally determined to sleep wrapped in a poncho under an old oak. But the rain seeping through the leaves, as well as the weight of the battle on his mind, made sleep impossible. The aide recommended that he stay in the log house; it was the only building available. Tents were at a premium also because the rebels had captured many of them that morning, so the ones that were left were reserved for the wounded.

Charles, still acting as brigade surgeon, began explaining, in his usual and gentle manner, that they needed the building to tend to the wounded. Of course, General Grant was welcome to one of the cots. The aide took his gentleness for pliancy, and underestimated the determination behind it, as many had done before him. Charles would not give in, and was prepared to defy the General himself no matter what the consequences. They were thus engaged when an imposing figure rode up to them. It was General Grant.

The two men stopped talking as the General

lowered himself carefully from his horse. It was then that Charles noticed a crutch suspended in a holster, like a carbine, from the saddle. Grant had been making the rounds among his commanders all during the battle despite his injury. All eyes were upon the General, as he removed the crutch and hobbled toward them in obvious pain. Grant had sprained his ankle two days before when his horse slipped in the mud and went down on his leg. He was lucky that the soft mud prevented further damage, but it was still bad enough. His pain was one of the things keeping him awake.

As the General approached, the aide began to explain the situation, emphasizing Charles's reluctance rather than the rationale for his position. If Grant was listening, it was not conspicuous. He was eyeing Charles up and down. Charles was covered with blood from shoulder to boot. His sleeves were rolled up as far as they would go, and his arms were red as much as you could see of them. His apron was supposed to be white, but one would not know upon seeing it. It was dark red in some places, and pink in other places where the rain was washing out part of the color.

Grant turned his eye to the open door of the log cabin. The lanterns illuminated a circle of people around a table near the door. In the spaces between the moans and the screams, one could hear the bone saw at work. He could see the pile of limbs spreading from the window along the side of the house.

Grant turned back to Charles. "Keep your hospital, surgeon," he said. "I can make do."

"That is very kind of you, sir," replied Charles, with a great relief in his voice.

"It is the least I can do for these boys," said the General. "My inconvenience is nothing to theirs. I owe them that. They saved us from being overrun by the rebels today. We'll lick 'em tomorrow though."

Charles said nothing further.

"Where do you hail from, surgeon?" Grant finally said.

"I live in Iowa," said Charles, "but my wife and I are both from Point Pleasant, Ohio."

"Point Pleasant!?" Grant exclaimed. "Why I was born there."

The General mentioned several family names that Charles knew well, and they exchanged gossip for the next few minutes. They soon discovered that they had an unusual and interesting connection. Carrie Thompson, who was married to Charles's brother-in-law, Will, was born in the same house that hosted the General's birth years earlier. Grant had lived lately in Galena, Illinois, and had not seen the house or the town for some time.

It was a pleasant respite, but after a short while the General mounted his horse to seek another resting place, and they bid farewell. While Charles returned to his work, General Grant returned to his "tree in the rain." Sherman found him there, and inquired about the Commander's reasoning for not seeking shelter. "I found the sight of the wounded more unendurable than encountering the enemy's fire," Grant told him.

The next day, Grant was as good as his word. Buell had brought his troops up in the night, and they were attacking all along the front. At 7:00 a.m., Grant sent word to the gunboats to cease firing. The army was advancing.

The rebels were somewhat disorganized, and not ready for the attack. Ground lost the day before was quickly regained, and many wounded still alive on the field, like Colonel Woods, were recovered and sent to the rear for treatment. Charles and his staff were among the first on the reclaimed ground, searching out the wounded.

The surgeons were moving their wounded out as soon as possible, transporting them in boats to hospitals in Cairo and St. Louis. Burial details were dispatched to the battlefield to bury the dead. Identifying the corpses was a difficult task after the ravages of war and hungry beasts. Many soldiers were buried as "unknown". The system for cleaning up after the battle was developing along with the system used to prepare for battle. The whole army was learning how to manage the logistics of war. Grant and Sherman, who had always thought so, were now convinced beyond any doubt that this would be a long and difficult conflict, and that this learning would not go to waste.

By afternoon of Monday the 7th, the battle was winding down. Sherman was the only field commander who took some initiative to pursue the retreating rebels. But after meeting with a formidable resistance provided by Forrest's Cavalry, he broke off the pursuit and sent his weary men back to the camp they had occupied before all this began. Sherman, himself, returned to his original headquarters in the extreme forward position, which was captured and then relinquished by Beauregard. It was a tent near a small, log chapel named Shiloh.

Eventually, the flow of wounded subsided, and Charles allowed his thoughts to return to their former bent. He became anxious that Sarah would hear of this great battle, and worry about him. So he went to his tent and retrieved the letter he had not yet mailed. To this he added the following account of events:

April 7th Continued

I can assure you my dear we have had two days of terrible strife. For two whole days the roar of cannon & the rattle of musketry have not ceased until later this after noon. Neither has the sound of suffering ceased from our ears since the beginning. But I can not describe to you the battle nor do I mean to try. It has been terrific but it is over and thank God the victory appears to be upon the side of the right. The enemy drove us little by little all day yesterday. But to day we have repulsed them - at first slowly, but steadily and towards evening we gave them a complete rout - They appear to be clean gone & our cavalry are after them sharply ---

I have been very busy & am unable to write any particulars. You will see them all in the papers & the most you care to know from me is the fact that I am still alive & well. My health is also improving. The Medical Director met me on the battle field yesterday & said he had not seen me look so well for a month - The reason I was not taken prisoner is that I had just fallen back to a hospital when the enemy drove in our lines & cut off our regt & several others. My assistant & hospital steward & nurses barely escaped - I had had also to leave that hospital & afterwards to fall further back but not in any especial haste. Jimmy's regiment suffered severely. He feels some better tonight. He is taking quinine. He received no wound though several balls passed through the flag. I suppose Toby is here somewhere but do not know.

Your loving husband, C.C. Parker

Charles worked steadily at evacuating the wounded. The hospitals nearest the landing were able to place their wounded on board first, thus leaving the more remote hospitals no room to transport theirs. Charles posted a lookout on the bluff near the camp to tell him when a transport boat was arriving. He needed to move some of his more severely wounded out as soon as possible.

Receiving word that a transport was docking, Charles rushed to have one of his worst taken down to the landing. Unfortunately, the boat departed for the opposite bank to load coal before Charles could disembark. He tried to speak to the captain, but there was no giving way. The captain had a schedule to keep.

Charles was agitated at first because this took him away from his duties with no easy way to get back. Finally, resigned to his temporary fate, he decided to take the opportunity to write to Sarah on some paper he found on board. There were no stools or chairs available, much less writing tables. So, he rolled up his coat to use as a writing surface, and wrote his letter as best he could, standing with his coat resting on the steamer's railing. It gave his penmanship an unsteady look.

Pittsburg Landing Tenn
April 9th 1862

My Dear Wife

I wrote you day before yesterday but fearing you did not receive it. I seize a moment to say that I am still safe & sound for which I know you will join me in thanks to God. I saw Jimmy to day also. He is much better also, able to walk down from his camp to see me.

I told you that nearly all our regiment were taken prisoners. But that I with a very few besides the disabled escaped. We are still finding our wounded & dead scattered every where. I believe 10 is all the killed of our regt yet found & identified. They went into the fight early Sunday & were surrounded about 4 o'clock. It was a terrible battle. The enemy had the advantage of us all day on Sunday but Monday morning we commenced driving them back. Our forces are still in pursuit but I have heard no account to day (Wednesday) as to the degree of success. I am on the Steamer City of Memphis, a hospital boat. Came on to bring one of my wounded & the boat pushed off with me on board & ran across the river to coal - She is about to start down the river with a large load of wounded (six or seven hundred). I do not know to what point she will go perhaps to Cincinnati -- I must go on shore & find a passage back to camp. Our position of the camp was undisturbed by the enemy except the bursting of a few shells - The camp of the Iowa 3d & many others however was occupied by the enemy Sunday night. Gen Nelson's forces arrived here on Monday & bore a conspicuous part in the fight. I am

unable to ascertain whether Toby Lakin is here or not but
suppose he is. I must go immediately.

Affectionately
C.C. Parker

The steamer had docked, and now Charles must
disembark and find some way of getting back across the
river. It would not be easy. Three hours later, he was able
to hitch a ride on a gunboat that had come for coal, and
was returning to its station on the river. The captain,
more agreeable than the last, dropped him off near the
landing. However, Charles was obliged to jump off the
gunwale to the shore. He waved his gratitude to the
captain.

The following day, Charles received a letter from
Sarah. He knew from her manner of writing that she was
not doing well without him. His thoughts turned again to
resignation. Now that the regiment was nearly dissolved,
it was a good opportunity to pursue that course. Several
officers told him that the men would probably be folded
in to other regiments. In any case, there was need for one
less regimental surgeon. He would write his thoughts to
Sarah, and try to ease her anxiety.

Pittsburg Landing Tenn
April 10th 1862

My Dear Wife

I have written you twice since the great battle here, but fearing you may not get the letters, I take every opportunity to send you a line. You have no doubt learned that our army here were attacked by the enemy in strong force early on Sunday morning the 6th inst. A fierce battle raged all day and the enemy drove our men back slowly until night. But reinforcements arriving from Buell's command - We attacked them early on Monday morning & compelled them to retire more rapidly than they had advanced the day before. It was a terrible two days conflict, & of course we call it a victory - The slaughter on both sides is great. The enemy were driven back & pursued in the direction of Corinth. There are various rumors afloat in camp to day. One is that they are preparing to attack us again. Others that they are badly whipped etc. etc. - The Iowa troops were early in the fight & suffered much. Many being killed & wounded & many more taken prisoners. The 8th, 12th & 14th are nearly all prisoners - Our Colonel was taken prisoner with the rest but being severely wounded the enemy left him & some other wounded when they were compelled to retire on Monday. So some of the wounded fell again into our hands. Most of our regiment however remain prisoners & we have heard no word from them since they were taken. We had a number of sick in camp when the battle commenced. We have them still besides a number of our own wounded & some of the other regiments. We have barely enough able bodied men here of our own to take care of them. Some boat loads of the wounded begin now however to be sent away to the general Hospitals at the different cities and we hope to be able to send some of ours soon - But we are some distance from the landing so that when a hospital boat arrives those nearer are carried on board & the boat filled before we can get the opportunity. But our sick & wounded are quite well situated in camp for the present, I think better than those of any other regiment I am acquainted with. We have found & buried ten of the dead of our regiment. I do not know the exact number of the wounded brought in to this time - perhaps 30 - Two Lieutenants were killed, (Lt. Moire & Lt. Ferguson) & brother of Lt. Henderson was killed. - Frank Moine is said to be wounded in the head & is missing. He may have been sent down to Savannah on the first boat load of wounded.

The Iowa 3d was in the hottest of the fight on Sunday. They were so badly cut up that few if any were able to go out on Monday - They have got back however into their own tents which were Sunday night in possession of the rebels -- Jimmy escaped unhurt though his comrades were slain all around him & some balls struck the flag he carried - He was taken sick on Sunday night however & staid with me - He is getting well, I did not see him to day but heard from him. Templeton & Swank were here to day & others. Swank is slightly wounded. So is Charlie Clark & Jack Hendrichson & Major Jones of W. Union & J. Earle of Albany. There were three killed in that company but not our acquaintances - Gen Nelson's forces arrived on Monday & took an active part in the fight. I can not learn as yet whether Toby Lakin is here or not. Yesterday I met Dr. Gay of Columbus, Ohio who is Gen Nelson's Brigade Surgeon. He was busy of course & so was I - I have not done near the amount of work here that I did at Donelson simply because I am not able - I do what I can however & the demand is very great. I had made up my mind before the battle to resign as soon as I could perfect the necessary arrangements. But of course the battle has deranged all our plans. I still wish to resign for my health's sake whenever I can do so honorably. But at a time like this I feel it as much my duty to risk my life in the service as it is the duty of the soldiers to risk theirs by fighting. I am somewhat better than I was. I cannot tell yet just what I will do. No indication for now what orders will be given concerning us only a fragment of a regiment - We may be disbanded - or attached to some other regiment or sent into quarter to recruit - or I may be detailed to some Steam Boat or other Hospital. Time only will determine these things. In the mean time let us await the dispensations of Providence with patience & faith that all things will yet be well. Your letter written March 30th & April 1st came to day. I am glad to notice that you & the children are well & enjoying yourselves so well with your kind friends. I should so much love to come & see you while you are there. I never can thank them all enough for their kindness to you & the children. I did at one time think I should come before you would leave Xenia. But you see now that such a thing is not probable. But do not worry & anticipate evil on my account. I will do all I can to take proper care of myself & God will care for the rest. I am willing to trust in Him. I am all the time afraid the children will be troublesome to your friends who are not accustomed to so much noise & confusion. But for me how I would love to hear their dear prattling tongues to night. Kiss them again & again for their Pa --

As to your going to Iowa do not be in a hurry or borrow any trouble about it for the present. I don't think we will ever make Fayette a permanent home again - I had a letter from Vines in which he sent me 20 dollars & said he had sent 10 dollars to you directed to Xenia. I hope you have got it. I have a letter also from Dr. & Mrs. Alexander. They say Mr. Mott's folks take first rate care of our things. The postage stamp & dollar bill you sent were recd & thankfully acknowledged some time ago. I embrace & kiss you.

Affectionately your husband C.C. Parker

Pittsburg Landing Tenn
Sunday April 13th 1862

My Dear Wife,

I have taken every opportunity to write you since the great battle a week ago in order that you may be well assured of my safety & health as well as the welfare of Jimmy & Toby Lakin. Both of whom I have seen to day. Jimmy & Brent Templeton staid with me last night but went away before breakfast. Jimmy is in tolerable health & spirits. Lt Templeton has just got his resignation accepted & expects to start home to day. I have just come in from a long ride over the battle field & through the camp during which I hunted up Toby's Regiment & found him looking & feeling quite well. He was in the fight here on Monday having arrived about midnight Sunday night. I also met several old Ohio acquaintances among them Robert Fee formerly of New Richmond, Charles Robb, Gus Penn & others.

Monday April 14th - You see I did not get to finish my letter yesterday on account of many interruptions. I have nothing new to write this morning but will send this along that you may know that I am still alive & well that is as well as usual - I have got all the wounded of our Regiment off on the boats to be taken to St. Louis or other Gen. Hospitals. We have here yet a few sick ones in hospital & there are here of our men about well ones enough left to take care of the sick & take care of what public property remains in our hands. We are expecting some order soon that will determine what disposition is to be made of us - only a fragment of our regiment - for I suppose you know if you have received my former letters, that nearly all the Regt were taken prisoners on Sunday last & we have heard no word from them since.

My health is considerably better than it was a week or two ago. I have not worked so hard as I did after the battle at Donelson. My labors have been more particularly directed to the care of the wounded of my own regt than on that occasion. This battle however has been a ten fold greater one than that in magnitude - a much larger number being wounded but yet a less severe class of wound generally -- There are hundreds of wounded here to be removed yet. The Boats sent from Cincinnati & other Cities are being crowded with them & all are doing all in their power to improve their condition which is deplorable enough at best. Our officer's mess is broken up. Myself & assistant have joined in with another however & get along very well - Our Colonel is gone home wounded. Lieut. Col. gone on Hospital Boat sick - Major ditto - Adjutant is a prisoner. Chaplain is still with us but quite sick. The Col. took one of the colored servants the Lt. Col. another & we have one still left with us. If I should get away to come home I may bring him with me. I think we could make him useful to us or else find him some other good place. I do not think I could get a resignation just yet but will probably try it on before long - Do not be impatient nor over anxious about me. I am trying to do my duty & have no fears but all things will come out right in the end. I have written to you several times not to be in a hurry about going to Iowa. I wrote to Vines to try to have Motts folks stay in the house & make garden. I do not think we will go back there to live. Tell the little boys that Pa thinks of them. God bless you, good bye.

Your afect Husband C.C. Parker

Pittsburg Landing Tenn
April 18th 1862

To the Asst. Adj't Gen'l.
Dist. West. Tenn.

Sir

Having this day delivered to Asst. Surgeon W.H. Finley, my successor in office, all the public property in my hands, and having been paid by Major Wallace to the 31st day of December 1861, and am not otherwise indebted to the United States, I have the honor herewith to tender my resignation as Surgeon of the 12th Reg't Iowa Inf. Vols.
Urgent necessity from ill health impels me to this course.

An obstinate chronic diarrhea with great emaciation & symptoms threatening pulmonary consumption have rendered me unable longer to perform the duties of my office either with justice to myself or to the public service.

Immediate acceptance of this to take effect at as early a day as practicable will greatly oblige.
Your obt Servt

C.C. Parker Surgeon 12th Iowa Inf.

Pittsburg Landing Tenn
April 18th 1862

My Dear Wife

I know your anxiety to hear from me often & so write every favorable opportunity. You will no doubt be surprised when I tell you that Will is here. He heard of the battle while at Burlington & his anxiety about Jimmy & me determined him to come home this way. I had sent in my resignation before he came - but the papers got lost some how by the frequent changes of commanders we have been subject to. So this morning I started a new set & followed them up till they had the signature of 4 superior officers approving them & they need but two more viz Genl Grant & Genl Halleck, & as their headquarters are not far from our camp now I have some expectation of getting away soon, I think in two or three days at most. I may have to go to St. Louis to get my pay but possibly I may get it at Cairo. In either case however I think you may look for me in a few days or a week at most after this arrives. I have now little doubt but that my resignation will be accepted. But if any thing occurs to prevent I will write to you immediately & in that case you must not feel disappointed. My health is improving a little yet but I think I am not really able for the service & it is my duty therefore to resign. Jimmy is pretty well now. I feel loth to go home & leave him in the army but his chances for promotion seem very good & that makes me feel better satisfied. I have little doubt but that he will be commissioned as 2d Lieutenant. I understand that he is already performing the duties of the office & has been recommended to the Governor by the Colonel for appointment. Abernethy is the only one standing in his way. Swank will probably be 1st Lieutenant. Will has just now (at noon) taken my horse & rode over to see Toby again. He & Jim went to see him day before yesterday & found Toby very well. I saw him last Sunday, as I wrote you. He looked real hearty & robust. I suppose you are now at Xenia & hope this will reach you before you leave. If you have already completed your intended visit there I shall expect to meet you in Milford or Cincinnati but if not - If you intended to stay longer I shall be pleased to meet you there for I want to see your dear friends of whom you always think & talk so much & then I want to see whether I would think Xenia a favorable location for us. I am not much inclined to that way of thinking but will try to look at the matter unprejudiced. I hope however you will not stay there waiting for me so long as to wear out your welcome. I fear the children are troublesome & then your folks always have so much company I am loth to add myself to the list of their visitors for fear of wearying them. I have written to Fayette to have Motts stay in our house if possible until they hear from us ---

Your letter of the 6th came to hand your fearful foreboding while writing about us being on the battle field were being realized at that very time. Kiss the dear frets & don't look for me too soon. My papers may have to go to St. Louis & back yet before I can leave.

Affectionately your husband

C.C. Parker

HEADQUARTERS, DEPARTMENT OF THE MISSISSIPPI

Pittsburg Landing, Tenn. <u>April 19th</u> *186<u>2</u>*
Special Field Orders No.<u> 15 </u>

    The resignation of <u>Surgeon C.C. Parker, 12th</u>
<u>Iowa</u> *Volunteers, is hereby accepted to take effect* <u>this</u>
<u>day.</u>
            By Order of General Halleck
               <u>M.H. McLean</u>
               Assistant Adjutant General

    Charles's resignation was approved along with that of Company C's Chaplain. He hastened to complete the last of the paperwork transferring his assignment to Assistant Surgeon Finley. Charles prevailed upon Caleb, one of the runaway slaves who had been working for the 12th Regiment hospital staff, to come home with him. Charles promised that he would help Caleb find work on a farm if he was not inclined to work in the clinic.

    Will was happy with the timing, that he might accompany Charles on his return trip. When they went to headquarters to finalize the paperwork, Charles had an opportunity to introduce Will to General Grant. They talked briefly about the house where the General and Will's wife, Carrie, were both born. The General was kind enough to include Will on the pass.

Head Quarters Disct of W. Tenn
Pittsburg, April 21st 1862

Guards & Any Steamer will permit

Rev A.G. Eberhart & servt
Capt. J.E. Ainsworth & servt
Surgeon C.C. Parker & servt &
Hon Wm B Lakin

to pass to Cairo, Ill
By order of Maj. Genl U.S. Grant
John A. Rawlins
A. A. Genl

They were on their way home.

Priscilla Malloy Parker's Journal - 1862

*C.C. went from St. Louis to Tennessee was at Ft.
Henry arrived there the day after the capture, was at the
taking of Ft. Donelson, had very severe labor with the
wounded after that terrible battle. Went to Pittsburg
Landing was there through that awful conflict, was on
the field where bullets flew thick, seeing to the wounded,
retired with some of the sufferers to the hospital a few
minutes before his regt was surrounded & taken with
Gen. Prentice, he remained there three weeks, his health
forbid him staying longer, he was sick & emaciated. He
came home here, stayed a few days, has now returned
with his family to Iowa. Again I mourn their absence. His
health not well restored.*

VII

"So, you came back to Fayette anyway," I said, smugly. "Obviously you didn't relocate after all that big talk about moving. Who talked you out of it?"

He glared at me for a moment. It was an uncharacteristically vicious glare. I could not tell if it was meant in earnest or in jest. Then, with a tone of thinly disguised resentment, he said "Elizabeth Alexander talked me out of it."

"Hmmm," I said, determined to make sport of it to lighten him up a bit. "Elizabeth Alexander. She was sort of like your mother, wasn't she?"

He turned up the intensity of his glare. Then, without any indication that it was coming, he burst into laughter. It was so spontaneous that I could not help laughing myself. It was one of those knee-slapping, gut-wrenching laughs that I had not had for a long time. It was fully five minutes before we could control ourselves. Tears were streaming down our faces. He was wiping his eyes on his sleeve; I with my handkerchief. I offered my handkerchief, but he waved it off.

"I had more than my share of mothers," he said, when his laughter had subsided to the point where he could speak.

"Don't we all," I said, still wiping. "But I think I know you well enough to know that it was your decision to stay."

"And so it was," he said, cheerfully. "I suppose

you want an explanation."

I nodded.

"This is such a beautiful and tranquil place," he said, gazing out the window. "In the midst of all that killing and dying, I had forgotten how beautiful. I suppose it was fortuitous that we returned here in the lovely bloom of spring, when life begins anew. And I suppose it was also fortuitous that I went first to Ohio. A few days in Point Pleasant reminded me of my reasons for leaving there in the first place. Ohio is a beautiful place too, but circumstances there would prove to be intolerable after a time. We returned here, and so many people were good to us."

"You were worried about your resignation," I said, thoughtfully, "and how people would take it."

"I suppose I was," he said. "But no one had a harsh word for me. I suppose that the condition of my health was obvious enough such that no one questioned my motives. Also, several officers preceded me here under conditions that no one thought shameful. When I again looked upon this beautiful little valley, I could not help but to feel that my place is here. Sarah was happy here also, and she did not favor another move. Besides, Will and Carrie decided to remain here."

"I'll bet you looked at most things differently when you came back," I offered.

He looked directly into my eyes, and said, "you have no idea."

"I would like to know," I said, hoping that this trend of revelation would continue.

He became pensive as he returned his gaze to the window. He seemed to be organizing his thoughts.

Finally, he spoke.

"I cannot tell you how good it was to see Sarah and the boys again," he said, with a tinge of emotion in his voice. "I thought my heart would burst when I first laid eyes upon them. I have always considered myself a humanitarian, but I never fully realized until that moment how precious life is, and how delicate. Life is truly a gift from God, and it should never be taken with only casual veneration.

"I say this to you," he said, turning to me with some force, "do not waste a moment of your life. Do not live to regret your failure to savor its most precious moments. Make the most of your opportunities to do the right thing, and take advantage of your time in the world. It is all you have."

I wanted to break in and argue that I try to live that way now, but he was on a roll.

"Take care to do that which brings pleasure to those you care about," he continued, "and you will know the greatest of pleasure yourself. Show kindness and charity toward everyone, for you never know how much your treatment of them can make a difference. You are a teacher. You should never lose sight of your responsibility to make the lives of your students into something of greater value. I had my doubts about teaching again after the war. I thought I had nothing of value to teach. But I finally realized that I do not teach the students. They come to learn from me. They see me live my life, and they must ask themselves 'is this the sort of life I would like to live?' I answer by living the kind of life I think they should live."

He stopped and narrowed his focus upon me.

Then he spoke as though his message was of the gravest consequence. "Do not take your students for objects. You must strive to see them as persons whose souls are seeking your guidance, and you must treat each precious life as an end in itself."

I could not argue with that.

"You are right," I said. I wanted to say something about how I would try to do better, but I could not think of any way to put it that did not sound insincere.

He was obviously waiting for me to say something more.

"I suppose," I finally said, "that I tend to just throw scholarship at them and hope something sinks in."

"The most important lessons for them to learn are not in the lectures," he said, with conviction.

"But," I said, somewhat defensively, "I do things in certain ways for a reason. I let them make their own choices. If they choose not to study, I let them do it and let their grades reflect their choices. If they choose not to ask me for help, I do not try to impose upon them."

"You must be more proactive," he said.

"Proactive?" I blurted out. "I didn't think that was a nineteenth century word."

"I saw it on the Internet," he said. "It is a good word. It would mean the same then as it means now. You must seek out those who need your help most, and press upon them the importance of a clean and useful life."

"You are right," I said, trying to sound as sincere as possible before arguing with him. "Let me ask a few questions."

"Of course."

"Is it possible to do too much for a student?"

"I am not sure I know what you mean," he said.

"Suppose I have a student who is clearly capable of good academic work, but is just not motivated to study or to come to class. Suppose I work with this student by checking on his assignments and constantly badgering him to pull his grades up. He resists for the most part, but through constant pressuring he does his work and passes the course. His attitude is 'All right, dammit, I'll do the work if you'll leave me alone.' If I did not put on the pressure, he would not have passed the course."

"Yes?" he said, indicating that he understood the premise.

"What did he gain?" I asked, sincerely.

"Well," he said, thoughtfully, "he gained the benefit of doing the work and passing the course."

"But," I said, springing the trap, "won't he just do the same thing the next time? Hasn't he learned that there will always be someone to carry him through and bail him out?"

"Ah," he said, stroking his beard, "I see your point. Yes, I suppose it is possible that this student has learned the wrong thing. But if he is capable of this work, then why is he not doing it in the first place?"

"Lazy."

"Lazy, or uninspired? Is it not your task to impress upon him the importance of doing this work? Perhaps if all you are doing is applying pressure, then you are not advising him properly. You cannot simply tell him what to do; you must bring him to understand that the doing of it is important."

"You are right," I conceded. "Usually, I inform him that he is going to fail, and if he continues to miss class and not study then I give him the grade he has earned. I can't do his work for him. What can I do except to let him go the way he's chosen?"

"Then," he said, solemnly, "you must be creative."

"I guess I have always believed that you can't save everyone," I said. "If a guy is headed for a cliff, I will tell him it's a bad idea, but if he keeps going then I let him go."

"There you are mistaken," he said. "Life has infinite worth. Some philosopher said that."

"Kant," I said, interrupting him.

"You must exhaust every measure you can conceive," he said, ignoring me, "to help bring that life to its fullest potential."

"Aristotle," I said. I might have said Maslow, but he would not know that name.

He gave me the look.

"I'm sorry," I said, "I can't help it. I think the secret to life is knowing things."

"Ah," he said, "there you are wrong. The secret to life is not knowing things. The secret to life is taking the best course of action. You do not help students by giving them information except that it helps them to make better choices. Your student has chosen not to study, and you must persuade him that he can make a better choice. You should not care if an idea was written down by Kant or Aristotle, what you should care about is that it helps one to live better."

"How did you do that with physiology?" I asked. "Isn't physiology and anatomy just learning names of bones and muscles?"

"You never studied those subjects," he said.

"Well, I had to take brain physiology, but not the other. It was not my favorite."

"It is true," he said, "that in my day a good deal of education was devoted to memorizing things. And it is true that anatomy and physiology requires knowing the names and bones, muscles and the like. But I took care to stress the importance of knowing these things, and how useful this knowledge becomes when choosing the best course of action. I like to tell the story of how Abraham Lincoln used medical knowledge to prove a man innocent of murder and spare his life. I often told stories of how knowledge can be used to save lives and relieve suffering. A thorough knowledge of the body's workings can help you to choose what to eat and when, and how to conduct yourself as to be healthy and happy."

I was quiet for awhile, thinking it over. "Tell me," I finally said, "how did you conduct yourself after your experience with the war?"

VIII

The steamer trip to Cairo might have been lighthearted but for the presence of over four hundred wounded and dying soldiers on board. Even though Charles had resigned, he was still in uniform, and still a surgeon. The need for his service pressed heavily upon him, and he had little opportunity for much needed rest. Will, appalled by his sickly appearance, urged him to leave the responsibility to the attendants, but to no avail. Charles would not be swayed from his sense of duty.

They debarked at Cairo, and Charles was able to find a paymaster and draw the pay due him for the three months of January through March. This greatly relieved him, and his health improved steadily as they made their way to Cincinnati where their families were waiting.

When Charles first looked upon Sarah, his heart pounded and his knees grew weak. The presence of so many family and friends prevented him from running to her as a lost little boy would run to his mother. That would be unseemly, he thought, and might embarrass her, though the urge to do so was almost overwhelming. Instead, he walked to her, calmly, and took both of her hands in his. The loneliness that had hung upon him like a weight about his shoulders fell away; replaced by a sensation of lightness and joy.

They just stood for a moment, neither having spoken a word, looking into each other's faces. Sarah's eyes glistened with tears, and her cheeks quivered with emotion. No one else could see her face but Charles. No one but he could possibly understand what she felt. She felt euphoria in seeing him again alive and well. Their time apart had been an endless torment of images and fears—images of him in danger, and fears for his safety and well-being. She knew that he would not be satisfied remaining at a safe distance from the fighting if he felt his duty was to be in its midst. She could now see that some of her fears were justified, and she also felt a depressing melancholy as the hardness of his features began to reveal to her all that he had been through. His ordeal was written as a testament upon his face, and the seeing of it was unspeakably painful to one who prayed ardently every minute of every day for his welfare.

The two boys sensed that it was their place to be patient and wait before greeting their father. They both knew of their mother's own ordeal, and instinctively understood her need to be alone with him.

And alone they were; in this crowded parlor, they were the only two people in the world.

Presently, Charles turned to his two young sons. Danny, the oldest, took the cue immediately and ran to his father's arms. Charley was more reluctant, unsure of himself. Even after a span of only seven months, his memories of his father were dim. In a lad not quite three years of age, it was a natural reaction to expect.

Charles, who was bent over with Danny still hanging about his neck, moved to sit in a nearby rocking chair. His weariness was pressing heavily upon him, but he would not let it spoil the reunion. Soon, with the reassurance of everyone in the room as support, the toddler walked slowly to the chair in which his father sat with his brother, and after a moment nestled into his father's embrace and smiled contently. Charles was home again.

Charles and Sarah had a great deal of catching up to do, but it would have to wait until the more pressing business of settling their affairs was completed. They could not remain long in Point Pleasant as a burden upon the family, and so plans must be adopted quickly. They decided to return to Fayette to dispose of their property and to pack their possessions. They would discuss the possibilities for resettling somewhere else during the trip.

Will and Carrie had decided to remain in Ohio for a number of reasons. Like Charles, Will had a solid future in Iowa if he chose to exercise it. But, he was not sure that that was precisely what he wanted. Carrie was quite content to remain in the vicinity of her family, especially her sister Sallie.

So, Charles and Sarah made their way back alone with the two boys. The return trip was made easier by Caleb, who was a good and faithful servant. He accompanied them to Fayette, and would eventually establish one of the first black households in the region.

The boys let out some of their pent-up energy on the return trip. Danny wanted to know everything about the war, and about his father's role in it. Attending to his questions was a full-time occupation. By the time they reached Fayette, nothing had been settled because the children left no time for the two to be alone.

It was a clear, sunny day when Charles stepped out of the coach in front of Gray's Hotel. He turned to help Sarah and the two boys, but Danny jumped down before anyone could assist, and ran over to greet a friend he recognized nearby. As Caleb helped bring down the baggage, Charles took a survey of Main Street. It was as though he had been gone for only a day or two. It was a strange sensation.

He tried to recapture the abject quality of the war, which had so recently run rough-shod over his psyche, but it was like a nightmare, the force of which was diminished by the light of day. Though his memory still contained vivid images of this nightmare, all threats of horror and privation were gone—overwritten by this dusty, peaceful little street with boys and girls running and playing and workmen going about their business. It was indeed a different world.

They had written ahead to inform the Motts that they were returning. When they arrived, they found their house in tip-top condition, and the Motts were happily settled in a new house on the east side of town.

Walking through the front door was, for both of them, walking back in time to an era of happiness. It was a sensation that both thought was lost forever. The close familiarity of the house and its memories filled in the blanks created by their recent nomadic existence and by a forced abdication to the goodwill of others. Thoughts of leaving Fayette were pushed aside by the joyful sensation of belonging. It was good to be home.

Their first night in town did not pass without visits from the Colonel and Elizabeth Alexander, and from James and Elizabeth Robertson.

"Oh, Dr. Parker," gushed Elizabeth Alexander, as she took his hands in hers, "we are so happy that you're back. Your presence here has been sorely missed. We were so sorry to hear of the plight of the 12th regiment.

So many good, young men. What is to become of them?" Her tone registered a deep and sincere concern.

"I heard," said Charles, "that they will probably be exchanged for Confederate prisoners in a few months. Then they will either form a new regiment or join others."

"What of your health?" said Elizabeth, looking into his face as though she were examining a melon for purchase. "You do not look well at all."

"I am better now," said Charles. "I was forced to resign because I simply could not carry my share of the work load. There were times when I just could not get out of bed, and I was more of a burden than a help."

"We understand," said the Colonel, conveying his approval. "We're just glad to see you back."

"Oh, your boys!" exclaimed Elizabeth. "I cannot get over how they've grown. Danny looks so big and strong, and Charley is such a delight. And Sarah, it is so good to see you too."

Sarah smiled, but did not say anything.

After looking at the boys for a moment, Elizabeth turned her attention back to Charles.

"You have come none too soon," she said, seriously. "Ever since the regiment went away, the students have become unruly. While you were gone, they put sheep on the roof, and took delight in hiding President Brush's carriage. If that were not enough, they've been stealing turnips right out of the Trustees' garden. Miss Sorin is at a loss as to what to do with them. I've always said that your discipline and influence kept them on the straight and narrow, and you are needed here more than ever. And that Dr. Alexander! Well, he's a good man. But, he just doesn't have your way about him. I will rest well knowing that I have you to attend to all my ailments."

Charles realized that it was too late to announce any intention to leave. His only opportunity to do so would have been before she had a chance to speak. To reveal his thoughts of leaving now would be to bring despondency to his good friends and benefactors. Now, some time must pass and plans must be firmly in place before any such announcement could have been made.

When Charles and Sarah were finally alone, they discussed the issue of relocating. Sarah was not strongly in favor of doing so. Charles tried to explain the advantages, but was suddenly at a loss. Now that he was home, he was reluctant to carry out what had before been such a strong desire. In part, the appeal of the place was more compelling than it seemed when he was away. The beauty of the hills and valleys, the serenity of the countryside, the close-knit circle of friends; this was all just the right combination of ingredients for living a good life.

His memory of life in Fayette must have been tainted by the appalling circumstances of his environs. What he desired to leave was that awful, brutal conflict with its unspeakable butchery and hardship. Yes, that was what he yearned to leave. Now that he had removed from that context, his impulse to push away from the familiar had disappeared.

Mostly though, he was just bone tired. The effort required to move again was prohibitive in itself. Sarah asked him pointedly why he would not take the easy course and stay in Fayette. His practice was established, the university would provide endless needs to satisfy, and there were many possibilities for his other avocations.

Charles was forced to admit that she was right. As he looked upon her face, staring anxiously into his, he was overwhelmed with the sensation of love for her. After all, what better place could there be?

By and by, Charles found himself in his old office in the museum in the Sem. The stuffed moose occupied its usual place in the corner. Everything looked pretty much as it had been except that the moose was more dusty than the last time he had seen it. Someone had been using the desk during his absence, and there were piles of papers to be sorted and disposed of. As he set about straightening his desk, he realized that his fears regarding a return to the classroom were greatly diminished. Nothing was as it had seemed at Fort Donelson. The memory of it was like the sort of images one creates when reading a novel. It was easy to believe that it all happened to someone else.

Under a stack of papers, he found an issue of the *Philomathean Journal* dated two months before. An article caught his eye: "Ye student smoketh one filthy pipe—stronger than last year's butter and blacker than ye ace of spades—and called ye same enjoying life. He spurteth liquid nastiness from his mouth, where he manufactureth essence of tobacco on an extensive scale."

Charles smiled to himself. No wonder Elizabeth was upset. The students were being themselves.

On June 26th of 1862, Jason Paine became the first to complete the full course of study in the preparatory and collegiate departments at UIU, and the first to earn a Bachelor of Arts degree. His decision to stay behind and not join the war was beginning to bear its fruit. Charles felt a strong affinity for Jason, and went out of his way to assure him that he had taken the right path. Jason was convinced that it was the will of God that set his direction, and he was grateful for the acknowledgement from someone for whom he felt such a deep respect.

Jason graduated along with John Clough, who was the first to earn a Bachelor of Science degree, in a commencement ceremony held in a clearing near the schoolhouse in Robertson's Woods. Dr. Brush gave the commencement sermon taking some of his text from Romans 14:7. Following the sermon, each student orated his or her lessons. Featured were the two graduates: John Clough delivered an oration entitled *Skepticism: In Relation to Philosophy*, and Jason Paine's valedictory address was entitled *Price of Liberty*.

While Jason gave his commencement address, he glanced occasionally at the schoolhouse in which he was teaching before beginning his university study. This gave him pause to consider how far he had come from those days, and how far he had yet to go.

Despite President Brush's efforts to emphasize study over socializing, both graduates were married by the time they graduated. That represented some cause for concern among some of the trustees that it set a bad example, but most felt such marriages were perfectly natural and were well within recommended standards of moral propriety.

That summer, Will and Carrie returned to Fayette. In the fall, Will was elected to the state legislature as the representative from Fayette County. He and Carrie would spend a lot of time in Iowa City for the next year.

In September, Jason Paine left to become a missionary in the Dakota Territory. When he came to say goodbye to Charles and Sarah, his mixed feelings about leaving were obvious. Charles suddenly realized that he was not envious of the hardships that Jason would face. The old longing for adventure was greatly diminished. Pioneering had become a young man's endeavor. Charles wished him well.

Also in September, word came that Jimmy had been promoted to 1st Lieutenant. Sarah was somewhat relieved that he was now an officer, believing that he would be less involved in the fighting. Charles decided not to tell her that many sharpshooters specifically target officers.

Charles had been appointed by the Commissioner of Pensions to the Pension Examining Board on which he would serve until retirement, except for a four-year period in the '80s when the Commissioner was a Democrat. As a former Regimental Surgeon, his qualifications were well established. There was only one problem:

West Union Iowa, Sept. 25th 1862
Genl Baker
Sir,
I should be pleased to know how, when & where I am to get my pay for services as examining Surgeon. R.A. Richardson, the Commissioner, also desires me to ask the same questions for him. My Post office address is Fayette Iowa.
Respectfully,
C.C. Parker, M.D.
Mr. Richardson's address is West Union

In October, Charles saw his good friend Daniel Vines elected President of the school board. His medical partner, Dixon Alexander, and his old friend Alex Winston, were also elected to the board. Charles was pleased that such capable people were involved in community education, even though Danny and Charley would have all of their schooling in the Academy. Danny would later say that he learned to read in Upper Iowa University.

In late November, Charles received an urgent summons to the Alexander house in Westfield. The Colonel was down with a very high fever. It did not look good.

"What happened?" asked Charles, as his old friend lay suffering.

"I was out huntin' bobcat," said the Colonel, in a weak voice. "I must've caught something else."

"I did get the bobcat though," he added, with a smile. "Carried it home on my shoulders. It's out back. You can have the pelt for your trouble."

Charles figured the Colonel had over-exerted himself lugging the heavy creature over hill and dale, and caught a cold. The cold seemed to be developing into winter fever. Charles was deeply saddened to see such a strong and vibrant man in such a weakened condition.

For three days, the Colonel drifted in and out of consciousness. And, for three days Charles was by his side attending him. He longed to tell the Colonel to take greater care in his advanced age, but that would be like telling a bear to be less furry and ferocious. It would not matter anyway.

In his last episode of consciousness, the Colonel,

who must have realized that he was dying, tried to comfort everyone else. "What more can a man ask?" he said. "I am surrounded by all that should accompany old age—honor, love, obedience, troops of friends."

On November 29th of 1862, Colonel Robert Alexander died in his home next to the sawmill that he had carved out of the Iowa wilderness. To the last he was true to his nature as the very essence of the pioneering spirit. He embodied the new American ideal for civic leaders; the social regard bestowed upon him was not obligated by birthright, but inspired by character. The depth of the sadness felt by everyone in the community could not have been greater. They looked upon his legacy—the town of Fayette, and especially the institution of Upper Iowa University—with renewed appreciation and commitment, and took it to be the best sort of memorial to the greatest man any of them had ever known personally.

Elizabeth spoke barely a word for the next three weeks. It seemed at times as though she did not understand that he was gone, only that he was away. Charles began to worry about her. Her daughters looked after her, but they were at a loss to offer her much comfort. She had never before seemed so vulnerable. The Christmas season reminded her of her late husband's recent conversion, and that all of this was God's will. With renewed spirit, she determined to carry on the work that he had begun.

Charles, too, felt a deep sense of personal loss. He had not appreciated the extent to which the Colonel contributed to his own sense of well-being. The tough old frontiersman could be counted on for virtually any form of succor. His word was gold, and his heart was true. He was, thought Charles, a man whose good will was worth more than money in the bank. That is what he would miss most of all; the Colonel was one of his most sincere admirers. The true-hearted respect that the Colonel never shied from expressing, augmented by the shear character of the man, was the most important factor in the decision to come and to stay in Fayette. It just would not be the same without him.

Sarah was sad for the Alexanders and for Charles, but she was preoccupied with her own condition of expectant motherhood. The two boys were more than a handful for her, and mothering was made more difficult by the winter and spring seasons. There always seemed to be an increase in the number of infirmed during that time, so Charles was away more frequently to attend them. He was home, however, to deliver his first daughter. On April 27th of 1863, Sarah Priscilla Parker was born.

A month later, word came that Will and Carrie had their first child and named her Mabel. Carrie had returned to Clermont County, Ohio some months previous, having found the life of a legislator's wife in Iowa City unsuitable for an expectant mother. Will joined her for the event, and they soon departed Ohio for Fayette. Carrie had secured a position teaching art in the university beginning in September.

It was a hot and muggy day in August when Sarah opened the front door to see her youngest brother standing proudly in his First Lieutenant's uniform. He did not look so young any more. Jimmy was on a twenty-day leave, and intended to use it all to rest. His health had been less than perfect, and had been one reason he used to request the leave.

Charles was delighted to see his brother-in-law in reasonably good health, and all grown up. Jimmy was twenty-five now, and seemed to have aged significantly since they last saw each other at Pittsburg Landing. Charles noticed that Jimmy's former youthful vigor and optimism were conspicuously absent. He was more quiet and reserved now. It was understandable.

For the past few weeks, Jimmy had been serving on detached service as an *aide de camp* to General T.K. Smith of the 1st Brigade of Division 17 Army Corps of the Red River Expedition. It was a political job, but he was happy to be mostly away from the fighting. Jimmy had had considerable trouble getting officially promoted. He had received his commission from Governor Kirkwood back in September of 1862, but the Army did not muster him at that rank until months later, about the same time he was ordered to General Smith's Headquarters. It took an affidavit from Aaron Brown, now Colonel of the 3rd Iowa Regiment. It was a paperwork nightmare, and Charles was reminded of what he liked least about the Army.

Twenty days was all too short, and Jimmy was reluctantly on his way. Charles and Sarah wished him well, and Jimmy promised with a decided certainty that he would leave the Army when his enlistment expired the following year.

When Jimmy's enlistment was up, he was mustered out of the 3rd Iowa as 1st Lieutenant on June 18th of 1864. Having been the second man in Fayette County, after Jacob Abernethy, to sign up for the war, and having been in some of the toughest spots in some of the toughest battles, he had had enough.

Jimmy Lakin left Fayette an idealistic young man in his second year of college. When he returned to Fayette, he was a battle-hardened veteran. Like so many young men, he was changed by all that he had seen. He was still good-natured, but there was an enigmatic edge to his character. Men he had known and loved, men who should be enjoying the best parts of their lives were now dead. Friends with whom he joked and laughed had been torn apart by rifle shot and blown to pieces by exploding shells in front of his eyes. He had heard their cries and groans as the balls thudded into their bodies. He had felt the puffs of air and heard the buzzing of Minié balls intended for him by young men just like himself who otherwise might also have been friends. He knew that these young men failed in their endeavors to kill him only because of a miscalculation of distance or trajectory, or because of an indiscriminant twitch of the body, or just simply because of a gust of wind or an unanticipated twig or leaf.

Upon meeting him, a stranger would sense that this was a serious man with a low tolerance for fluff and nonsense. Come to the point, and do it honestly. His eyes, brought fully to bear upon you, spoke his mind; life is too short to waste on foolishness. Don't squander my time and energy with frivolity. The name "Jimmy" did not seem to suit him any more, so most people took to calling him just Jim.

Jim moved back in with Charles and Sarah, though it was soon obvious that the little house on Washington Street would not hold three adults and three children for long. There was some discussion of his returning to his studies in the university, but that did not hold the appeal for him that it once had. Jim was confident that he could make his way in the world without further study of science and philosophy. Besides, considering that the students of his new class were much younger and less mature, he felt out of place. He could no longer relate to the sophomoric antics that the students were pulling from time to time.

In July when Will arrived, he, Charles, and Jim together purchased a plot of hilly farmland north of Fayette. They built a small house for Jim to use while he tended to the affairs of the farm. Jim was anxious to go into business, and Charles always had a dream of owning a big place as his father did. He had bought and sold several properties in Fayette before the war, but he made little money on them. Now, he hoped to build something new.

Since his recent discharge from the army left Jim with no money to speak of, and since Charles had no money because that was his usual state of affairs, Will was obliged to finance the whole venture. Will made it clear that he was not to be relied upon for any heavy responsibility toward running the farm. He had other business to keep him occupied. Jim agreed. Charles would keep his hand in it, but between his commitment to the university and to the growing population in need of medical care, there would be little time.

The farm was set up to feed, graze, dip, and winter sheep. They bought and imported sheep and lost money doing it, but it satisfied Charles's need to be involved in building something, and it gave Jim something to do for the present.

The difficulty in caring for sheep was complicated by the amount of time and effort required to fit them out for the region. The 1860s saw increased interest in sheep in Fayette County. The sheep that were brought in from other states usually had pelter. They lost their front teeth, and they were covered with ticks. Most of them also had a contagious skin disease called "the scab" that was caused by mites and resulted in the loss of large splotches of wool. Those who were successful with sheep had to raise tobacco also. They would make a potion with the tobacco, and dip the sheep in it. By killing the old sheep, and those which lost their teeth, for mutton, and by treating the young ones that were left with tobacco, a period of three or four years would yield a flock of twenty-five or thirty good, healthy sheep. It was a business strictly for the patient and for the highly determined.

As the sheep business progressed, or not, (depending upon the objectivity of the observer) Charles proceeded to plan a larger house. The children were growing, and the house on Washington Street was becoming exceedingly cramped. Building on the farm was a thought, but there were no ideally suited spots for a large house. Still, he could plan anyway.

Before a move could be undertaken, something must be resolved about the clinic. When they were settled in the new house, Charles would need to vacate the clinic in the rear of the house on Washington. It was less than satisfactory as a clinic and he desired to sell the property. His old friend, H.B. Budlong, suggested that a nice new clinic he would build on a vacant lot he owned on Main Street between State and Clark would be just the thing. It would be centrally located, and it would adorn the downtown area nicely. Accordingly, Budlong had a handsome one-story brick building with a full basement constructed to Charles's specifications. Centered near the top of the façade, above the two front windows, a limestone block with the name "Parker" carved elegantly upon it was placed. Budlong, knowing first-hand the kindness that Charles extended to people in need when they could not afford to pay, charged a very moderate rent for the facility. It was a much-appreciated contribution to the community.

Late that summer, word came that Lieutenant Colonel Jacob Abernethy had been killed in the fight for Atlanta on July 21st. Jacob had been the first student from Upper Iowa University to sign up for the war. Even though he was one of Jim's rivals for promotion from his old outfit, Jim was shocked by this news and remained in poor spirits for some time. It was not just a matter of losing a friend. Jim was troubled by guilt at having quit the war before its conclusion. The compulsion to stick it out had imposed itself upon him when his enlistment was up, but he shook it off. Others, like Jacob, re-enlisted to see the thing through. Jim was alive, and Jacob wasn't.

That fall, Jason Paine returned from his missionary work in the Dakotas to accept a ministerial position in the Upper Iowa Conference. He was also invited to teach ancient languages in Upper Iowa University. His status as the first and most available alum—John Clough was doing missionary work in India—prompted the extension of an invitation to join the Board of Trustees. It was a position he would hold for the next thirty years.

In February of 1865, Will, Jim, and Charles bought another plot of land, adjoining the first, north of the Fayette bridge and east of Lima Road from UIU President William Brush. On this land, they built a house large enough to accommodate everyone. It was a farm, even though it was barely a stone's throw from downtown Fayette. From the lot, Charles could see his house on Washington Street, but still the new place was in a nice rural setting.

Will and Carrie had their primary home in West Union, where Will did a good portion of his business, but Carrie would stay in the Parker place when she was teaching art courses in the university.

As the new clinic was nearing completion in early 1865, Dixon Alexander accepted a commission as Regimental Surgeon of the 16th Iowa Volunteer Infantry. Charles did his best to warn his partner of what was in store for him, but Dixon would not be dissuaded. It was a matter of honor, he said. And, furthermore, several close friends had answered the call and would need looking after. The fall of Atlanta and Sherman's march to the sea were encouraging developments.

Charles understood, and he felt a bit guilty that he did not rejoin the 12th when the university recruits were released from imprisonment and the regiment was reformed. His health had improved to the point where it would have been possible. Even though he was serving his country as Pension Examiner for the whole of Fayette County, he might have done more. Privately, he wondered if this accursed war would ever end.

The answer to that question was not long in

coming. On April 9th of 1865, Robert E. Lee officially surrendered at Appomattox Courthouse. Word of the surrender reached the telegraph office in Fayette late in the day, and by morning, everyone had heard and the university bell was chiming the victory.

There was celebration in the streets such as had never been seen in Fayette. Grown men wept with joy and relief. While the fighting had not reached this part of the frontier, the grief and despair of the war had.

The celebration was just winding down when the same telegraph line that had brought the best news of the war now brought the worst. On April 15th, President Lincoln died of an assassin's bullet. The sorrow of the news was deepened by its contrast with the euphoria so recently experienced at the war's end. The same grown men wept yet again, but now for a much different reason. For the remainder of their lives, most people could tell you where they were and what they were doing when they first heard the news.

Charles and Sarah, like most other people, went about their business in a mechanical, deliberate, and detached sort of way. They could not help remembering the eager lawyer from Springfield who was so odd, and so extraordinary. They could not help but to reflect on his presidential accomplishment, and how profound and difficult it actually was. It was a very sad affair.

Jim was more affected than most. He had often entertained his friends and comrades with his first-hand account of the brilliant Mr. Lincoln in the courtroom. Jim understood before most others did just what sort of genius Abraham Lincoln brought to the nearly unimaginable task of keeping the union together. It was his personal connection with the President that inspired his active participation in the war and his optimism about its outcome. Now, he could find no ground for optimism.

By June, the shock of the President's assassination had not worn off, but it had been superseded by the pressing demands of everyday life. People carried on because there was really no other choice. In Iowa, most people would be spared the painful injustices of the reconstruction, and would be removed from the debates in Washington between President Johnson and his cabinet, which was punctuated by the constant bickering on Capitol Hill.

Charles received routine assignments for his services as Pension Examiner, so accordingly, on June 14th of 1865 in his brand new clinic, Charles examined Ole Iverson, a wounded veteran applying for a pension.

Ole was a weathered, gaunt looking Nordic man of thirty-seven years, about five and a half feet in height with light brown hair and blue eyes.

"When did you enlist?" asked Charles, making notes for his own records.

"I enlist on the 27th of January in the year eighteen and sixty-two," said Ole, in a heavy Norwegian accent. "It was in Company H of the 15th Wisconsin Volunteer Infantry that I serve. We call ourselves 'St. Olaf's Rifles', an' we brought glory to the Union."

Charles looked up from the notes he was taking. "You are living in Iowa?" he asked, gently.

"I live in Marion when Cap'n Simes recruit me," Ole said, blinking his eyes. "I'm from Clayton County."

"Ah, yes," said Charles, as he returned to his notes. "What is your occupation?"

Ole looked at Charles vacantly, as though he should already know the answer to that question. "I'm a farmer, of course," he finally said.

"Tell me about your service," said Charles.

"Well," Ole began, somewhat impatiently, again expecting that someone learned like Charles should already know these things, "we were mustered in at Madison, and we spend a lot of time building forts. They send us down to Island Number Ten, and that's when I get sick the first time. I had the dysentery. That was for the two months in May and June of eighteen and sixty-two. Then I left there an' I soon got sick again. This time they left me behind in a hospital in Iuka, Mississippi. I stay there about three months. Then, they send me back to my company in Murfreesboro, Tennessee and we go into action at Stone River. I get lost, and I wander around for a few days until I find them again. That's where I get shot, so they put me up in a hospital in Nashville."

"When did you receive your wound?" Charles asked.

"It was on New Year's Eve," said Ole. "That would be on December 31st of eighteen and sixty-two, it was at Stone River. I did not get back to camp until three days later. I spend a lot of time in the Convalescent Camp there in Murfreesboro. They finally put me in the Invalid Corps in August of eighteen and sixty-three 'cause I can't shoot no more, but that don't do no good. I get sick with the bad cough. They finally put me out of the army on February 9th of eighteen and sixty-four an' I come back to Iowa."

"Yes," said Charles, "very good. Show me your wound."

Ole held out his right arm as far as he could. It was not far. Charles had to hold and manipulate it himself, because Ole could not. Charles unbuttoned Ole's flannel shirt to see what was there. There was considerable damage and scarring. It looked as though the ball had entered the anterior of the forearm, about four inches from the wrist, and exited on the posterior about four inches below the elbow. The bone, and shattered muscles, tendons, and nerves must have deflected it as it went. His hand was nearly and firmly closed, making it almost impossible for him to pick up anything of any weight. His entire arm was partially paralyzed from the shoulder down, and the soft, cool flesh indicated that circulation was severely restricted.

It was not the worst wound Charles had seen, but it qualified as severe. It was amazing how such a small piece of metal could do so much permanent damage in such a short amount of time and space. One inch to either side, and Ole would not need to apply for a pension.

"What sort of treatment did you receive?" asked Charles.

Ole just looked at him blankly, as though it was a trick question.

"Did a surgeon stitch it up?" asked Charles, even though there was no evidence of stitching. He hoped the question would encourage Ole to talk about it.

"He didn't do nothing," said Ole, finally. "He just put a cloth around it an' told me to lie down. He said it will heal up fine, it got no gang green."

"How long," asked Charles, afraid to hear the answer, "after you were shot did you see the doctor?"

"'Bout three days," said Ole. "I got lost, an' had

to watch out for rebs, so I hide out."

No wonder it was so badly damaged. It was obvious that the bone had been shattered and had not healed well. The surgeon could have arranged the fragments of the bone in better order and treated the skin if he had seen it sooner. Charles examined the wound closely. Ole's use of it would always be very limited. Satisfied that he understood the nature of the wound, Charles turned his attention to Ole's labored breathing.

"How long have you had trouble breathing?" Charles asked.

"I got the bad cough when we was in Murfreesboro," Ole answered, matter-of-factly.

"You did not have any cough before that?" asked Charles.

"Nope."

"Does it bother you when you are working?" asked Charles.

"I can't work good," said Ole. "I try, but, I can't work."

After the examination, Charles sat to fill out the standard form that required filling in blanks, beginning with the date.

Examining Surgeon's Certificate
Fayette Iowa June 14th *1865*

I hereby certify, That I have carefully examined
Ole Iverson, *late a* Private in Company H. of the 15th
Regt. of Wisconsin Volunteers (Inf.). *in the service of the*
United States, who was discharged at Murphreesborough
on the 9th *day of* February, *1864, and is an applicant for*
an invalid pension, by reason of alleged disability
resulting from Phthisis Pulmonalis & gun shot wound.
In my opinion the said Ole Iverson *is* three fourths
incapacitated for obtaining his subsistence by manual
labor from the cause above stated.

Judging from his present condition, and from the
evidence before me, it is my belief that the said disability
originated *in the service aforesaid in the line of duty.*

The disability is permanent.

A more particular description of the applicant's
condition is subjoined:
Private Iverson has incipient phthisis - says he was well
previous to enlistment. On this point, I have no other
evidence.

Private Ole Iverson received a wound at the battle of
Murphreesborough, on the last day of December 1862
while in the line of duty. Said wound is caused by a
musket ball which passed through the right fore arm
greatly lacerating the flexor & extensor muscles &
fracturing the ulna. Flexion & extension of the fingers
and thumb are nearly destroyed as also rotation of the
fore arm.

C.C. Parker, M.D.
Examining Surgeon

"There," said Charles, "You should have no trouble getting your pension now."

"That is very good doctor," said Ole, "Thank you very much."

Charles then turned his attention to the second form.

Examining Surgeon's Receipt
Fayette Iowa June 14th *1865*

Received of <u>Ole Iverson</u>, *late a* <u>Private in Company H.</u> <u>15th Regt Wis. Vol. Inf.</u> *in the service of the United States, the sum of one dollar and fifty cents, being the fee authorized by law for an examination which I have this day made of the said* <u>Ole Iverson</u>, *as an applicant for an invalid pension.*

<u>C.C. Parker, M.D.</u>
Examining Surgeon.

"Are you sure you can afford to pay all of this now?" Charles asked, as he handed the receipt to Ole.

"Sure," said Ole, tentatively, "I can give you the money now."

Charles was skeptical, but he decided to accept the payment. Ole left and mounted his plough horse to take the long ride back to Marion. Charles wished him well knowing it would not be easy for him.

In July of the following summer, The Fayette County Board of Supervisors was obliged to hold a special meeting to take quick and decisive action. Responding to pleas from farmers to do something, the Board had two months previous ordered that a bounty of twenty-five cents should be paid for every gopher scalp presented to the Supervisor of the township in which the gopher was caught. Every farm boy and many of those from town as well, turned his endeavors to catching gophers. Some were even turning in scalps that were mysteriously missing the ears. Some Town Supervisors were only paying for whole heads. Now the Board was obliged to repeal the order. It seemed that the townships were running out of funds.

Also that summer, the personal tragedy of a good friend imposed itself on the Parkers. Jason Paine was stricken with total blindness while ministering in Cedar County. He moved back to Fayette, to his small residence in town. His wife took on the responsibility of his care, but he relied heavily upon Charles to assist him in adjusting to his unexpected and tragic condition. Charles spent a good deal of time in conversation with his old friend, and the Paines were frequent guests in the Parker home.

There were some in town—those who had an interest in liquor—who tried to suggest that this affliction was divine retribution, presumably for Jason's active campaign against drinking. But if townspeople took those rumors seriously, they did not say so.

In October, Charles found himself examining Ole Iverson again.

"How have things been going?" Charles asked, as he took Ole's arm to examine it.

"Not so good," said Ole, with a hoarse cough. "They still have not got me my pension."

Charles examined Ole's chest, and determined that he had not improved since the last time he was in for an examination. It was clear that Ole could not work to support himself, and that must be reflected in the report.

Examining Surgeon's Certificate
Fayette Iowa Oct 9th *1865*

I hereby certify, That I have carefully examined Ole Iverson, *late a* Private in Co H. of the 15th Regt. of Wis. Inf Vols *in the service of the United States, who was discharged at* Murphreesborough *on the* 9th *day of* February, *1864, and is an applicant for an invalid pension, by reason of alleged disability resulting from* gun shot wound.

In my opinion the said Ole Iverson *is* one half *incapacitated for obtaining his subsistence by manual labor from the cause above stated.*

Judging from his present condition, and from the evidence before me, it is my belief that the said disability originated *in the service aforesaid in the line of duty.*

The disability is permanent.

A more particular description of the applicant's condition is subjoined:

Priv't Ole Iverson was wounded at the battle of Murphreesborough, Tenn. by musket ball passing through the right arm fracturing the ulna, some fragments of which came out. Flexion & rotation of the hand are very imperfect and somewhat painful. The wound is healed.

In addition to his wound, Ole Iverson has decided dullness of the upper portion of the left lung, slightly hurried respiration - and cough. Pulse about 100 per minute at this examination. His condition is about the same as one year ago. The condition of his lung increases his disability in my opinion about one fourth.

C.C. Parker, M.D.
Examining Surgeon

Again, Ole was on his way, and again Charles wished him well.

Charles had little time to wonder about Ole, or about any of the other veterans he saw on a regular basis. On October 29, 1865, Caroline Ritchey Parker was born. The Parker family was now rounded out nicely with two boys and two girls. Of course, the two boys were old enough to help with the chores, which included taking care of their sisters when their homework was finished.

Will was elected again to state legislature, this time to the Senate, for the 1866-67 term. He was becoming more successful in his business ventures and real estate transactions, and was widely respected throughout the region for his honesty and skill at negotiation. In July of 1866, Corwin Thompson Lakin was born to Will and Carrie, complicating the logistics of Will's term. Carrie lived in the Parker house when Will was in Iowa City. The two Lakin children along with the four Parker children made for a lively household.

In April of 1867, Will ventured back into one of his rare business failures. He and his partner, Wood, assumed the ownership of the *Fayette Public Record* from O.C. Cole. Will Lakin had originally acquired the paper from Rev. Brush, and named it the *North Iowa Observer*. It was near death from neglect when Cole took over. By fall though, Will had had enough of the newspaper business. The paper finally died, but was resurrected a third time by Daniel Vines, who named it the *Fayette Journal*.

The newspaper business was difficult in Fayette not only because businesses did not need to advertise— everyone knew them—but also because nothing newsworthy could make it into print before everyone had already heard about it.

One newsworthy item of 1867 that was cause for celebration in more than one quarter was Upper Iowa University's resolution of its debt. The manner in which the funds were raised was an indicator of the changing times.

More than over slavery, the Civil War was fought over a changing social system. The south clung to the class structure of the feudal era, with its refined aristocracy and its need for cheap, easily controlled labor to farm the fields and to do the work. The slaves represented an indentured peasant class over which lords and masters could rule, and from whom subjugation could be enforced.

However, by the mid-nineteenth century, slaves were not cheap, certainly not as cheap as peasants were to the kings and queens of Europe. The rulers of Europe had leverage; they could reward their favorites and impose punishment and death upon those who defied them. The aristocratic plantation owners of the southern United States had no such luxury. Killing slaves was literally throwing money away. In fact, any form of severe punishment that disabled a slave, even temporarily, required careful consideration.

American aristocrats' prospect for a peasant class was all but eliminated, intentionally, by the Constitution of the United States. Ironically, it was the industrial technology of the north in the form of the cotton gin that allowed for slavery to be maintained economically.

Unlike any ruling class before it, the founding fathers of the United States, in the creation of their new government, outlawed the form of indentured servitude that gave the aristocracy its power. It was this form of servitude that brought many Europeans to America in the first place. Many immigrants used indenture as a means to finance the journey, and once their indenture was satisfied, they were determined to die rather than return to that way of life. This determination, dubbed the American Spirit, was what fueled the American Revolution, and it was to this particular issue that the Declaration of Independence was addressed.

Still, aristocrats such as Washington and Jefferson, were not entirely prepared to let go of their station in life and the slaves from Africa allowed them to retain the illusion that they supported freedom for all men. To them, Africans were not exactly men.

Less than one hundred years after its first experiments with the new mechanisms of industry, the north was embracing a new order. Production efficiencies and advances in technology were stabilizing the food supply, which reduced the number of farmers needed to maintain it. Smaller, less efficient family farms saw their children seeking employment in the manufacturing centers in New York, Massachusetts, Connecticut, and in other northern states. These young, single workers lived sparing lives in boarding houses so that they might send their extra income back home.

Slaves were not needed for factories because there was plenty of cheap labor available from willing workers. Free black men were as welcome to provide cheap labor as any other man. Business owners were relieved of the requirement to invest capital in their cheap labor, and they could be lords and masters over all of their employees, regardless of their ethnic origin, without enduring the stigma of slavery. The death or departure of a worker provided no more inconvenience or expense than hiring a new one. Business owners were becoming the new aristocracy, with the distinctive American twist that it was an aristocracy defined more by business knowledge and gumption than by birthright. The Civil War was fought primarily over what would define an aristocrat—ownership of land and family connections, or knowledge of economics and skill at commerce. The winner would rule the land, and business became the foundation of the new order.

Business opportunities were materializing for people who would otherwise be the poor, rural denizens of the lowest feudal class. More and more individuals were realizing new possibilities and advancing their own standing by working in the factories. People would now work hard willingly to exercise their opportunities and to obtain their share of industrial output.

The Civil War had redefined the country. What had been a loose agglomeration of states and territories was now a single nation with a unified vision of the future. Men returning to their homes, both north and south, now knew their country intimately. They had fought in its farms and fields; they had seen its mountains and rivers; they had trodden its roads. They now knew that their country was more than just an abstract idea. The frontier represented by Illinois, Iowa, Wisconsin, Missouri, Kansas, Texas, and California was now the western franchise of the new civilization. This new civilization was nourished by business, and it was obvious to many that the road to business success was paved with education.

In the fall of 1867, twenty-four-year-old Henry Hurd opened Hurd's National Business College on the Upper Iowa University campus. Applying capitalist economics to business enterprise was the latest fad. Like many other business schools sprouting up around the country, Hurd's school was affiliated with a traditional liberal arts college. The traditional schools were more than happy to share the revenues from the new area of study, and like Upper Iowa were seeing their debts resolved.

Hurd's program was called the Mutual System Business Training. Simulated businesses were set up for students to run. They hired staff, managed accounts, ordered stock, managed inventories, and developed promotions. Initially, students began by managing a small business, usually a store. When they had learned the basics, they graduated to railroads and shipping companies. Eventually, they became proficient in running a commercial bank. In three to six months, depending on the skills and abilities of the individual, students graduated with a certificate of Master of Accounting.

The fall of 1867 saw another innovation in Upper Iowa University. Dr. Brush installed changes in the curriculum that would prove to be popular with students, who were beginning to look for relevance in education. Electives were offered for the first time; students could substitute French, German, Hebrew, or calculus for advanced courses in Latin and Greek for the A.B. degree.

Perhaps it was this modernization of the university that encouraged the citizens of Fayette, or perhaps it was just simple frustration with what most saw as pure injustice. In any case, the movement to bring the county seat to Fayette caught fire again. On October 8th of 1867, after much politicking, a general election was held to decide the issue. The maneuvering undertaken to bring the question to a vote would have impressed the most cynical of political pundits. On the question whether to remove the County Seat to Fayette from West Union, the vote was 1,360 for removal and 1,715 against removal. They lost again.

In the big, new Parker house, the disappointment over the vote was short lived. In fact, the whole issue was very much in the background. On February 11th of 1868, James Donaldson Parker, the last of Charles and Sarah's children, was born, bringing the family to three boys and two girls. Charles often sat in the parlor of his grand home, surrounded by noisy, active children, gazing across the room at his loving wife, and reflected on the depth of his blessings. He could not have been happier.

In March, Joseph E. Boyce bought the house on Washington Street, and infused the Parker household with some much-needed cash.

April and May brought spring showers, and the usual round of disease and illness. Spring was also a time when there was an increase in farm accidents. One unusual accident issued a call that brought Charles, Dixon Alexander, and J.A. Aldrich from Fayette, and Drs. Armstrong and Robertson from West Union to Wadena. A local resident had been cleaning his rifle when it discharged while his arm was over the muzzle. To five Civil War surgeons, the remedy was obvious— amputate the arm at the shoulder.

After the patient was put to bed, the five surgeons went to the hotel to get a bite to eat. It was then that they discussed the possibility of organizing a medical society in Fayette County. Drs. Parker & Robertson were enlisted to prepare the by-laws and regulations. All the physicians in the county were invited to a meeting in December. Charles was elected first President of the Board of Officers.

At the end of the school year that May, Carrie relinquished her position teaching art in the university. The demands of mothering young children, coupled with the need for her husband to spend most of his time at their home in West Union, proved to be too much of a distraction for her. Many students and faculty alike were very disappointed. She left promising that when her children were older, she would return.

Shortly thereafter, Carrie's younger sister, Sarah Thompson, came out to Iowa from Ohio to visit and to help with the children while Will was away. Sarah was known by the nickname Sallie, because there were too many Sarahs in the family to keep track of all of them. Sallie had been teaching school in Cincinnati, and was well suited to childcare, but her family suspected that there might be another reason for her interest in helping out.

Sallie had always shown a fondness for a certain young man six years her senior, whom she remembered from her youth. This certain gentleman left Ohio when she was only fourteen, and much too young to make her wishes known. Besides, he had not indicated any particular interest in her. But now, she would have plenty of opportunities to see if she could attract his attention.

He came to West Union often to visit his brother. Accordingly, Sallie would see him every time she accompanied her sister to Fayette to visit their in-laws, the Parkers.

If there was a strong desire for Carrie Lakin to remain on the faculty of UIU, there was a growing consensus calling for President Brush to leave. Thinking the students needed more discipline than the current president was enforcing, a faction of the board called for Dr. Brush to resign. The whole business reeked of unsavory politics. Because the school owed him more than eleven hundred dollars in back pay, he refused to resign. The forces seeking to oust him did not have enough support to force the issue.

In January of 1869, Jason Paine was appointed County judge and ex-officio auditor. He gave the appointment a gallant effort, but his continued blindness proved to be an insurmountable problem. He resigned his position as judge in October.

In June of that year, Dr. Brush resigned formally, and Professor Charles N. Stowers was appointed as his replacement. President Stowers fulfilled the board's expectations as a harsh disciplinarian, but he managed to alienate the students and many members of the faculty. The following year President Stowers asked to be reinstated to the faculty, and the presidency passed to Professor Byron M. McLain who would serve in an acting capacity for two years.

At a reunion of the 3rd Iowa Infantry Volunteers in August of 1869, Colonel Aaron Brown, the former town doctor who had since distinguished himself as commander of the regiment, proposed a drive to erect a monument. Jim Lakin took an active role on that committee as Treasurer. Almost as soon as the committee was officially organized, the effort was abandoned. The committee remained in existence, though, more out of optimism than out of any progress toward their goal. By 1878, Jim had some money on account, but nothing on which to spend it.

For Charles, the routine of his work had the effect that it tends to have on everyone. That is, the days of this latter portion of his life blended together as the swirls of a marble cake flow through its whole. There were a few notable activities and events that punctuated the continuity, but there was little to convey the reality of a ceaseless passage of time. It had been nearly five years since the close of the war and fourteen years since Charles first came to this county.

The sole evidence of progress was the growth of the children. The older boys were well on their way to becoming young men. The youngest children had a way of keeping their parents active and consumed with their care. Parents of young children have precious little occasion to notice time's passage. A parent awakens periodically to the realization that time is fleeting, but soon that realization becomes enshrouded again in the routine of living.

It was not quite tedium that Charles experienced. One must not think of a rich and rewarding life as tedious. Much of his impulse to remove himself from the familiar and strike out in search of adventure had faded, replaced by contentment with his present condition, and by a relatively aggressive campaign of exploration in the territory surrounding Fayette. In his travels, he was able to explore quite a bit, and to collect a large variety of wild plants. These he delighted in carefully uprooting and bringing back for his garden.

It was more of an over familiarity brought on by sameness that imposed itself upon him, and encouraged him to look for creative ways to engage his boundless energy. The same places, the same people, the same state of existence all blended into the marbling of his life. To think of it as tedious would be to forget the sort of horrific circumstances that can distinguish excitement from tedium. It did not require much effort to recall a form of excitement that he could well do without. In view of memories that still haunted both his conscious moments and his dreams, it was a welcome sameness indeed. The insidious onslaught of age was tempered by the consummation of comfort and happiness, and he did not wish it otherwise. But nothing good lasts forever.

In early February, after a particularly harsh day of winter and a particularly difficult day of treating the infirmed, Charles returned home late to find Sarah deeply distressed. Their oldest daughter, Sarah Priscilla, had been down with a cold, but was now suddenly and gravely ill.

Charles was not overly concerned at first. Anytime the children were sick, Sarah experienced trepidation. It was to be expected, considering the manner in which their first child had died. She had never really recovered from that. Charles tried to calm her fears, and his quiet confidence helped to restore her peace of mind.

A quick examination, however, served to unsettle Charles. Sarah Priscilla appeared to have pneumonia, also called winter fever, and she was failing rapidly. He did his best not to alarm Sarah, but she sensed his concern, and it induced in her a terrible foreboding. For the next few days, Sarah Priscilla was constantly attended by one or both of her anxious parents. But, they were helpless to prevent the inevitable.

On February 8th of the year 1870, Sarah Priscilla Parker died before reaching her seventh birthday. It would be a challenge to the most expressive of artists to characterize the depth of the anguish that hung over the Parker household. The entire community shared in its severity. It was an enormous loss, and everyone felt it.

Charles was devastated. Sarah Priscilla was his princess, and he had delighted in discovering those thousand little things that she had in common with her mother. She would have grown up to be the best of women. It was a tragedy beyond description.

Still, Charles was accustomed to tribulation, and was prepared to cope with it. He soothed his aching heart with intensified affections for Sarah, and with his concern for her needs. By now, it was his habit to escape his troubles by providing service for others. It was a strategy that worked very well for him.

From the outset, Sarah had prepared herself for the worst. She had been through this before, and she determined to be steadfast to the last. After their son had died so tragically, she and Charles forged into the wilderness to build a new life, together and alone. But this time such a dramatic reconstruction was not possible. She tried to push herself through it, but it was a hopeless endeavor; strong as she was, she could not endure under her present condition using only self-reliance. She would not think to ask for help, but it happened that she did not need to do so.

The outpouring of sentiment from the community surprised her, and provided a form of support she had not previously known. She never presumed to be important enough to be the object of anyone's attention but Charles's, and it had never occurred to her that she was present in anyone else's thoughts. The sincere empathy from other mothers who knew intimately the same anguish helped her to inure.

Having already lost a child, Sarah knew that she could get through it. She knew she had the strength to accept what God has decided and to carry out His work as He indicated. Besides, she knew unequivocally that she could count on the love and emotional support that Charles provided. She was at least prepared to cope with the grief. Now, with the support of a community of friends, she would conquer this.

The responsibility of caring for four other children, ranging in age from two to thirteen, complicated the issue. On one hand, they distracted Sarah from her sorrows, and prevented any sustained contemplation of her loss. In caring for them, she could lose herself, and almost forget what had happened. On the other hand, attending to her children's needs interfered with the resolution of her grief.

Though Sarah preferred to immerse herself in the care of her children, she was thwarted in that endeavor by a conspiracy of her relatives. Charles, whose own grief was tempered somewhat by war memories which were monstrous in comparison, had the presence of mind to arrange with Will and Carrie to allow Carrie's sister,

Sallie, to stay in the Parker house and help with the children.

It had originally been Sallie's offer to do so. Besides providing help for Sarah, her object was to be in closer proximity to a certain gentleman, with whom she was now deeply infatuated. Her fond memories of him as a young man in Ohio had been strengthened in the past few months by their frequent encounters. She had come to know him as the excellent man he was. It was obvious to all that the affection was reciprocated, and no one was surprised when, on April 19th, Jim Lakin and Sarah "Sallie" Abigail Thompson were married. It was a particularly poignant event, and the prospect of such a union between two lovely and illustrious people did a great deal to heal the wounds so recently afflicted.

Frederick Lakin was born to Will and Carrie later that year, and Jason Paine, still looking to make his life useful, was appointed to the position of county auditor by the Board of Supervisors when that office was first created. He would serve in that capacity, and later as Superintendent of Schools.

As a blend of felicity and despair, the flow of life persisted. Those who had been here a long time knew that blessings must be enjoyed as they were bestowed, because it was only a matter of time before the next calamity. Following that calamity would be further blessings.

One such calamity befell the institution of Upper Iowa University on October 2nd. James A. Doremus, a student, committed suicide. He was found early in the morning in the student's hall of Lamb's Hotel sitting slumped over at a table with a revolver by his side. James had been studying bookkeeping under Professor Hurd. In fact, it was determined that the professor had walked by the deceased student at least once without noticing; he was apparently one of several people to do so.

James was rumored to have spent all of his money keeping some number of wild women satisfied, and that the women had left him when the money was gone. Beside James, on the table, was a note chiding his mother for not giving him more money. It was all a great scandal, and it cast a pall on the institution for the remainder of the school year.

In the summer of 1871, Frank Calhoun Lakin came from Cincinnati to live with his Uncle Jim and Aunt Sallie in Fayette, and to attend Upper Iowa University. Frank was the son of Jim and Sarah's older brother, John, who had died ten years earlier while on a business trip to San Francisco. Frank's mother, Celeste, raised him well, but was now seeking help in completing his education. Now that Jim was married and settled on his farm, he offered to keep the boy. Frank would help his Uncle with the family businesses as well as attend school in the fall.

Acting President Byron McLain asked for a sabbatical in June of 1872 to conduct his research in Palestine. The board granted his leave and replaced him as president with Roderick Norton, Minister of the Fayette Methodist Episcopal congregation. Acting President Norton faced severe financial difficulties, and was forced to take some extreme measures to balance the budget. Most faculty did not receive their pay. Three faculty members were hired that year with the stipulation that the university was not to be held responsible for paying them.

Enrollment had dropped to the point where few students came from outside of Fayette County. So many electives had been added to the curriculum that Upper Iowa University became the first college in Iowa to grant degrees to students who had no courses in Greek. The beautiful hills and valleys that made Fayette attractive to its founders now proved to be a substantial barrier to railroads. The potential for profits did not exceed the cost of building the lines. Fayette was not developing according to the grand scheme envisioned by Colonel Alexander. The limits of available transportation discouraged outside students.

Professor McLain returned from his sabbatical, but declined to accept the presidency. It fell to a young science professor who was ill-prepared for the task. To Charles, and to many others, it appeared that the university would not endure long. It was a sad affair, but most considered it inevitable.

Charles soon had added responsibilities to distract him. On July 10th of 1872, he was appointed to Board of Trustees of Iowa Hospital for the Insane at Independence. Construction of a magnificent facility had begun nearly four years previous, and it was near completion. The level of care was to be the best anywhere. Charles would serve a term of four years, until he was replaced by an appointee of a Democratic administration. The board he joined was charged with the task of organizing the institution. They elected officers and governed the implementation of policies and procedures they created, helping to bring the facility into effective operation.

The same year that Charles was pressed into the service of the State Hospital, Jim was appointed to the staff of Governor Carpenter. He served as the Governor's aide in Fayette County until 1876, when he was obliged to devote more time to his business ventures.

In September of 1872, Jim's company, Burch, Lakin & Co. took a contract for grading a railroad bed from Fayette to Cresco. They worked hard for a year, and completed most of the grade, but financial pressures forced the railroad to abandon the project. They worked until the fall of 1873, even though they had not been paid since the previous May. The financial panic of October killed any hope of the railroad renewing its interest. There was simply not enough potential to warrant the investment. It was yet another disappointment in Fayette's quest for growth and development, and more than one business owner packed up and moved west because of it.

If the disappointment over the railroad's abandonment of the region was not enough, dejection was heaped upon Fayette residents in the form of another near miss. At nearly the same instant Jim's company took the contract, another event had encouraged optimism among the businessmen of Fayette. On Sunday morning, September 15th of 1872, the courthouse in West Union burned down. Because the citizens of Fayette County had repeatedly declined to appropriate funds for a county jail, a jail room had been improvised in the courthouse. James Thompson, who was awaiting trial for larceny, attempted an escape by enlarging the hole cut for the stovepipe. He enlarged the hole by setting a fire. When the fire burned the hole to sufficient size, he broke through the outside brick wall. Soon, the hole in the six-inch thick wood lining of the room was large enough for him to fit through, and he made his escape. He did not stop to put out the fire, and the building burned to the ground.

Those in favor of removing the county seat to Fayette saw another chance to press the issue, and called for an election. Two years of intense struggle and bitter politics ensued. Finally, the struggle was ended when those who sought to keep the seat in West Union maneuvered a contract to reconstruct the original building before an election could be held. It was now quite clear that Fayette would never enjoy the status, political advantage, and financial benefits accorded the county seat.

Eighteen seventy-three would bring better tidings. After nearly eight years of total blindness, Jason Paine recovered partial sight. Charles knew of similar cases, but was still at a loss to explain what was happening. He worried little about the explanation though, and rejoiced in his friend's recovery. It became much easier for Jason to get around, and to fulfill his duties as County Auditor.

Better tidings were also in store for the university. In June of 1873, John William Bissell was appointed to the presidency. Right away, he had to wrestle with the disarray left from the previous administrations as well as from the ravages of the financial panic. The board sent letters to those who owed money to the institution and to those who had made pledges of contributions. Many simply had nothing to pay. The university was at the lowest ebb in its short history. When Dr. Bissell took the helm, Upper Iowa University had graduated only twenty-three persons and enrollment was down. Things did not look good.

Perhaps it was optimism generated by the appointment of so obviously qualified a president as Dr. Bissell, or perhaps it was just something that was inevitable. The Ladies Professorship Association was incorporated on November 28th, with Mrs. A.N. Ingham as President. Mrs. Ingham was the wife of Rev. Septimus Ingham, Professor of Moral Philosophy and Biblical Literature. Also elected to the Board of the Association as Corresponding Secretary was Abbie Mills, Professor of Painting and Drawing. The LPA was founded in part as a benevolent association intended to receive bequests and donations for the development of the university. More specifically, the Association endeavored to endow a chair to be known as the "Lady Professorship of the Upper Iowa University," the professor to be chosen by a joint action with the Board of Trustees.

There had been talk of a professional association for the development of women, who made up half of the faculty during that era. There was a general feeling among the women that it was time for an official action committee that served women's interests and that brought common sense to the decision process. Following the 1873 Commencement ceremonies, one of the graduates offered a large donation toward the development of such an association. By 1874, the LPA had elected Ella Torbet, a graduate of Baldwin University, to hold the endowed Chair as Professor of Modern Languages and Greek. Miss Torbet would also serve as Preceptress the following year.

An association that would have been unthinkable in many institutions, and impossible—for various reasons—in others, was taken in stride in the Upper Iowa University. Elizabeth Alexander still lived, and was a powerful influence on decision making at all levels. She was regarded by faculty and by administrators as nothing less than the mother of the institution, both figuratively and literally. Her stern guidance was present in virtually every high level administrative meeting. The LPA was an outgrowth of her presence, and if opposition to such an organization existed at all, it was not heard in public.

In addition to sponsoring lectures and academic events, the LPA was a great aid to the president by adding to the endowment. Another effort to add to the endowment and to create a sense of community among graduates was the formation of the "Old Students Association" with Jason Paine as its president. In addition to being the oldest and most prestigious graduate, Jason had become the institutional historian. It was a role he enjoyed immensely.

If these developments were not enough cause for optimism, then there was the biggest of them all. On September 16th, the railroad spur from Manchester to Fayette was finally completed, and saw its first service. To distract attention from the fact that the line went in only one direction out of Fayette, President Bissell made a list of over two hundred destinations that one could choose upon boarding the train. Special trains were arranged to take students directly to Chicago in the spring, and bring them back again in the fall. Finally, it looked as though Fayette was taking on the mantle of a growing city, and prosperity was just around the corner.

Just as the rail line was making preparations for its grand opening, Charles was surprised to see Ole

Iverson in his office again.

"Howdy, Doc," said Ole, clearly not feeling cheery, nor in good health. His breathing was better and the cough was gone, but he looked gaunt.

"Ole!" exclaimed Charles. "How have you been?"

"Not so good," replied Ole. "I come to see about getting more in my pension. I think you are the only one who can help me."

"How long has it been since I last saw you? It must be years."

"I was here last on October 9th of eighteen and sixty-five," said Ole, who was always good with dates. "It has been 'most eight years."

"You still haven't received your pension?" asked Charles, incredulously.

"No, I get my pension," said Ole, "but I come because I try to get more in my pension. It's not enough for me to live an' I can't work."

Ole was not the sort of man to complain. If he said that he had difficulty, you may imagine it ten times worse and still underestimate.

"Have you applied for an increase?" asked Charles.

"Yeah," replied Ole, "I did back in sixty-eight, but they said no. I got to have more. I can't live on what I got now."

"Is this your paperwork?" asked Charles, gesturing to a packet in Ole's left hand."

"Yeah," said Ole, handing the papers to Charles. "This is it."

Charles looked at the documents. The first two were certificates he himself had issued. The third, dated

December 26, 1865, granted the pension of four dollars a month retroactive to February 1864. Then, there was a request from an attorney in Elkader for Ole's discharge papers, an application for an increase in his pension benefit dated November 26, 1867, an Examining Surgeon's Certificate dated December 30, 1867, and a rejection of the application dated March 17, 1868.

Charles sat to read the examiner's certificate. It was written by Dr. Hanna of Elkader, who was well-known to Charles. Dr. Hanna was a competent surgeon, but did not seem to understand bureaucracy, and how to deal with it. His report made sense to another surgeon, but would give the wrong impression to a clerk. Dr. Hanna implied that Ole's disability would improve over time. This impression must have been surmised by the attorney, who then must have asked for a clarification.

On January 28, 1868, Dr. Hanna wrote the following addendum on the bottom of the report: "I admit the incoherence of the above, but time will produce a great change for the good, in his case - yet I am of the opinion that the disability is permanent. I am also of the opinion that he is entitled to more and should draw two dollars per month in addition to what he now does."

No wonder the application was denied. Charles wanted to help Ole, but the rules were strict and he was obligated to portray the situation as it was. There had been a good deal of cheating on disability pensions, and the system had been revised to prevent it. He examined Ole again, and filled out the new form.

Surgeon's Certificate
of
Biennial, Annual, or Semi-annual Examination,
on which the Pensioner draws his Pension.

State: <u>Iowa</u>   *County:* <u>Fayette</u>
          Post Office: <u>Fayette September 8th</u>, *1873*.

<u>I</u> *hereby certify, That* <u>I</u> *have carefully examined* <u>Ole</u>
<u>Iverson</u>, *who was a* <u>Private in Co H. 15th Wis Vols</u> *in the*
war <u>against the Rebellion</u>, *and was granted an Invalid*
Pension under Certificate No. <u>54.528</u> *to be paid now at*
the agency in <u>Marion</u> *by reason of alledged disability*
resulting from <u>Gun Shot wound</u>, *which he states to have*
been received in the line of duty while he was in the
military service of the United States.

In <u>my</u> *opinion the said Pensioner's disability, from the*
cause aforesaid, continues at <u>One half = $4</u>

A more particular description of the Pensioner's
condition is subjoined:

Height, <u>5 6 1/2</u> *; weight,* <u>130</u> *; complexion,* <u>light</u> *; age,*
<u>47</u> *, respiration,* <u>17</u> *; pulse,* <u>100</u>

Shot obliquely through right fore arm fracturing the ulna
& producing unusual laceration of flexor & extensor
muscles resulting in adhesions; which almost entirely
prevent the flexion of the hand.

<u>C.C. Parker</u>
Examining Surgeon.

Charles hoped that the last statement would excite some empathy from the clerks, but he was afraid that is all it would do. He handed the completed form to Ole.

"Will I get more in my pension?" asked Ole, hopefully.

Charles knew that Ole could not read, and so would not know what the report said. He hated to give Ole bad news, but it could not be helped.

"I do not think so," said Charles. "Your problem is that you were only shot in one arm. You would get more if you were shot in both arms."

Ole looked downcast, but he did not say anything. Charles told him that there was no charge for this visit because it was for the same pension as before. Ole looked greatly relieved, and managed a slight smile and a nod before he turned to leave.

Things at the university continued to improve. In 1874, President Bissell reported to board that he had generated enough revenue not only to pay the faculty, but to paint the roof as well. The roof had been leaking and causing great discomfort and inconvenience, which would be corrected with a good painting. University expenses had been covered without borrowing any money and the hope and trust placed in Dr. Bissell was now clearly justified.

In May, Jim and Sallie had their first child. Marie Thompson Lakin was born on the 31st in West Union. Because Jim was so consumed with his work and with recovering from his severe financial losses incurred from the railroad contract, Sallie stayed with her sister for the last few weeks of her pregnancy. Carrie was pregnant herself, and gave birth to Caroline Louise Lakin shortly thereafter. It was a blessed event that just added to the optimistic feeling of the times.

Good news is always accompanied by bad. That August, Priscilla Parker, Charles's mother, died in Cincinnati at age 81. Since the older children were on summer break from their studies in the Academy, and because the railroad made things so convenient, Charles took the whole family to Ohio to visit their relatives. It was a brief and uneventful trip that left no one with a strong desire to remain in Ohio. Iowa was home now, and family ties to Ohio were weak to the point of nonexistence.

That November, Jim was appointed Assessor of the Town of Fayette. It was a welcome relief from the pressures of running his own business, and an excuse for giving up some of his responsibility in that regard. It was also good experience for his appointment two years later as County Auditor to replace Jason Paine. Jim was developing a reasonable career as a public servant.

In addition to the pranks, the sort of which intelligent folk are often given to, levity has always been a staple of university life, used both in good times and in bad to remind us not to take ourselves too seriously. It is fairly indispensable in an institution whose primary mission is to criticize its own core tenants. A series of events too complicated to explain in print led to a report of a robbery of Hurd's Bank published in the April 1875 edition of the *Fayette News*. It was reported that $30,000 was stolen from the bank, but the report neglected to mention that it was a simulated bank run by business students in the university, and that it was not real money. The story was, of course, intended as a spoof, but other newspapers picked it up and began wiring for details. With a great deal of embarrassment, the paper was finally forced to print a retraction.

The following month, all five members of the senior class, many of whom were behind the story about the robbery, went into the woods looking for a fitting monument to commemorate their academic success. There they found a large boulder, which, with great difficulty, they hauled to campus. Their intention was for the boulder to be placed in a conspicuous location as a memorial to their class. During the night, the five member junior class, including Jim's nephew, Frank Lakin, dug a hole and buried the stone entirely. The next day, the seniors were obliged to dig it up again. They placed it where it now rests, on the north side of the walkway near the west door of the Sem. After the last day of classes, the seniors made a great ceremony of burying their textbooks underneath it.

In September, Ole Iverson came again for an examination. He was even worse off than he had been the last time Charles saw him two years previous. This time, Charles determined to make a strong appeal for an increase.

Surgeon's Certificate
of
Biennial, Annual, or Semi-annual Examination,
on which the Pensioner draws his Pension.

State: Iowa　　　　*County:* Fayette
　　　Post Office: Fayette September 6th, *187*5.

I *hereby certify, That* I *have carefully examined* Ole Iverson, *who was a* Private in Co H. 15th Wis Inf Vols *in the war* Against the Rebellion, *and was granted an Invalid Pension under Certificate No.* 54.528 *to be paid now at the agency in* Dubuque *by reason of alledged disability resulting from* Gun Shot wound of right arm, *which he states to have been received in the line of duty while he was in the military service of the United States.*

In my *opinion the said Pensioner's disability, from the cause aforesaid, continues at* One half = $4 (rating unjustly low from first)

A more particular description of the Pensioner's condition is subjoined:

Height, 5 7 *; weight,* 130 *; complexion,* light *; age,* 49 *, respiration,* 20 *; pulse,* 88

Shot through right fore arm fracturing both radius and ulna. On account of adhesions of the muscles he has very little power to flex the hand or wrist or to rotate the fore arm. In my opinion his rating has always been unjustly low. He is a feeble man now beginning to grow old with very little use of the right arm--no power to grasp any small object. His rating should be equal to Private total or intermediate above that rate.

　　　　　　　　　　　　　　C.C. Parker
　　　　　　　　　　　　　　Examining Surgeon.

When Charles handed the certificate to Ole, he said, "I have done my best to get you an increase. The government is decidedly inflexible, and does not always seem to be interested in justice. I have done all I can."

"Thank you, Doc," Ole responded, and left saying no more.

Charles was distracted by his frequently occurring restlessness. On March 21st of 1876, he purchased two lots on King Street, which was a new development on the south end of town, recently platted by James Robertson on what had been a portion of his cornfield. It was one of many speculations Charles made on lots in town.

The purchase of these particular lots near the Robertsons stirred in Charles an increasing inclination to move their residence. There was nothing wrong with the big farmhouse; in fact, it was most homey and convenient. Charles was just... well... restless.

It was as though Heaven acknowledged and acted upon his desire. At eight in the evening on Tuesday, April 11th, a severe rain and hailstorm broke loose over Fayette. Hail one inch in diameter broke windows all over town. There was flooding everywhere from the two-hour storm. One of the casualties was the cozy farmhouse occupied by the Parker family, which sat on the north bank of the Volga River. The damage was not as severe as it might have been, but it was sufficient enough for Charles to successfully argue that a house away from the river would be safer for the children.

By August, the new and what would prove to be final Parker House in Fayette was finished. The family moved in with great relish and a sense of a new beginning. After a short period of time, several close friends moved onto the same block, and now frequent visits could be made without hitching up the wagon.

In November, Ole appeared again before Charles for an examination. This time, he had an application for an increase in his pension, and Charles was to evaluate the circumstances for that increase.

Examining Surgeon's Certificate
IN THE CASE OF AN APPLICANT FOR INCREASE OF PENSION
No. of Certificate: 54.528

State: Iowa   *County:* Fayette
        Post Office: Fayette November 21, *187*6.

It is hereby certified, That Ole Iverson *formerly a* Private *of* Captain Wilson (afterwards Brown) *Company* H *in the* 15th *Regiment of* Wis Vols., *in the war of* the Rebellion, *who is now at* Dubuque *Agency at the rate of* four *dollars per month, on account, as he states of* Gunshot wound of right fore arm, *while in the line of duty in the military service of the United States, on or about the* 31 *day of* December, *186*2, *at a place called* Stone River, *in the State or Territory of* Tennessee *is still suffering on consequence of said wound .*

The disability originates entirely from the injury or disease on account of which he was originally pensioned as follows:

Height, 5 7 *; weight,* 125 *; complexion,* light *; age,* 50 , *respiration,* 16 *; pulse,* 100

Wounded by musket ball passing through the right fore arm obliquely between radius and ulna fracturing the latter bone (possibly both). On account of which there now remain muscular adhesions with considerable atrophy & partial paralysis of the fore arm and hand. Motion of fingers only partial and imperfect, grasping power very slight. Disability increased rather than otherwise with increasing age: But in my opinion his former rating is unjustly low & therefore

I find his disability, as described above, to be equal to, and entitling him to-- <u>Private total (=$8.00)</u>

<u>C.C. Parker</u>
Examining Surgeon.

The Surgeon will forward his report of examinations direct to the Pension Office whether the pensioner is thought to be entitled to increase or not.

The second page was a form upon which four perspectives of the male body were outlined. Charles indicated by arrows the path of the bullet through the arm.

Ole stood waiting for his papers.

"I will send these directly to the Pension Office," said Charles.

"Will they get me more on my pension?" Ole asked, hopefully.

"I think so," answered Charles, optimistically. "We must now wait and see."

In January of 1877, Danny Parker, Charles and Sarah's oldest son who was by now in his junior year of college, was elected Secretary and Treasurer of the Methodist Episcopal Sabbath School. It was a great honor for such a young man, and was a formal recognition of the promise he had demonstrated as a student and as a citizen. Charles was equally as proud of Sarah, who was elected President of the Ladies Working Band. Their elections were particularly significant in light of the building of a new church undertaken by the congregation.

Later that month, Francis Alexander, twenty-one years of age and daughter of Charles's medical partner, died of consumption. This tragic event left Dixon and Mary with only one son, Ed, of what had once been a family of four children. It was a common enough occurrence on the frontier for children to die young, but still it was a tragedy that affected the whole town. There was supposed to be a greater degree of civilization here now. Such tragedies should be less frequent.

Another death would soon have a profound affect upon the town. On April 1st of 1877, Elizabeth Alexander died at age eighty after an acute illness that she battled for eight days. Charles attended her day and night, but there was little he could do. Tough as she was, she finally succumbed.

Elizabeth left a legacy of three sons, seven daughters, many grandchildren, two towns, and an institution of higher education. The endurance of this institution surprised everyone, even her. For twenty years, she had fretted over its difficulties and rejoiced in its triumphs. For twenty years, she had poured her heart and soul, and most of her wealth, into the most needy of its recesses. She had always carried on as though success were inevitable, but privately she marveled at the university's frequent recovery from near-disaster. She took these to be miracles, signs from God that her efforts supported a divine mission. Many old-timers likened her death to the death of President Lincoln in its affect, and the town endured an extended period of mourning and a deep sense of loss. For many, it was like losing their mother.

The loss of such a vital force in the institution compelled the Board of Trustees to take an unusual action, which was intended to fill the void left by Elizabeth's death. Faith in the president's abilities ran so high that the board transferred complete power to manage and settle all accounts to President Bissell, Vice President Adam Fussell, and Henry Hurd for a period of three years. It was an ingenious ploy that removed certain fetters from the president's ability to administrate, without violating the integrity of the board. It was a move that proved to be particularly helpful in coping with the difficulties imposed by the crop failure of that year.

"I'm here for my examination," said Ole, in much better spirits than Charles had seen him before.

"Did you get an increase in your pension?" asked Charles, as he took the papers from Ole's good hand.

"Yup," said Ole, directly. "I ain't livin' high on the hog, don't cha know, but I'm doin' ok."

"Good," said Charles, as he proceeded with his examination.

Surgeon's Certificate
of
Biennial, Annual, or Semi-annual Examination,
on which the Pensioner draws his Pension.

State: Iowa   *County:* Fayette
   Post Office: Fayette September 4th, *187*7.

I *hereby certify, That* I *have carefully examined* Ole Iverson, *who was a* Private in Co H. 15th Regt. Wis Vols *in the war* Against Rebellion, *and was granted an Invalid Pension under Certificate No.* 54.528 *to be paid now at the agency in* Des Moines *by reason of alledged disability resulting from* Gun Shot wound of right arm, *which he states to have been received in the line of duty while he was in the military service of the United States.*

In my *opinion the said Pensioner's disability, from the cause aforesaid, continues at* Total(= = $8)

A more particular description of the Pensioner's condition is subjoined:

Height, 5 7 *; weight,* 130 *; complexion,* light *; age,* 51 *, respiration,* 18 *; pulse,* 90

Shot obliquely through right fore arm Fracturing Radius & Ulna on account of which there now exists muscular adhesions with atrophy and very little power to flex or rotate the hand.

C.C. Parker
Examining Surgeon.

In the margin of the form, Charles wrote a note. *"Ought to be Exempt from Biennial Examination."* Ole was definitely not going to improve in the future, and the state could save some paperwork.

"There," said Charles, as he handed Ole the paper. "See you, Doc," said Ole as he left. Charles would never see Ole in person again.

In June of 1885, Ole would apply again for an increase in his pension because of increasing pain in his arm and shoulder. Charles, as President of the Examining Board, received and approved his request and forwarded it on to the Pension Office. Ole's pension was then increased to twelve dollars a month. It was increased to fourteen dollars the following year as a result of Ole's failing health.

In March of 1887, Ole and his steadfast wife, Margaret, sold the farm they had painstakingly managed together all these years to Ole and Belle Reierson. In addition to one thousand dollars in payment, the Reiersons were to provide each year for as long as Ole and Margaret lived, pasture, stable room, and feed for three cows and three calves, twenty bushels of wheat, thirty bushels of oats, forty bushels of corn, a piece of ground for the Iversons to use for growing potatoes, and one half of all the chickens and eggs produced on the farm. The Iversons were also furnished one bedroom, and the use of the cellar and other rooms in the house. Most importantly, the Reiersons would "treat them kindly and attend to them during their sickness & give them good and kind treatment at all times."

In March of 1890, Charles, as President of the Examining Board, approved what would become the last of Ole's requests for an increase in his pension. Despite the elaborate description of Ole's ailments placed on the form by Dr. S.E. Robinson, the Pension Office denied the request citing old age and not the war wound as the cause of disability.

Ole received his last pension payment on December 4th of 1890. On January 24th of 1891, he died on his farm in Pleasant Valley Township, Fayette County, Iowa, one of hundreds of thousands of good men who answered the call to arms and suffered as a result of it. Still, he lived a good life, and he did the best with what he had. In the end, he fared better than most.

In 1878, Charles saw his two oldest sons blossom with the potential they had always shown. Danny was elected Critic, and Charley was elected Prosecuting Attorney of the Philomathean Society. Danny was clearly the intellectual of the family, and his skill at Greek, oration, and philosophy was widely appreciated. Charley was something less of a scholar than his older brother was, but he showed a keen interest in business and in the law. Both brothers took Hurd's commercial program, and Charley was the clear winner in that round of the ongoing sibling rivalry.

On a Saturday night in June of 1878, a severe rainstorm reinforced the Parker family's decision to move their residence. The Volga rose four feet above any point reached previously since the town was formed. Thirty bridges washed out along the river, and several mills were destroyed. The town of Oelwein was awash in a lake.

The house from which the Parkers had moved was shifted off its foundation by the force of the floodwater, and had to be torn down and rebuilt by the Hoyt family, who bought it. Water ran down Main Street, and flooded most of the homes and businesses on Water Street. But it did not reach the new house on King Street. Great relief was felt by all at the south end of town.

Spring of 1879 saw Daniel Mason Parker graduated from Upper Iowa University. He had originally been slated for graduation in 1875, but he delayed completion of his degree requirements that he might take every course open to him. Danny's academic achievements were widely acknowledged, and Charles could not have been more proud of his oldest son. Everyone could plainly see Danny's potential as a teacher, and this seemed to be his own express wish. Upon graduation, he attended Garrett Biblical Institute, and was employed variously as an instructor and as a minister while he continued postgraduate study on his own. It was said of him that he was a Thoreau, Marvel, and Starr King all rolled into one—after Henry David Thoreau, the famous essayist; Ik Marvel, pen name of Donald Grant Mitchell, an agriculturist, landscape artist, and author; and Thomas Starr King, clergyman, lecturer and author.

Nearly coinciding with Danny's graduation, on June 4th, Lee Henry Thompson Lakin was born to Jim and Sallie. In what now seemed like a family tradition, Carrie gave birth to a strapping son, William Parker Lakin, shortly thereafter. The two sisters had certainly perfected their timing.

The year of 1880 was not a particularly good year from the Parker family's perspective. There was good news from the university—the Board regained control of accounts and thanked the three administrators for eliminating the school's debt and for returning it to financial health. And there was bad news from the community; Jason Paine was stricken with nervous prostration while ministering in churches in Postville, Cresco, and Monticello. He was obviously attempting to do more than his constitution would allow, and he suffered for it.

But, the worst possible news came from within the family. Caroline Ritchey Parker, Charles and Sarah's only remaining daughter, died of consumption at age fourteen, on August 21st. It was a particularly insidious and painful death, and the trauma of watching their beloved daughter wasting away was almost more than they could bear.

The boys were old enough to care for themselves—J.D., the youngest, was twelve, and the two older boys were adults—so Charles took some time off to stay at home and tend to Sarah.

She did not seem to show as much emotion this time—not that she had shown much to the public with the deaths of her other two children. But Charles sensed that this was different. Sarah was at the end of her rope, and it would be very easy for her to just give up. She was strong, and very stubborn when she wished to be, but now she was just tired—tired beyond rest, anguished beyond recovery. There was no consolation that would heal her wound. It was a wound inflicted upon a wound inflicted upon a wound. Each time was harder to bear than the last, and with each successive death of a child she worked harder at suppressing the hurt and the sense of defeat. She felt as though she had died herself.

Charles could barely stand to see her in this condition. He had trouble coping with his own grief. How could God allow this to happen? Charles could accept that he was a sinner, but Sarah was virtually without fault. How could this happen over and over again to hurt her so deeply? What must he do to bring this continuing tragedy to an end? He could not blame God. God does good by definition. Charles tried to see it from God's perspective, but he was at a loss to explain why two such lovely and innocent young girls should be taken without having the chance to truly celebrate God's gift of life. This is certainly not the sort of thing one expects from a god that demands devotion when that devotion is given wholeheartedly and without qualification.

Despite his own feelings, Charles could not falter from his care and concern for Sarah. One of them must be strong. One of them must be able to hold the other up. One of them must see some purpose in going on. Given the affliction they had experienced, this was the most difficult time in their lives. Neither of them would ever fully recover.

Life does continue, and Charles and Sarah were bound to continue on with it. Their sons needed them, and their needs could not be denied for discouragement or lack of energy.

In June of 1881, Charles Lucious Parker, became the second son to graduate from Upper Iowa University. There was a great celebration marking the beginning of the institution's silver anniversary at commencement that year, and Fayette was overwhelmed with a surge of alumni, former faculty, and friends. Lucious Bugbee could not attend, but sent a congratulatory letter, and pointed out that the silver anniversary was not official until 1883, twenty-five years from the date that the seminary became a college. Everyone decided that if the university survived until then, they could celebrate again.

Among the speakers at the celebration was David B. Henderson, now a lawyer practicing in a firm in Dubuque, who chose "The Future of Upper Iowa University" as his topic. He noted the removal of debt and the optimism that Dr. Bissell had brought to the institution. "The next twenty-five years will outshine the first as gold outshines silver."

The university thrived under Dr. Bissell not only because of his skill in managing accounts, but also because his was a modern view of education. Gone were the days when college was something for the idle rich, who needed education to bolster their social stature by fine tuning their "breeding". Development of technology and business demanded a new sort of student: one who could apply technical, economic, and management skills to new industrial problems. Gone were the days when knowledge of Greek and Latin classics identified you as a member of an elite club, with upper-class standing.

"Three tons of coal," said Dr. Bissell, "will pump as much water or shovel as much coal as an average man will pump or shovel in a lifetime; so that if a man proposes to do nothing but work with his muscles, he had better dig his three tons of coal and set that to work, and then die; because the work will be better done, and without any cost for the maintenance of the doer."

Dr. Bissell took his cues from Aristotle's recommendation for the preparation of good citizens. To reach their full potential, students must develop their minds as well as their bodies. Minds and bodies are best developed in an harmonious and balanced atmosphere, where music, art, and other intellectual activities were engaged as well as physical exercise. These activities were necessary components of daily life. The traditional college curriculum did not provide sufficient quantities of these activities, therefore students must be encouraged to involve themselves in their personal growth outside of class.

In the heyday of the Bissell administration, nothing summoned and energized students quite so readily as debate and oratory. The opportunity for developing creative argument was an oasis of exhilaration compared with the tedium of lectures and recitations. If the thrill of competition were not enough, prizes were offered. The expanding popularity of debate extended outside the institution, and colleges formerly isolated unto themselves challenged each other for the right to claim superiority. Students from Upper Iowa frequently won these debates, and prevailed in regional contests with much larger schools.

In 1881, Minnie Brunson won the right to represent Upper Iowa at the State contest. She became not only the first woman to compete with a memorized speech, but the first woman to win that event. At the regional event, at the University of Illinois (set up by a senior named William Jennings Bryan who did not compete), Minnie's speech drew spontaneous applause from the audience. This outburst was interpreted by the judges to be the result of overly dramatic deportment on the part of the speaker, and enough points were deducted from her score such that she did not win. It is likely that such deductions would not have been made if she were male.

Participation in these contests gave students incentive to pay attention to politics and world affairs. Interest in public issues and debates encouraged like-minded students to form societies around parochial positions on those issues. The Young Republicans, the Young Democrats, and Christian societies were established.

Christian societies such as the Young Men's Christian Association and the Young Women's Christian Association worked toward the improvement of physical culture and fitness. Physical activities were activities that minimized the effects of social standing and class distinction. Competition was based solely on the skill and abilities of the individual. Physical competition was the perfect symbol of important American ideals.

The first formal physical programs on campus had been military training. To the Manual of Arms was added particular training that would benefit the modern combat soldier who relied on strength and endurance. Later, the YMCA and the YWCA promoted the benefits of physical conditioning for sound mind and body, and the benefits of honest competition for a healthy and happy life. These programs provided an alternative to preparation for war.

On September 19, 1881, President James Garfield died of wounds inflicted by an assassin. It was a tragic event, but the effect on people in this part of the country was not the same as the assassination of President Lincoln had been; they continued much as before.

The following year, Jason Paine had recovered

enough from his illness to become President of the Prohibitory Amendment Campaign. He worked diligently to close saloons and other places of ill repute. Jason was also elected President of Fayette County Farmer's Institute. In this capacity, he promoted agriculture as a science.

Jason elicited many responses from those who encountered him. Some respected him, and some despised him. Charles admired him for his conviction, and for his willingness to suffer any consequences that resulted from his efforts to act on his convictions. He had come a long way from the cocky young man he was when they had met so many years ago. But he still retained his enthusiasm, and a rather unshakable confidence in the correctness of his beliefs. This is what Charles admired about him.

That same year, Charley followed the path taken by his father, his grandfather, and his great-grandfather before him: he left the family home to seek his fortune out west. He would return on occasion, but for the most part he disconnected himself from the house of his father. He was not the same sort of person as his older brother, Danny, and did not wish to compete with him any longer. He sought to define himself on his own terms, just as his forefathers had done. He went to Bathgate, North Dakota to try his hand at farming, primarily because it was not Fayette. It was a part of the country that was also seeking to define itself, and it offered opportunity to all those willing to risk everything to build their own future. After finding farming unsuitable for a number of reasons, Charley took the course that was most natural to him and delved into banking and real estate.

Charles was sorry to see his son leave the family, but understood perfectly why he would do such a thing. He could not help but to see his own personal struggles and impulses to wander reflected in his middle son. Sarah was less understanding, but had been so numbed by the losses of her other children that she feigned approval for her son's sake. She knew full well that there was nothing she could do to make him stay. In a way, it helped her to better appreciate the devotion Charles had shown to her all of their married lives. Charley was enacting that aspect of his father that she liked the least, but she was grateful that it was as it was, for it could have been much worse for her.

In June of 1882, Philo Woods graduated from Upper Iowa University, the only member of the University Recruits to do so. He finished nearly twenty years later than he had originally anticipated before the war. It was a reminder of the true nature of the sacrifice that those idealistic young men made when they signed up for the glory of their country.

Most of those who survived the bullets and the disease returned, as Jim Lakin had, with experiences that displaced their former youthful innocence and optimistic abandon with a rather more somber perspective. College studies demanded a certain degree of naivete that was for them, now hopelessly lost. How does a recitation of Cicero fit into the world of a man who has seen his fellow soldier cut in half by a cannon ball? Where does the scolding of a fussy teacher fall into the priorities of a man whose unit suffered thirty percent casualties in one battle because an officer gave an inappropriate order? What value does the musing of a great philosopher or theologian hold for a man that has seen first-hand the horrors of war and the suffering imposed by slavery? They could never go back.

Sometimes, however, people can go back. In the fall semester of 1882, Carrie Lakin returned to teaching art in the university. Her sister, Sallie, was expecting her next child within the month. Carrie and Will, for their part, had decided that five children were enough for the present, and Carrie longed to be active in something besides motherhood. Mabel, Carrie's oldest, was nineteen, and was responsible enough to look after the other children. The next oldest, sixteen-year-old Cory, was not yet reliable in that regard, but he was of some help to his older sister.

On October 4th, Irene Ritchie Lakin became the third child born to Jim and Sallie. Sallie was maintaining tradition in that she stayed in her sister's house for the last few weeks of pregnancy. The house would not be blessed with two newborns this time, however.

About the same time in another home, the tradition of multiple newborns was also missed. Charles was summoned to a small farm in Frog Hollow, north of Fayette. The farmer came to fetch him early in the afternoon.

"She's about to have 'em," the farmer told Charles, hurriedly. "Ya gotta come now!"

On this particular farm, Charles had delivered babies twice before. The first time, about three years previous, the farmer's wife gave birth to healthy twin boys. About a year before, she had triplets; that time girls. Charles impressed upon the farmer a sense of urgency with this pregnancy—when the time came he was to send word immediately. The probability of another multiple birth increased the risk of complications.

They arrived in time, and Charles delivered a healthy baby boy. Mother and son were doing well, and Charles was relieved to see that only one would be delivered this time. He took the child outside where the farmer was waiting with his five other children.

"You have a fine son," said Charles, thinking the farmer would be happy that it was a normal birth.

The farmer looked down at his son, and then he looked blankly up at Charles. He looked down again, and then looked toward the door as if he expected to see someone coming out.

"My gawd, Doc," he finally said, "came within one of not bein' any."

The following spring hosted the first edition of the *Collegian*. It was a monthly publication of twelve pages and it featured literary works written by UIU students. The *Collegian* also contained some campus news and reports made by the four literary societies. School papers, such as the *Collegian*, became one more of the increasingly diverse activities in which a student could choose to participate. These activities had an object beyond purely learning or purely recreation. Working on the school paper could lead to the development of skills one would use in a career in journalism. Higher priorities were placed on those activities that had practical application for the enterprising student. Education was moving away from the Aristotelian ideal of contemplation on the Isle of the Blessed, and toward Aristotle's ideal of the citizen of civic affairs. The citizen of affairs in the modern world was involved in commerce.

That summer, Charley returned from North Dakota for a visit, or so it seemed to his parents. He did not spend much time at home, however, and in what appeared to them as a sudden and impulsive move, he married Violet Truman of Decorah on August 20th. Violet had been a student in the Music Conservatory when Charley was studying in the university. There was some suspicion that Charley was sweet on Violet, but speculation that they would marry ended when Charley moved away.

The Parkers and the Lakins all managed to attend the hastily-arranged wedding in Decorah. It was a joyous event, but there would never be any close ties with the bride or her family. Shortly after the wedding, Charley whisked his new wife off to North Dakota, and it would be some years before Charles would see his son again.

Family troubles notwithstanding, Charles found solace in his avocation. That summer he completed his scheme of planting pines around campus with the help of the junior and senior classes. He had solicited the help of graduating classes for a period of years, and now, twenty-six years after planting that first elm, the project was completed. He could now turn all of his attention to his own garden.

Extended buggy rides onto the prairie would yield, in the next few years, one of the most complete plant collections west of the Mississippi. In addition to collecting plants, Charles picked up interesting rocks; a heart-shaped rock graced his office desk as a paperweight. Other stones collected found employment lining the rather elaborate garden south of the house on the plot intended for that purpose.

On many such forays, Charles took his youngest son, J.D. One excursion to the southwest brought them to a spot where the prairie extended to the horizon in all directions. Charles stood up in the wagon and lifted J.D. up on his shoulders.

"This is the last spot in Iowa that is untouched by civilization," Charles told his son. "When I first came here, it was all like this; as far as you can see there are no trees or farms."

By now, J.D. was the only child remaining in the Parker household, and he was at the school most of the time studying and romping with his friends. After Carrie had died, Charles took in Esteling Ackley as an aide to the family. Normally such a woman would be referred to as the hired girl, but Charles and Sarah thought of Estel as part of the family. She was a thirty-seven-year-old dressmaker from Wisconsin whose husband had died of diphtheria and left her essentially stranded in Fayette. She was very helpful to Sarah, and there was quite a demand for her fine dresses to keep her busy.

It was a shame to let so many rooms in such a large house go unused. Charles extended an invitation to eighty-year-old Willis Burston, a widowed minister from Kentucky and active member of the church, to live with them. He accepted the invitation and the four of them passed many evenings enjoying each other's company. It was a good way to make the time pass more quickly and to divert attention from such recent and painful losses.

On campus, more changes were in the wind. Literary societies were slowly being replaced by the

student-oriented groups that offered activities which were
less academic in character. There were the political clubs,
there were music, art, and poetry clubs, and there were
the others which emphasized physical fitness.

Physical culture, such as tennis and gymnastics,
was not ordinarily to be found in those societies bent on
intellectual pursuits. However, those clubs that offered
physical exercise were increasingly in demand.
Accordingly, on March 25th of 1885, the campus charter
for the YMCA was formalized. John R. Mott, from
Postville, was the fourth student to sign the constitution,
and his experience in the university chapter carried him
into the "Y" as a career. He became heavily involved in a
global organizing effort that stimulated many
humanitarian enterprises. Franklin D. Roosevelt would
later declare the UIU alum to be a national treasure. Mott
would be awarded the Nobel Peace Prize in 1946 for his
work with prisoners of war.

The campus would also add its first new building
in the year of 1885. South Hall was built to house fifty
women and to feed one hundred students in the dining
hall. The new dorm was administered by the Ladies
Professorship Association. Fall of that year brought the
largest class so far to Upper Iowa—three hundred
twenty-four students. An observatory was built with a
five-inch Alvin Clark telescope, donated by Rev.
Sedgewick of Camanche, Iowa.

In 1886, the first recorded football game at the
university was played on the street adjacent to campus.
The only rule was to get the ball over the opposing goal
line, and any means for doing so was acceptable. The
first game ended when the ball smashed the straw hat

being worn by Grandpa Pierce, who was working in his garden at the time.

Football's reputation for brutality and corruption prompted the board to prohibit the games initially, but arguments that intercollegiate track events were not corrupting led to reconsideration. Soon, long traditions of rivalries with Luther College, Coe College, and Cornell College were underway. In 1893, Upper Iowa won its first sanctioned game against Lenox College. Admission was five cents.

In 1887, the observatory was moved to the northeast portion of the campus ground to make room for North Hall, which was built as a men's dormitory. The second floor of the new building was occupied by Hurd's business school, which left only the first and third floors for housing. The partition in the third floor of the Sem that had helped to maintain the illusion that the men and women were separated was removed, and the floor was turned over to the literary societies for meeting rooms.

On June 21st, Danny Parker married Sarah McDonald in New Hampton. Danny would become the second son to be mostly removed from Fayette. He and his bride traveled to North Dakota to see what held the attraction for Charley. The following February, on the 17th, Danny and Sarah had their first child, Charles Sherman Parker, in Grafton. The desolate regions of the Dakotas did not have the same appeal for them, so Danny applied for a ministry in the Upper Iowa Conference and was appointed to New Hampton.

Eighteen eighty-eight would herald nearly complete devastation for the Parker household. The bad news began early and came often. First, Charles diagnosed Sarah with consumption. When it became obvious that she was infected, he devoted himself almost entirely to seeking out treatments of any sort that might help. He corresponded with experts, and experimented with ideas for treatments that materialized during many sleepless nights of contemplating the problem while listening to her cough incessantly.

On March 14th, Sallie Lakin died suddenly of winter fever. Jim was distraught beyond consolation. Carrie had to help with their children because Jim just could not muster enough energy to do it himself, and their aunt Sarah was too sick to be of much help.

Charles began to feel overwhelmed. He had been treating his long-time friend and benefactor, Daniel Vines, for dropsy. It had been a long and painful bout—a continuous degradation of the quality of his life. Dan's misery finally ended on June 10th. It seemed to Charles that everyone close to him was dying, and there was nothing he could do.

The idea of losing Sarah simply could not be accepted. Something must change to prevent that from happening. Charles prayed, as he had never done before, for a miracle. He called upon all the power of God to acknowledge the good things done by this good woman, and to relieve her suffering and make her whole. He appealed to God for mercy for His most faithful and obedient servant. But, as with all else it seemed, his efforts were in vain.

On December 3rd, Sarah Lakin Parker, at age sixty, loving wife of a good man, mother of six children, three of whom died before her eyes, a woman who never lost faith or hope or brought grief to anyone, lost her struggle for life. She ended her life as she had lived it, quietly and in solitude. The one blessing of her death was that she would no longer be forced to endure the pain of losing those close to her.

Sarah's funeral was delayed to allow enough time for Charley to travel to Fayette from North Dakota. When it came time, Danny was too ill to attend. The pallbearers reflected how well Sarah was regarded in the community; they included James Robertson, W.F. Boyce, J.E. Budde, James Percy, Alex Winston, and Professor Duncan. All were pillars of the community; all but Professor Duncan were among the first to settle the town. She would likely have been embarrassed to know how honored and how deeply saddened they all felt in performing such a service.

Charles was numb. He went through the motions of the funeral for everyone else's sake, but for the next several weeks he remained in seclusion. In his isolation, he went through every dusty corner of his memory searching for all of those things he had done and said that may have hurt her or detracted from her happiness. These he collected, and psychologically beat himself with them mercilessly. He castigated himself for being a disappointment as a husband and father. He punished himself with remorse for all those times he had abandoned her to seek adventure. He thought of all those things he should have done differently. When he had finished with that, he began all over again. He was rapidly losing his will to live.

J.D. feared for his father's health. Showing a mature presence of mind, he pleaded with his uncle Jim to do something. Jim had still not recovered from his own loss, now increased in magnitude by the loss of his beloved big sister, but he roused himself into action. With his children, Jim moved into the Parker house temporarily, and assisted J.D. in working on Charles. Together, they brought him back. The effort was a healing experience for all of them. Still, none of them would ever feel the wholeness they had known before.

In June of the following year, James Daniel Parker graduated from Upper Iowa University, the third of Charles and Sarah's children to do so. By this time, only graduating seniors were required to present an oration. In the middle of his memorized speech, J.D. forgot his lines and lost his train of thought. In a humorous way, he asked the audience to sing while he thought about it.

At first, Charles was mortified. J.D. had a reputation as a carefree, some would say careless, young man. He was the baby of the family, and was treated, some would say, with a faulty degree of indulgence by his parents. This display did not help to rectify that impression. Charles was glad Sarah was not here to witness this excruciating embarrassment. But when he thought of Sarah, he realized that J.D. must have been thinking of her too. She should have been here to see this. She would have been so proud.

Most of the audience could not correctly interpret the minute inflections of J.D.'s voice that indicated his sudden thoughts of his mother and how much he missed her, though there were some in the audience who knew him well and were not fooled. He hid with humor the abrupt wave of sentiment that washed his thoughts clean. Unable to recall the rest of his speech, J.D. suggested that anyone interested could peruse the copy he had prepared, and that they would find it in his father's office. Then, he sat down. Charles had to look away and wipe the tears from his eyes. He no longer cared what anyone thought about this unorthodox exhibition, he was as proud of his son as he could be.

The fall semester brought a peak enrollment at five hundred thirty-two students. It seemed that just about everything had peaked.

As is always inevitable in the course of human affairs, what had been the strongest energy binding the fabric of the community dissipated that it might regenerate as something new and different. On February 11th of 1890, Jim Lakin married Helen Nelson Sabin in Duluth, Minnesota. He had met Helen through one of his business associates. This marriage was not quite what his marriage to Sallie had been, but it was what he wanted. Helen was a good woman who would provide the companionship that Jim needed, and would be a good mother to his growing children. The children now ranged in age from eight to sixteen, and proved to be too much for Jim to handle on his own.

Helen was not interested in moving to Fayette. It was not that she did not like the town, but that she was concerned that there were too many memories and ties to the past that would haunt her new husband and diminish their relationship. Jim agreed reluctantly, and sold his land. Shortly thereafter, they moved to Brighton, Colorado to begin a new life together.

Jim said good-bye to his brother and Carrie and to all their children in West Union, and then he and Helen traveled to Fayette to say good-bye to Charles. They spent all afternoon and most of the evening reminiscing about their adventures with Mr. Lincoln and his now infamous trial, and about their war experiences. Jim, Helen, and the children caught the morning train that would take them out west. They promised to return for a visit, but Charles knew that he would not see them in person again. Will and Carrie now remained as his only tie to Sarah's family.

Charley's connection to the west was by now quite permanent. He sent a letter to his father telling of his move to Neihart, Montana to try his hand at mining.

On campus, the Old Students Association was reorganized as the Alumni Association with the object of "creating and maintaining a sentiment of union and fellowship." A new Chapel that held six hundred students was built just east of North Hall. The Chapel had a stage, and was used frequently for lectures and artistic performances sponsored by the L.P.A. Commencement was moved to the Chapel to eliminate the chance that poor weather would spoil the occasion, as it had done frequently in the past.

Every institution and political party had its colors, and the track team decided it was time to display the colors of the school when it was competing off campus. Upperclassman William Mabry planned to travel by train to Chicago for the Christmas holidays. He was tasked by the team with picking the school colors during the break. William forgot all about the assignment until he was on the train back to school. Fortunately, among the vendors on the train was one selling sewing kits and bits of colored ribbon. William picked two bits of ribbon, one of peacock blue and the other of white, and presented these to the track team. Later, Henry Dickman and William Baker bought a stuffed peacock as a mascot. These symbols of the institution endure today, not only representing the school itself but also the sort of students one may find there—resourceful even if they are not always highly organized and efficient.

In 1891, the science department took over the first floor of North Hall reducing the amount of dormitory space available for the men. There were ample apartments and boarding houses in the town, which made up for the loss and encouraged the move in the first place.

During this period, class rivalries became more intense. It was an outgrowth of a highly competitive, industrialized society. Competition was so intense at the Fawcett Oratory Contest for a fifty-dollar prize that two of the speakers fainted, one in the middle of his speech. Increasingly, students resorted to buying canned speeches from oration companies to increase their chances of success.

In June of 1892, J.D. graduated with an M.D. degree from the University of Michigan Medical School. Charles reminded his son to take care with his writing while he was away at school. Fifty cents was promised for every letter J.D. wrote while in Michigan that had no spelling or grammatical errors. J.D. did not collect many half-dollars from his father, and would show an aversion to letter-writing for the remainder of his life.

On August 23rd, J.D. married Nellie Klemme in Ridgeway, Iowa. Nellie had graduated from UIU the year following J.D.'s graduation and she attended a private music school in Boston while J.D. was in Michigan. She did not require perfect grammar and spelling in the letters she received, and therefore received many more than Charles did. Nellie went to St. Charles College in Missouri to teach music for the 1891-92 school year, but returned to marry the young man her father did not favor wholeheartedly.

The Klemmes were a wealthy and powerful family in the region, and Mr. Klemme had hoped that his daughter would marry someone higher on the social scale. But Nellie was as strong and as stubborn as her father, so there was never any question of who would prevail. Mr. Klemme took heart in the young man's completion of medical school. He welcomed J.D. into the family, and rejoiced in his father's eminence as a pioneer and physician, if not in his business savvy.

The couple moved into the Parker house on King Street. Charles gladly relinquished the master bedroom to the newlyweds, and made it clear that this was their house now, that they were the core of the family's future now. It was the beginning of a new era.

Nellie was a jewel. Her wisdom and common sense were the perfect complement to J.D.'s natural gifts for healing and humanitarianism, and she was the perfect complement to his sense of humor. She became the chief advisor for family financial matters, and took it upon herself to help resolve the massive debt that Charles had accumulated. Nellie would provide a much-needed stability to the Parker household.

One morning, she glanced up from her work in the kitchen to see Charles outside behaving rather strangely.

"What is your father doing?" she asked J.D.

J.D. walked to the window to have a look. "He's after eggs," was the reply.

"After eggs?"

"Yeah. He won't eat an egg unless it's fresh, and he doesn't think eggs are fresh unless they're still warm from the hen. So, he follows the chickens around waiting for them to lay. He'll be in soon."

And so he was.

The following year, a gymnasium was built on the northeast corner of the campus entirely with funds raised by student organizations. Men used it three days a week, and women the other three. No athletics were permitted on the Sabbath. Tennis courts and a track were also built. President Bissell began installing electricity on campus, and adding to the landscaping that Charles had begun.

On September 12th of 1893, Danny, Charley, J.D., and Will Lakin organized a 70th birthday party and family reunion for Charles. Charles was finally coming to grips with Sarah's loss, and was settling pleasantly into old age. J.D. was successfully taking over the medical practice at the clinic, and the university was, currently at least, in good hands. Charles sought out the companionship of some of the old timers who were left, such as Alex Winston and James Robertson, each of whom lived only a few blocks distant. Many hours were devoted to the loving care of his garden.

On April 11th of the following year, Hugh Klemme Parker was born in Fayette to J.D. and Nellie. Even though Charles had grandchildren already, the immediacy of this child and the current circumstances surrounding the Parker household gave him renewed optimism for the future.

With the birth of the new comes the death of the old. Charles received a telegram that on June 13th of 1894, James Kennedy Parker, his oldest brother, had died in Clermontville, Ohio at age seventy-six. Charles sent his regrets to the family, but did not attend the funeral for health reasons.

That same month, Charley graduated LLB from the University of Michigan Law School. Taking the cue from his brothers, Charley decided that additional education in his area of interest would increase his ability to pursue his desired ends. After a brief visit in Fayette, he returned to the west, this time to Seattle, which was as far west as he could go without getting on a boat. He would remain there, practicing law and dealing in real estate, for the rest of his life.

In April of 1895, the Grand Army of the Republic held a thirtieth reunion in Clermont. Charles attended with several other members of the University Recruits. During dinner, an old soldier with a glass eye seated directly across from Charles took a sudden interest in him.

"Yer Surgeon Parker, ain't cha?!" said the veteran, more as a statement than as a question.

"Yes, I am," replied Charles.

"I gotta thank you, sir," said the veteran, emphatically. "You saved my life. Don' cha remember? You took that mini ball outta my eye at Shiloh. I'da died if'n you hadn't operated on me."

Charles did not remember him at all. The men he worked on were just a blur in his memory; he did not think of them as men at the time, just as work that needed to be done.

"Yes, I remember," said Charles.

"Thank you again, sir," said the veteran, who proceeded to relay to Charles everything that happened to him after his recovery.

A few months later, Charles received word that Jim and Helen moved from Colorado to Salt Lake City. They were fine, and Jim was seeking new business opportunities. They repeated their promise to return for a visit, but Charles held out little hope of that.

On April 29th of 1895, William Brush died. Except for Charles, he was the last link with the university faculty's foundational years. He was widely known by reputation, but most of those now affiliated with the institution could not remember back to when he was president.

In the fall of 1895, students returned to find new floors, new wallpaper, and electricity in Old Sem. It was a fresh start in anticipation of the coming turn of the century. The following year, the science department added the third floor to its space and eliminated housing accommodations altogether in North Hall. The campus was spreading out, and preparing itself for a new age of business, science, and technology.

On March 28th of 1896, J.D. and Nellie bore their second child, Dorothy Lakin Parker. It was a joyous occasion, and Charles now had two grandchildren to bounce on his knee.

On February 18th of 1897, Dr. Dixon Alexander died. His wife had passed on three years earlier, and with only one son left to carry on, Dixon had just given up.

Dixon's passing brought on an interlude of

reflection for Charles. He thought a lot about the vibrant, brash, and passionate man who had been his partner, and how in recent years he had deteriorated so much. The tragic losses of his wife and children left Dixon languid and lifeless, with little of his former energy. He just seemed to be marking time until his death.

Charles wondered if he was showing the same symptoms. After all, he had suffered much the same tragedies as Dixon had. Was he, too, becoming so useless and burdensome? He brought the subject up one night after dinner. While J.D. listened intently to his father's inquiry, preparing a technical explanation, Nellie looked Charles straight in the eye and, very sternly, said "No!" The discussion came to an abrupt end, and the subject did not come up again.

Charles would not be lacking in grandchildren, even if he could not visit them all as regularly as he desired. On November 22nd of 1897, Sarah Blythe Parker was born to Danny and Sarah in New Hampton.

In February, Nellie Parker bought the lot upon which the Parker Clinic had been for over thirty years, thus bringing it into family ownership for the first time. This tact removed any threat of increased rent for her husband's practice. Nellie's father helped her finance the purchase, and he insisted that it be recorded in his daughter's name. J.D. and Charles had no objection to that at all. In fact, Charles was so pleased with Nellie's management skills that ten months later he signed over the house and all of the vacant lots he owned to her as a Christmas present.

"You have found the perfect wife," he told his son. "You should cherish her."

"I do," was J.D.'s reply, "I do."

Eighteen ninety-nine brought upheaval to the university after twenty-six years of steady growth. President Bissell resigned after presiding over an administration that saw many controversial changes, from electricity to a modern one-speaker commencement. Whatever the reason was that prompted the resignation, only the board knew. Dr. Bissell left an institution fully prepared to face the new century, though it appeared that the new president was inclined to undo much of that preparation.

Dr. Bissell was replaced by Guy Potter Benton, a staunch Methodist, who, in his inaugural address, derided the changes taking place in the modern world. The New Man, he said, was a worthless emasculate, and the New Woman had traded decent home life for the cigarette, the bicycle, and the ballot. The sensuality represented by modern art, theater, and literature was disgraceful.

After his speech, President Benton asked former President Bissell to stay on as a consultant. Dr. Bissell declined, and embarked on a trip to the Holy Land. After his return, Dr. Bissell was appointed a presiding elder in the Methodist church. He attended every major event at Upper Iowa, and eventually joined the Board of Trustees.

Despite President Benton's assessment of modern art, its encroachment on modern society was unstoppable. That fall, Charles attended a play produced by the combined forces of two student societies. It was called *The Houseboat on the River Styx*, authored by John Kendrick. The only other play Charles could remember attending was in the summer of 1858, after they returned from Mr. Lincoln's trial. It was presented at a Philomathean public, and it was called *Major Andre*. William Warner had written it when he was a student there.

The following year, in 1900, Charles particularly enjoyed a production of *The Merchant of Venice*. Thus began a tradition of theater at UIU that would be formally incorporated into the curriculum of the School of Oratory, and would continue as a tradition at the university for the next century. In 1902, Charles attended the first of what would become the traditional senior class play; it was called *The Rivals*.

The catalog for the 1900-01 academic year indicated that there were six buildings on campus; courses were taught by twenty-six full time faculty, there were ninety-one students in the collegiate programs, there were one hundred students in the Academy, and there were eighty-five students in the normal school. Forty-eight students made up the Art department, one hundred eleven the Conservatory of Music, one hundred nineteen the School of Oratory, and sixty-five the Business College. All in all, given some duplication in the numbers, there was a total student body of four hundred and one.

On September 6th of 1901, President William McKinley was shot by Leon Czolgosz, an anarchist, at the Pan-American Exposition in Buffalo, New York. He died eight days later, and was succeeded by Vice-President Theodore Roosevelt. It was a national tragedy, but it was not of the magnitude the old timers remembered of President Lincoln's assassination. Everyone hoped this new Roosevelt fellow would be a good president.

Twenty days later, the President of the Board of Trustees, Samuel B. Zeigler, laid the cornerstone for the new library. David Henderson had encouraged Dr. Benton to travel to New York and ask for a donation from Dale Carnegie, who was sponsoring many such projects at the time. Carnegie had already committed funds for a large library in Dubuque.

Dr. Benton went to see the famous industrialist, but had his patience tested immediately. University presidents have always needed patience and persistence as indispensable qualities in the pursuit of funding. On his third try, Dr. Benton was issued into the presence of the skeptical philanthropist, who, upon hearing the request, said that he only funded public libraries. That would be fine, suggested Dr. Benton, Upper Iowa did not have a library building, and desperately needed one. There were no community libraries in the region at all. Dubuque was seventy-five miles away by horse, and further by train. Carnegie took the information under advisement and sent Dr. Benton back to Iowa without a commitment.

The next time Carnegie met the Speaker of the House, he informed Mr. Henderson that Fayette was too small to warrant the investment. Henderson refused to accept that answer, and finally persuaded Carnegie to contribute $25,000 to the project. Carnegie included the following in his letter to Henderson: "My dear Friend-- You will receive a cheque for $25,000 which you can use as you think best for your alma mater for her permanent interests, preferably for a library. I think that any institution that made so much of a Scotsman is entitled to some recognition." When Dr. Benton wired his appreciation, Carnegie responded that it would please him greatly if the library were named after his good friend David Henderson. And so it was.

On July 16th of 1902, Danny and Sarah added another grandchild to the family with the birth of Laurice Daniel Parker. J.D. took his father along with the rest of the family to Postville to see the baby.

That fall, the town received several bits of shocking news. On September 16th, David B. Henderson resigned from the House of Representatives. He had held the speakership since 1899, and had just been nominated for his twelfth term in Congress by a unanimous vote of his party. His resignation was completely unexpected, and ranking Republicans begged him to reconsider. He said that he had had enough of the bickering and mudslinging inherent in politics. He also had health problems that he chose not to make public.

On October 2nd, Henry Hurd died. Hurd was the last surviving faculty member to have been appointed by Dr. Brush, though he had ceased conducting classes some time before his death because of his ill health. Still, Hurd was an institution in Fayette, and his school was one of the first steps the university had taken toward the modern era. More than a few local businessmen owed some part of their success to what they learned from Henry Hurd. Hurd's National Business College became the Commercial department of the university.

By the time the library was dedicated on November 11th, Dr. Benton had accepted another position, and attended the dedication and the ceremonial football game as the President of Miami University of Ohio. On this occasion, the new President of Upper Iowa

University was inaugurated. He was Thomas J. Bassett, a graduate of Asbury University and Professor of Greek in that institution when the name was changed to DePauw University. President Bassett would establish the gallery of portraits in the library of Upper Iowa's presidents, as well as have the old wooden sidewalks replaced with concrete walkways illuminated by streetlights between buildings.

In April of 1903, the Faculty Committee of the Board of Trustees submitted its report on student discipline to President Bassett, who was quick to take action. The report indicated a number of problems, but the most disconcerting was the discovery that the young men were commonly found in the private rooms of young women after ten o'clock. Dr. Bassett decreed that young women would only entertain young men in the rooming house parlors, and never after ten. Housing managers were further called upon to crack down on obscenities, drinking, gambling, and use of tobacco.

On January 22nd of 1904, James Robertson, last of the town's founders, died at age eighty-three. Charles was deeply saddened at the loss of his old friend, and particularly concerned that there were no others with whom he could reminisce about the early days. Jason Paine was one, but Jason was too young to have been involved in the town's politics.

James Robertson had been a pillar of the community in so many ways. He took on the role of town patriarch back when the Colonel died, and that responsibility only increased when Elizabeth Alexander died. Having been the founder of the Methodist Church in Fayette, as well as a founder of the university and one of the primary landholders of the town, James was a dispositive force in local politics. His interest in the community's welfare, even at his own expense, made him the last of a rapidly dying breed. He could never be replaced.

That October, on the 31st, Eleanor Bolles Parker became the last child Charles would see introduced into the family, and would be the last of his grandchildren. No matter how old he became, Charles never ceased taking delight in his grandchildren. He remarked to Nellie one evening that he was afraid that Eleanor would never know how much her grandfather loved her.

The following May, David B. Henderson suffered a stroke in Dubuque. Upper Iowa University's most famous alum died from a second stroke on February 25, 1906.

Meanwhile, Dr. Bassett reorganized the post of Steward into Superintendent of Grounds and Buildings, and hired Albert Miller for that position. Miller bought a horse-drawn lawn mower, replacing the hand mowers used by students to that point. Students were upset with the loss of income by the replacement, but they soon were placated by their increasing interest in the sports programs developing on campus. Track, tennis, bicycling, skating, and bobsledding was available for those not interested in baseball and basketball.

Dr. Bassett dropped football from the sports curriculum, partially because the murderous game was literally killing students all over the country, partially because the Upper Iowa team was not as strong as it had been initially, but mostly because of the game's dishonesty. Many schools hired thugs to play for them, and traditions at Upper Iowa made condoning such practices unthinkable.

In the summer of 1905, citing student disciplinary problems, the Board asked for Dr. Bassett to resign. He was replaced with Dr. William Arnold Shanklin, minister at St. Luke's in Dubuque. The sweeping changes President Shanklin had in mind for the university to bring it in line with the modern academic world in the areas of curriculum and facilities were no longer of much concern to Charles.

On the morning of January 12th of 1906, Charles came slowly out of his room to sit at the breakfast table. He had relinquished the entire upstairs portion of the house to J.D., Nellie, and their children. Charles kept his bedroom in what had originally been the dining room of the house on the first floor. Dining had been moved into a portion of the living room.

"Good morning, father," said J.D., as he sipped his cup of coffee.

"Good morning," said Charles, in a weakened voice.

"Are you going out today?" asked J.D. He knew his father was failing rapidly, but he had gone for a walk just the day before yesterday.

"Not today," was the reply.

Nellie brought food from the kitchen, but Charles declined. He was not hungry, he said.

After a bit of typical morning conversation, in which Charles did not participate, he excused himself and said that he was going back to his room to rest. J.D. went to check on him at noontime, and found him resting peacefully in a permanent slumber. At the age of eighty-two years and four months, Charles Coleman Parker left the trials and tribulations of life behind to begin his most important adventure, and to be with Sarah once again.

IX

I came in the side entrance of Old Sem, as was my habit since moving into the Winston House. It has now become my habit also to refer to it affectionately as "Old Sem" even though everyone else calls it Alexander-Dickman, or just AD. I suppose that name means more to me than it does to most others. The three flights of stairs provided most of my exercise in the winter. I stopped at my mailbox as usual, and headed into my office. Everything was normal until I opened the door and stepped inside.

He was not standing at his usual post gazing out the window; nor was he seated at the computer. He was nowhere to be seen.

I plopped down in my chair in half disbelief, and in full disappointment. Was he gone? From the moment I first saw him, he never left my office. Where could he be? Yesterday, he was telling me stories. He never said good-bye; never gave any indication that he was leaving. Did I do something wrong?

As a terrible feeling that I had seen the last of him came over me, I searched my memory in vain trying to find some scrap of information that would explain his absence. What was the last thing he said to me? I don't remember. Wait, I do remember. He said, "Take care not to slip on the ice." Was there some hidden meaning in that? I don't know.

Racking my brain for an answer seemed to

stimulate a flood of images and memories. I remembered the first time I saw him, and what I felt. I remembered our conversations, and the times I was annoyed with him. I remembered why he said he came—to help me.

There's an interesting question. If he is gone for good, did he accomplish his mission? I don't feel any different than I was, but maybe I should think about it. Yes, there are several things.

For one thing, I see Upper Iowa University differently now. What began as a last resort for me has become a first choice. Seeing the university through his eyes has given me an appreciation for its true value. The more I learned about the institution and its history, the stronger my belief became that this place deserves all the devotion and sacrifice that one can give it. When times are tough, it always seems to bounce back on the strength of special people who bring special qualities to its hallowed halls. The right people always seem to show up at the right time to bring the institution back from the brink of oblivion, or to give it a push toward a brave new world. If ever there was an organizational embodiment of the power of faith, this is it.

UIU is not Harvard or Stanford, but it has qualities that those institutions and others like them will never possess. It deserves devotion and sacrifice not because it is prestigious or graced by academic elite, but because it is genuine. It is not a place where students come to make social connections and to adorn themselves with celebrity, but a place where students can come to find out who they are and to discover their potential. It is not a place where graduates leave with their destinies written, but a place where the future will be what they make of it.

Let's see... his biggest criticism was the way I relate to students. Has that changed? Well, I'm still arrogant. God himself could not change that. But, my arrogance has always been directed more at the faculty and administrators than at the students. I do see many things differently now. For one thing, I have seen how one may be gentle and still be strong. I have seen how one may be tolerant and supportive without being unsubstantial. I suppose what I have seen is a different view of success and how it should be understood.

I know what I've learned! Students were goofier then than they are now. I still laugh when I remember his stories about sheep on the roof and cows in the chapel, and the illicit dancers trying to hurry back from Lima on a quarry sled. Yet these same students were the people who made this country what it is. These were the people who defended the flag, forged the government, built the cities, fed the nation, and healed the sick. These were the people who grew up to become teachers, scientists, spiritual leaders, inventors, actors, writers, artists, and entrepreneurs. I guess I've learned to let students express themselves and still keep my faith that they will turn out all right, to impress an academic standard not as an absolute but as a flexible guideline. I guess I've learned that the aim of education is ultimately to improve life, and not just to rack up accomplishments.

I suppose I see them more as individuals now and not simply as a generation with their collective obsessions for material wealth and good times. What has always appeared to be apathy to me is probably more like bewilderment. He was somewhat bewildered by the modern world; I guess we all are. But, he showed me that a simple application of old values still provides a beacon in the fog. He put me in mind of my own bewilderment and cluelessness at that age, and how it is never fully resolved.

I was a goofy kid, and not well-understood by most of my teachers. Many of my students need my attention, and the small numbers here afford an opportunity for that. I now guard less against the demands on my time, and invite more interaction outside of class. I guess I realize now more than ever that I am here for them and not just for myself. They deserve my faith in them, and my efforts on their behalf. Yes, he has done all that for me.

As all of this was coursing through my mind, I attended mechanically to paperwork. When that was finished, I left my office and descended the central stairs to drop it off in the Registrar's office. I was too agitated to return to my office directly, so I headed out the front door to walk around for awhile. I missed him, and I was annoyed that he did not say goodbye.

I stepped out into a driving mixture of rain and sleet. Where did this storm come from? It was supposed to be clear today. I fought the wind down the front walk, until, just before the street, I decided that a walk would not be the remedy for which I had hoped.

It was then that I noticed something was wrong. It was not a conscious thought as much as it was a sense of being lost. As I searched for an explanation, I noticed that the street was different. It was not paved. And, the arch over the walk was missing. There was a line of people moving down the street toward the church. Wait a minute! All the buildings are different. C.C.'s tree, to my right, was different—much larger—and there was no marker. So, that's what an elm looks like.

I looked at my watch. It said Monday, January 15th. But today's not Monday, it's Tuesday.

Just as I was beginning to realize that I was in the twilight zone again, a petite woman stepped into my view. She was dressed completely in black. Her dress was old-fashioned, and it covered her from chin to ground. Her hair was gray and naturally wavy, and was kept close to her head under her modest brimmed black hat. She was not young, but it was hard to determine her age; she could have been forty or seventy. She was attractive once, but her face was now etched with hardship and sacrifice, and no makeup had been employed to cover the deep lines at the corners of her mouth and under her eyes. Her mouth made a straight line above her square chin, and guarded her expressionless face. But, her sunken, pale-blue eyes were gentle, and reflected compassion.

She did not speak, but I knew she was Sarah. Her presence had a calming affect, and I knew, somehow, that I was to follow her.

She led me to the church. No one seemed to be aware of our presence. I should have received many stares because of my modern dress, but no one turned to look at me. Once inside, we approached a tall, slender, balding gentleman who was speaking quietly with a group of other men. I knew somehow that this was James D. Parker, C.C.'s son. They were reminiscing about old times, telling the sort of anecdotes that can be heard at any funeral.

"Reverend Paine has been kind enough to handle all the arrangements," said J.D. "He offered to do it, and I had too much on my hands to refuse the service. I think we're starting now."

Everyone moved quietly into the pews as an imposing figure took the podium. He was slender, not too tall, with gray hair and a scraggly beard, and a dashing look about him. So, this was Jason Paine. He looked weary, but as he began to speak, his presence outweighed his appearance.

Rev. Paine spoke a brief prayer, and then introduced the hymn "Nearer My God to Thee" which was sung beautifully by a quartet of two men and two women. When that concluded, there were readings from the Bible—the 90th Psalm and 1 Corinthians 15—and another prayer offered by the current President of UIU, Rev. Shanklin. Finally, Rev. Paine took the podium again. His voice came as though from the top of a mountain.

"We are today a congregation of mourners. While some of our number, allied by kinship are especially bereft, there is not one but feels the soreness of heart that comes of severed ties. Dr. Parker belonged to the entire community. I use the word advisedly. He was a veritable asset in the heart-possessions of every member of this community. We have been rich in his presence among us, we are poorer by his passing away.

"The question arises with you, as it did with me, why, from among these distinguished brethren beside me, all in the vigor of their manhood, learned and gifted, each bearing titles of honor and distinction, I, a plain old man, should be asked to speak to you today, but I am assured that I am not called merely to speak beautiful words of praise, arranged in well-framed sentences, but rather to give testimony, as a witness testifies in court, of that whereof I have personal knowledge of him whose remains lie before us today.

"Fifty years ago last December I was teaching in the log school house which stood in the grove hard by the residence of Brother James Robertson, who was one of the directors. According to custom of the day, the teacher 'boarded round' among the patrons of the school and the Robertson home was one of my first places of entertainment. Dr. Parker and his most excellent wife had just arrived and were staying at Brother Robertson's until his own house could be occupied. Amid the freedom of frontier conditions, a week domiciled under the same roof and gathering at the same table furnished excellent opportunity for intimate acquaintance. I recognized at once the princely character of the man, and his generous nature seemed to reach out and embrace me, and we were close friends at once and ever after.

"It is a custom among Christians when they assemble to bury their dead, that the word spoken be based on some portion of God's word and so, when I learned that I was to speak to you today, I bade my memory bring me to some passage which would be a fitting suggestion of such a life and such a nature as that of our brother. First my memory quoted me from David, 'Mark the perfect man and behold the upright, for the end of that man is peace.' Good, I said, but that points more especially to the closing moments rather than to the long and fruitful life. And then it quoted me from Job 'Thou shalt come to thy grave in a full age like a shock of corn cometh in his season.' Good, again, but while this pictures most beautifully the rich, golden ripening of his soul, I would like to speak also of the kindly, helpful life he lived.

"This then from James, quoth memory, pure religion and undefiled before God and the Father is this, 'To visit the Fatherless and the widows in their affliction, and to keep himself unspotted from the world.' True, I said, true, a most comprehensive summing up of Christian work and duty, yet the spirit of self-denial, of self-sacrifice so characteristic of our brother is not shown.

"Would this from the Master himself meet your wish then? 'For the Son of man came not to be ministered unto, but to minister, and to give his life as a ransom for many.' Most excellent indeed as showing the spirit of humble service always so marked in our brother, but there was, when occasion required, such a heroic spirit, which could not be turned aside by obstacles; is there not some text which will bring out this trait? Yes, there is one from Paul, as he laid down his pen just before he was beheaded. 'I have fought a good fight; I have finished my course; I have kept the faith, henceforth there is laid up for me a crown of righteousness, which the Lord, the righteous judge shall give me at that day.' Good, all good, not one of those passages can be omitted in a delineation of this most unusual character, unusual because of its wondrous purity and symmetry and strength.

"There are too many texts for one short discourse. How shall I combine them? And these words came to me 'Ye are our epistle, written in our hearts, known and read of all men.'

"If the inspired author of those immortal epistles of the New Testament was warranted in declaring those Corinthian brethren to be his epistles, to be known and read, as such, of all men, surely I am doubly warranted in taking our brother's blameless walk as a text from which to draw instruction and encouragement.

"Dr. Parker's devotion to his wife attracted my attention and won my admiration from the first. Every degree of tenderness, every measure of affection was manifest and manifested not by sentimental words but by kindliest action.

"He was a lover to the last—dignified but informal, chivalrous but sincere.

"As children came to bless the home, the same traits were prominent. Their physical, intellectual and moral well-being were carefully guarded, and no outside interest, however pressing, was permitted to come between him and his family.

"But his solicitude for his family did not stop with them; it reached out to all his acquaintance and especially to those to whom he ministered professionally. He did not choose his profession merely as a means of worldly gain and promotion, but as offering him the best field in which to exercise his God given talents and by that exercise to bless humanity.

"He felt that, having entered this work, responsibility was laid upon him by the Almighty from which he did not wish nor dare to flinch.

"Wherever there was a wail of distress brought to his ear, be it from hovel or from palace with promise of reward or without hope of emolument, by night or by day, in heat or in cold, 'neath balmy skies or in raging tempests, there lay his path of duty and he faltered not. No soldier ever rushed into battle at the command of his general more promptly than he rode to the help of the afflicted.

"I see him now, as memory's picture brings before me those early days, sitting his little brown mare, plunging into the oncoming darkness, out onto the unfenced and almost trackless prairie, through a storm, which compared with which this fierce tempest raging without today, is but a pygmy. The cry of the afflicted was to him the call of God.

"Kindness was in the very warp and woof of his nature and extended to brute as well as to human being. Bishop Berry recently said, pungently, though in homely phrase 'A man's mule knows more about his master's religion than does his pastor,' and judged by this standard Dr. Parker's religion was genuine as all who saw him among his animals will testify.

"He was eminently industrious. He followed Wesley's counsel to his preachers, 'Never be unemployed; never be triflingly employed.' He seemed to act upon the conviction that he was debited with sixty minutes of every waking hour and for each minute thus debited he sought to show a corresponding credit of something worthy accomplished. I remember entering his office one day and saying as I entered the open door 'Dr., if you are not busy I wish you would look at my arm though if you are in a hurry I'll come in again.' With the trace of a smile coming over his usually grave countenance he replied 'I am always busy, but never in a hurry.' It was the key to his busy life, by which he was able to accomplish so much.

"While carrying a large practice he found time to study and keep abreast with the very front of his profession, to take part in public enterprises, to mingle largely in social life, and to cultivate, chiefly with his own hands, both vegetable and flower gardens which were the pride and admiration of the city. He said once to me, 'I make it a rule never to allow a weed to go to seed in my garden.'"

Jason paused for a moment. He seemed to be waiting for his words to take affect. Then, he said "Dr. Bissell has asked to be included among those to offer praise in honor of Dr. Parker, and we are honored to hear his remarks. Dr. Bissell."

J. W. Bissell, former president of Upper Iowa University, took the podium. He reminded me a great deal of Charles in his appearance.

"Thank you, Reverend Paine," began Dr. Bissell. "Some one may say he was not a financier. Perhaps, and yet it depends on how we estimate it. Men differ in the forms in which they invest their earthly accumulations, some in broad acres, some in vast flocks and herds, some in merchandise, and some in stocks and bonds. All seek investments that are safe, where values will not shrink, where possession is secure. Visionary schemes for the rapid increase of wealth sometimes allure men to their undoing, and everywhere wrecked fortunes warn us of unwise placement. Dr. Parker, looking beyond the uncertainties of earthly investments, looking for more productive fields and more enduring returns, laid up large treasure for the hereafter. With him, a dollar given to better the condition of a fellow human being or a call made to relieve human suffering, though it brought no moneyed return, was not deemed lost. It was so much laid up. He preferred to suffer inconvenience himself rather than to distress another. I remember years ago, perhaps thirty-five, in a time of great stringency, I had occasion to talk with him concerning his financial affairs. He was in need of money and I said to him 'You have a large amount on your books, why not urge collections more vigorously? Your accounts are good, are they not?' And I shall never forget his grave, earnest look, half reproach, half sympathy, as he said, 'Yes, they are nearly all good, sometime, and I am urging those who are in circumstances to pay, to do so now, but most of them are very hard-pushed just now. I went to them to relieve their suffering, and I cannot bring myself to distress them again unless I am in great personal need.'

"We read one of those grounds brought forth plentifully, so that he had not where to store his increase, and he said within himself, 'I will tear down my barns and build greater that I may have where to bestow my goods, and I will say to my soul, Soul, thou hast much goods laid up for many years, take thine ease, eat, drink and be merry. But the Lord said, Thou fool, this night shall thy soul be required of thee, then whose shall these things be? So is every one that layeth up for himself treasure on earth and is not rich toward God.' I have no condemnation for those who accumulate. It is a God-given faculty and His condemnation rests only upon those who lay up treasure for themselves and are not rich toward God. Our brother had not gathered great earthly treasure, but who in all this community, who in all your acquaintance can you name today as richer in good deeds, richer in kindly helpful acts and words, richer in the grateful affections of the thousands to whom he ministered and with whom he lived, richer in the sympathies which were stirred and the love that was cherished when it was whispered upon our streets and in our homes and away out in the regions beyond, 'Dr. Parker is dead', and when it was answered with subdued and trembling voice and moistening eye, 'Oh! dear old Dr. Parker.' The richest man in the world today would give millions upon millions if he could hold the same place in the affection of his neighbors as does our dear departed brother. The one, when he goes, must leave behind him all his immense gettings and hoardings; the other is just entering upon the full, blissful, undisturbed possession of his abundant treasure. Moth and rust and thieves and death will not come to trouble; it is his forever. He was rich in the true riches, a financier in the treasure that fadeth not away.

"I walk along the narrow streets of the beautiful city on the hill and note monuments which loving hands have placed at the graves of the departed. I notice that some are becoming discolored and roughened by the action of the elements, and moss is beginning to appear on some, and ever the names so precious to those who inscribed them are beginning to be less distinct. And I bethink me that in a century or two, or three, names now so distinctly seen upon the marble will be wholly effaced, and only lumps of unsightly, worthless stone will encumber the ground. But he who engraves upon men's hearts, engraves for eternity, and there a thousand hearts beating warm in this community today, and a thousand more in the region round about, and yet others, many, who have scattered abroad, and there are as many more whose hearts have ceased to beat upon earth, and upon all these, our brother, by deeds done, by kindly words spoken, by warm sympathies expressed, has carved his name and written his very character. And you and I who believe in an intelligent immortality will at once agree that these inscriptions shall be fresh and undimmed when centuries and cycles and eons shall grow old.

"To you whose homes are invaded by this bereavement, what shall I say more than to these others? Dr. Solon C. Bronson wrote to me the other day, 'The death of my father was a triumph. If you have a profounder sorrow than do we, you shall also have a larger share in the glory of the triumph. You have a richer heritage of blessed memories. You open the door to the room now vacant and find it filled with delightful recollections; mementos of the past and of him so recently passed from you, mementos and recollections that appeal to every sensation of your being, radiant and beautiful to your eyes, harmonious and musical to your ears, redolent of patient cheerfulness and fragrant with grateful words, sweeter than honey to the taste, those expressions of sympathy and love, while feelings of courage and faith follow every reminder of the good man gone. His life has been to you a devout and faithful service like that of the Sabbath morn; may his death be as the benediction at its close, until, in the eternal Sabbath, you reassemble to go no more out forever.'

"Dr. C.C. Parker, whose acquaintance I formed thirty-four years ago, was one of the best men I ever knew. Through all the long years that he practiced in Fayette county, he was the ideal Christian physician, ever bringing cheerfulness to the sick room which often provided more effective than the medicine prescribed. He was a warm friend and liberal supporter of the Upper Iowa University; a great lover of the beautiful, a generous provider, given to hospitality, and a friend of the needy and deserving. He was undemonstrative but sincere to his Christian life. A man of sterling character and noble life has gone to his reward."

Dr. Bissell's voice quivered with emotion as he spoke this last. It was the sort of delivery that under any other circumstances would have drawn spontaneous applause. In fact, the audience seemed to be exerting quite a bit of energy in refraining. He gave a little nod with his head to acknowledge the applause that was being restrained from, and turned from the podium.

There were a few more prayers and utterances, and then the casket was borne from the church by six area physicians to the funeral wagon waiting outside. Sarah, who still had not spoken a word, followed the procession with me two blocks down Washington Street until we reached Alex Winston's house. I stopped to look at it more closely. I decided that I did not need to go to the cemetery; I had already seen his monument. Besides, I thought of a better place to say good-bye.

The Winston house was basically the same as it was when I purchased it. It was white instead of gray, and the porch from which Charles and Alex watched the library go up was smaller and more ornate. I would have loved to have seen inside, but it was not my house just now. Alex Winston must be with the procession that was still making its way south on Washington to the road that would lead directly to the cemetery. He is old, and near his own death. It must be doubly hard losing old friends when you know that your time is near.

I thought briefly on the irony of all this. From where I was standing, I could look south down Washington to the very spot where he took his first glimpse of Fayette. It is very near that spot where he is about to be buried. When I turned completely about, I could look north on Washington and see his first house in Fayette three and a half blocks away. A slight turn to the right would then leave me facing Old Sem, into which he invested a good part of his life and energy. It was all right here. Nothing in my life had ever been so neatly contained.

Sarah must have thought I was an idiot, spinning around as I was. She apparently decided to stay with me instead of following the procession. I was very happy that she did. Perhaps she knew where I was going.

We walked in silence down Madison Street the two blocks to King Street and turned south toward the house in which they both died. When we reached it, Sarah proceeded ahead of me into the garden. The garden was so much a part of who he was. She must have been reminiscing; there was not much to it in winter. There was a large shed and a greenhouse that were not there in my own time. I stood for awhile trying to imagine it in all its glory. Even in its depleted condition, it exhibited signs of splendor. It must have been magnificent; even Jason mentioned it in his eulogy.

As I stood there, I could not help remembering something that Alan Watts once said. The beauty of a garden is not so much in the discipline of its rows, but in the growth that the discipline makes possible. Maybe he's not gone after all.

Author's Note

Charles Coleman Parker lived the archetype of an authentic life. As noted by Herodotus in his infamous fictional account of a dialogue between Solon (the archetype of a wise man) and Croesus (the archetype of a rich and powerful man), those who live authentic lives are rarely well known, wealthy, or powerful. More to the point, people who live authentic lives do so in relative obscurity and entirely unselfconsciously. If the paparazzi are following you around, your life is probably something less than authentic. Charles, not thinking he had done anything extraordinary, would probably wonder why anyone would write a book about him. Nellie Parker urged him to write an autobiography, and he declined in order to compile his father's (Daniel Parker's) story.

As Dr. Bissell and Rev. Paine noted, Charles lived entirely for the sake of others. His was a life of service to those who needed whatever he could provide. I have no doubt that if Herodotus were to write his account in modern times, he would have named someone like C.C. Parker as "the happiest of men," ignoring people like Michael Jordan, Queen Elizabeth, and Bill Gates. It is characteristic of such a man that few realize his true value until he is gone.

Herodotus was of the opinion that the authenticity of a life cannot be judged until it is over, and that it must be judged by others. The greatness of such a life is defined primarily by the void it leaves behind. When

C.C. Parker was alive, everyone who knew him knew he was good. They did not seem to understand how good until he was gone, when they took the opportunity to reflect upon what he meant to them personally. These are the sentiments expressed by virtually every person who commented on his life.

This development of C.C. Parker's story was based primarily in historical fact. All of the materials I used in compiling the story can be viewed in the Henderson-Wilder Library on the Upper Iowa University campus. Some books are on the shelves; other materials are located in the Parker Archives. By necessity, some of the specific content, such as dialogue, was based on informed speculation. All letters and documents portrayed were transcribed verbatim with no editorial corrections other than some punctuation. Though fictional, nothing in this account should be taken as pure fiction. All speculation was formulated on a variety of indicators. As many particulars have been incorporated into the story as possible, and descriptions of the events associated with the town of Fayette and with Upper Iowa University were taken from documents and histories. All of the characters portrayed were real people, though about some, little is known. For example, Keaser was listed in an ad placed in the West Union paper in 1856 as the person to contact in Fayette to inquire about purchase of the Davis Inn. Nothing else is known about him. It is known both from family lore and from certain documents that Charles brought a black servant home with him from the war, and that this servant settled in the Fayette area. The name Caleb was common for the time and convenient for the story, but no one recorded what his name actually was. Caleb was the only character whose name was unknown; all other names mentioned are authentic. With the lives of ordinary people, it so often happens that precious little detail has been preserved.

At the time of his death, *everyone* knew of the kindly, generous, capable Dr. Parker, and they assumed that his memory would live forever. So, they did not make much of an effort to document it, and what they did document was soon forgotten by succeeding generations.

Charles Coleman Parker was a man who touched many everyday lives, and was fondly remembered by those who knew him. He was important enough in a small corner of Iowa to have been the subject of biographical sketches included in local historical accounts, but not so prominent as to have attracted any serious attempt to chronicle his life. C.C. seemed to have escaped the notice of some editors tracing the progress of Fayette. It was surprising to me that an 1878 history of Fayette County offered a full biographical sketch of Alexander Winston, but only C.C. Parker's name and his occupation. Either the details of his existence were common knowledge and taken for granted, or not thought to be remarkable enough to warrant rehearsing. Other editors did notice him and wrote glowing, though altogether too brief, biographical sketches.

Of Sarah Lakin Parker, virtually nothing is known except the dates of her birth, death, and marriage to Charles, her membership in and devotion to the church, her attendance at Clermont Academy, and the cause of her death. That she called him "Charles" is speculation, based upon my presumption that she preferred the elegance of formality in expressing her affection. I can imagine also that she desired to differentiate herself, as his most intimate friend, from his many other friends who probably called him "C.C." I made assumptions about her character and personality based partly upon the sort of woman I presumed would be married happily and successfully to Charles, and partly upon the observations of their relationship briefly alluded to by Rev. Paine in his eulogy. Sarah's father was a notable character in Point Pleasant, but died long before having any real influence in her adult life. Charles could well have embodied several male roles for her, and aside from her brothers, William and Jimmy, was apparently the only man in her life.

C.C.'s great-grandsons could not remember anyone in the family mentioning anything about Sarah. Her death must have been very traumatic for Charles, and I suspect that discussion about her in the family was minimized in deference to his feelings. He lived for seventeen years following her death and after that period of time family members were out of the habit of discussing Sarah. They may even have forgotten most of the details.

One of the two obituaries I have for Sarah reports that she was serene and happy; she was devoted to serving God and His church; she was discreet in her words and charitable in her thoughts and actions, and she bore her long and fatal illness with composure, patience, and abnegation of self. I interpreted this description to mean that she was an intensely private woman who did not complain, share feelings, express opinions, or impose herself on anyone. The other obituary merely rehearsed summary details of her life. Apparently, no one but

Charles knew her, and he wasn't talking.

Abraham Lincoln once remarked, regarding a biography of Edmund Burke, that biographies tend to make heroes of their objects and to preclude descriptions of any mistakes or failures, that biographies commemorate lies and cheat posterity out of the truth (thank you to John E. Walsh for providing that remark). I am confident that I have included every known mistake and failure of Charles C. Parker. He does not seem to have had as many as the rest of us. Aside from a few minor eccentricities, his biggest defects seem to include his complete and utter failure at business (a natural consequence of his unbounded generosity), and his wanderlust (acknowledged by the family to have permeated the Parker men). C.C.'s middle son, Charles Lucius Parker, as his father, grandfather, and great grandfather did before him, left home to seek his fortune out west. Danny Parker, the oldest, apparently spent little time in his father's home after coming of age.

Charles demonstrated an apparent desire to remove himself from the society of his parents and siblings. Though I did not make this much an issue, it seems to me that this desire was the result of a particular alienation from his mother, Priscilla. She might have been a bit overbearing for his taste, and her oldest son, James, was probably favored with the bulk of her attention and approval. I have supported this notion with verbatim entries from her journal, delivered in context. The support is gained as much by what was missing from those entries as it is by what was included. I apologize to the family if I have been mistaken.

Charles seems to have been painfully honest,

exceedingly gentle, remarkably talented and effective at everything except business, fully self-reliant and loath to impose on others, devoted to his wife and children, and decidedly devoid of all but a very modest ambition. One of his obituaries stated "he was an exceptionally expert surgeon... and the best, gentlest, and most sympathetic of physicians as our family can testify." Another: "pure, gentle, gifted, skillful, generous, affable, sympathetic, the very sole of honor and integrity... if there is a man in Fayette county who will be missed more than Dr. Parker, we don't know his name."

A biographical sketch written in 1910, after his death, included the following: "Doctor Parker was always a friend to struggling young men, and his kindly counsels and fatherly advice led more than one young man into the proper course to insure future usefulness." The author, in mentioning it, implies a personal knowledge of such instances, the sort of which are never officially recorded. Therefore, I was obliged to submit myself as the wayward soul in need of his counsel as an example of that which could likely have been his most important legacy. Placing myself thus was not much of a stretch.

The obituary written for the UIU *Collegian* by students who knew him, verified all other accounts: "Doctor Parker was modest to a fault; energetic and active in serving others; courteous and kindly under all circumstances; earnest in his profession and practice as a physician, and beloved by all who knew him."

I have made less, perhaps something different, of his religious makeup than some accounts would have it. The obituaries I have, as well as the biographical records, make a point of his Christian character, of his church membership, and of his devotion to the local congregation. In my view, those depictions could indicate more a man of his time, who would naturally subscribe to the prevailing social etiquette and would use conventional means to display his sense of community responsibility. Charles was also a man who would adopt such a demeanor in deference to Sarah's wishes. He apparently joined the ME church in Pt. Pleasant because she was a member.

There is no strong evidence, such as there is for Jason Paine, to indicate extraordinary piety. Charles was certainly not an activist, evangelist, or missionary, in the same regard as his father and mother were. I thought it instructive that he chose to sit in his tent writing a letter to his wife rather than to attend the first religious services conducted in camp in some weeks. He was close enough to hear the proceedings, upon which he commented in his letter. I found it also instructive that, having reported his situation, he felt no occasion for an explanation of his motives. My characterization of his beliefs and his orientation toward church is indicated by a host of minutiae, though perhaps I see it that way because of my own leanings. Dr. Bissell, who knew him a good long time, provided further indication when he said that Charles "was undemonstrative but sincere to his Christian life." That he was faithful, and put his trust in God, and embodied Christian ideals, there can be no doubt. Again, if I am mistaken, then I apologize.

Many accounts indicate that Charles was in ill health nearly all of his adult life. Some people believed that he would not live long following his return to

Fayette after the war. Attaining the ripe old age of eighty-two is certainly a testimonial to the depth of his energy and constitution. There is some argument over the cause of his death. The cemetery record indicates "unrenic poisoning" which, of course, means uremic poisoning. This record was recreated at a time when his son, James D. Parker, the physician, was still alive and was probably consulted regarding the specific cause of death. Other records in the same book were left blank, indicating that when the cause of death was unknown, it was left out. Some of those commenting on his life had speculated that the same disease that had forced his resignation from the Army caused his death. His son, J.D., has been quoted by family members as having asserted that Charles had amoebic dysentery during the war, but no one can know for certain. According to the family, he experienced chronic diarrhea following the war and for the remainder of his life, which would explain his sickly appearance. It is all the more remarkable that he accomplished so much and contributed so vitally to his community in light of this affliction. Diarrhea was one of the most common illnesses among the soldiers during the war, and many died from its consequences. Chronic conditions sometimes have psychological bases. I left room for that possibility, and indicated its probable cause if indeed that was the case. Again, no one can know for sure.

In the Parker family accounts, it is not known for sure where the amputated limbs incident and the discussion with Grant took place. Either of them could have happened at Fort Donelson or at Shiloh, and there is no hard evidence for either possibility. I constructed the story around the most probable occurrence based upon facts known of the two battles which were provided by several sources, upon the Commander's report of Charles being "on duty in the hospital" and citation for "bravery and efficiency" at Fort Donelson, upon Grant's own account of the battles including his "tree in the rain" at Shiloh that he chose in order to avoid staying in the hospital, and upon small indications in C.C.'s letters. A detailed map of the Shiloh battlefield, revised and amended by Gen. Don Carlos Buell, shows the position of the 12th Iowa camp across a ravine—400 yards away—from the only log house on the map. Shelby Foote mentioned a spreading pile of limbs outside a log house where surgery was being performed on the bluff near Pittsburg Landing, in his novel about Shiloh. I was unable to confirm the source or validity of Mr. Foote's description, however it occurred to me upon reading it that such a sight might well have been seen at any and every battle in the Civil War.

Finally, I feel compelled to comment on my reasons for undertaking this project. I am sure it came as quite a surprise to members of the Parker family. I tried to incorporate as much speculation on my own motivations as I could into the story, though I am not altogether clear myself as to what they were. Charles Coleman Parker was the sort of person I would like to have been, he lived the sort of life I would like to have lived, and he was remembered in the manner in which I would like to be remembered. But I did not really know any of that at the point when I determined to write his story. I have just enough talent to recognize his greatness, but not enough to imitate it. I am honored just to be able to fantasize that such a man might have been my friend.

My greatest concern is that I did not depict his greatness greatly enough. I do not consider myself a writer. The influences on my style and the inconsistencies in its application should be transparent to the literary scholar. I received—nay, earned—low grades in English and history courses all the way through school. I was often the target of natural-born counselors and educators, such as C.C. Parker, who seek out the clueless and the academically needy. Perhaps I am merely the next in a line of students to benefit from his counsel. Since undertaking this project, there is no doubt that everything about me has improved though not as much as might be desired.

My first view of the plaque commemorating C.C.'s tree did not occur on the day of the interview as in the fictional account, though it could have. I noticed it the second or third week of my first term, and it did provide the inspiration. The images that came to me the first time I saw it were pretty much as related in the story, and were embellished by my own experience with the beautiful countryside and natural attractiveness of northeast Iowa. Finding that there was no existing biography of this character led me to contemplate the creation of one. At first, I thought such an endeavor could be no more than fictional. However, information began heading in my direction bit by bit until there was enough to attempt a biographical story. That was good because my imagination is certainly not up to the task of writing pure fiction.

Even though I was distracted by many obligations, providence pressed me—sometimes gently, sometimes firmly—in the Parker direction until I could think of little else. I feel strongly that this is not my project alone, but that it does belong to providence. I cannot say why I should feel that way. Virtually every word had to be hammered, whittled, and tweaked in order to find its proper place in the story. To me it has been a miracle of Biblical proportions. To you, who have just read it, it may be something else. In any case, it has been the most satisfying and challenging thing I have ever attempted.

Richard A. Barker, Ed.D.
Alex Winston House in Fayette, Iowa
November 2002

Acknowledgements

None of this would exist but for the love and support I receive every day from my wife, Barbara. The relationship depicted between Charles and Sarah is primarily a projection of our relationship adjusted for cultural variables, and for the fact that we are neither quiet nor reserved, nor do we keep our opinions to ourselves. Charles was probably a better husband. He was definitely thinner.

The greatest debt in the creation of this story is owed to Dr. James Donaldson Parker, retired physician, and to Dr. Thomas Parker Goebel, retired aeronautical engineer, both great grandsons of Charles C. Parker. The wealth of information and materials they were able and willing to furnish made all the difference in too many ways to mention. The Parker family is riddled with physicians, ministers, scholars, teachers, and scientists, and has provided more than its fair share of distinguished alumni of Upper Iowa University as well as of other institutions. Charles Coleman Parker represents the family norm rather than the exception, and is notable only in relation to his time and place in history.

Another great debt is owed to Dan Crawford, an alum of UIU, for writing an unpublished manuscript, dated 1988, entitled *Treasures of Our College Home*, on the history of the school. The amount of research Mr. Crawford conducted in preparation for this endeavor saved me untold hours of digging through the archives

The author in his office in Old Sem.

and organizing bits of information. Some documents to which he had access apparently no longer exist, and some of the people he interviewed are now deceased.

Other extremely helpful publications included *University Recruits, Company C* by Charles B. Clark and Roger B. Bowen, which documented the fortunes of the 12th Iowa Regiment, and *Moonlight: Abraham Lincoln and the Almanac Trial* by John Evangelist Walsh, which illustrated the "Duff" Armstrong trial. This latter work is an extraordinary piecing together of the details of a much-discussed and poorly-documented event. Previous accounts of the trial neglected the role Charles Parker played. Walsh's account not only described Parker's role, but cited a document written by the judge commenting on the value of Parker's role. Thanks are also due to Barry Zbornik, Fayette history enthusiast, who has variously created and maintained web sites with useful information. In addition, Mr. Zbornik was kind enough to provide a wealth of information in personal communications.

I would like to extend my deepest gratitude to Becky Wadian, Director of Library Services at UIU, and to Associate and Assistant Directors Carol Orr and Mary White. Their assistance, their vigilance for anything Parker, and their leniency regarding the use of library and archive materials proved invaluable. I must also thank the volunteers at the Fayette County Historical Center, located in West Union, for that same sort of assistance.

I mentioned that my skill at writing, such as it is, was long in development, and I must acknowledge its stimulus. The first clue regarding the writing process did not materialize for me until I was teaching at the graduate level. Masters thesis committees in the University of Redlands required a university examiner. For most of the thirty some theses for which I was committee chair, the examiner was Dr. Edward K. Williams, classic professor of classic English. Listening to him explain to my students what was wrong with their work became one of the most important elements of my own education. That and practice has produced whatever it is that resides here.

Finally, I must acknowledge the contribution of the Alex Winston House, within which I found levels of inspiration and spiritual support that I cannot effectively relate. While the idea for the project was formulating itself in my imagination, I could not foresee any opportunity to act. The commute, as well as the normal demands of teaching and scholarship, simply did not leave enough time or energy. I was thinking in terms of years, if at all. About six months after the seeds of the project were sown, cosmic forces I cannot explain directed me to a house for sale in Fayette situated across the street from Henderson-Wilder Library. The rest was like magic. Go figure! The house was the perfect vehicle for the task. Plus, it was cheap.